9-10 M+W B 311 Moore
10-12 Tu

Southern Christian University Library
1200 Taylor Rd.
Montgomery, AL. 36117

95-100 A
85-94 B

Property of
FABS

NATURE RECREATION

Group Guidance for the Out-of-Doors

BY

WILLIAM ("CAP'N BILL") GOULD VINAL

Emeritus Professor of Nature Education,
University of Massachusetts

SECOND EDITION

Southern Christian University
QH 51 .V5 1963
Vinal
Nature recreation; group guidance for the out-of-doors
3 4141 0002 9612 1

DOVER PUBLICATIONS, INC.
NEW YORK

QH
51
.V5
1963

29612

Copyright © 1963 by Dover Publications, Inc.

Copyright © 1940 by William Gould Vinal

All rights reserved under Pan American and International Copyright Conventions.

Published in the United Kingdom by Constable and Company Limited, 10 Orange Street, London W.C.2.

This new Dover edition, first published in 1963, is a revised version of the work first published by the McGraw-Hill Book Company, Inc., in 1940.

Library of Congress Catalog Card Number: 63-4588

Manufactured in the United States of America

Dover Publications, Inc.
180 Varick Street
New York 14, N.Y.

To My Father

WILLIAM RAYMOND VINAL

Who gave me my first dog, Dandy. Who encouraged me to raise frizzled fowl, game birds, black ducks, Canada geese, and homing pigeons. Who taught me the fun of berrying, horn pouting, and bobbing eels. Who left the meadow uncut for the pitcher plants. Who planted the big spruce and rock maples for their beauty. Who set the flowering dogwood by the drive.

To My Mother

MARY ELLEN FARRAR VINAL

Who taught me to protect the robin and the bluebird. Who kindled the desire for dandelions, cowslips, huckleberry pie, and gooseberry tarts. Who nursed fluffy chickens back to life. Who fed the snowbirds. Who sent me with flowers to the shut-ins and the sick. Who raised the honey locust and the catalpa from seed sent from Cambridge. Who filled her windows with beautiful sword ferns, fuchsias, and flowering geraniums.

PREFACE

Today we are witnessing a shift in economic and social life patterns of enough gravity to merit the thought of scientists as a whole and of nature leaders in particular. Those teachers who can adapt themselves to change will be the most successful.

The study of nature has been constant, but the objectives of nature study have been continuously growing and changing. Nature lore originated with the pioneer who loved his woodsy home. Through observation and experience, he built up a body of nature understanding and knowledge that both guided and enriched his existence.

From rail splitter to horse trader, nature practice met and solved social needs. It was the way of Thoreau and the training school for Lincoln. Our first textbook dealing with nature materials was the *New England Primer* (about 1690) with its religious precepts. Then followed *Poor Richard's Almanac*, first published by Franklin in 1732. Every household had a copy of the *Old Farmer's Almanac*, which was used faithfully in weather prediction. Even today, in rural districts, it is fastened to a string and hung on a nail for ready reference.

But with the development of industrialism and the concentration of population in cities, there disappeared both the need and the place for daily intimacy with the out-of-doors. In some schools, nature study degenerated into an ambitious accumulation of facts chained to the pickled and desiccated biology of the past.

Louis Agassiz aroused a new enthusiasm for living material and strove to emphasize the importance of firsthand contact with nature. Unfortunately, his sphere of influence did not touch the life of the average citizen. John Muir, John Burroughs, and Dallas Lore Sharp saw nature with an artist's eye and could put it into literature for others to enjoy. Ernest Thompson Seton brought woodcraft and Indian lore into social significance for youth. Perhaps Enos Mills was the first to start an organized school to teach nature lore to others. He called it The Long's Peak Trail School and Nature Guiding.[1]

[1] Enos Mills's guiding dated from about 1888. Probably his first article on guiding was "Guide Wanted," *Saturday Evening Post*, Jan. 6, 1917. "The Children of My Trail School" appeared in the *Saturday Evening Post*, March, 1919.

It is true we no longer need to learn the signs of the zodiac, nor is it necessary to hew logs and thatch the roof. But we still live and move and have our beings in a world of nature, and upon our ever-increasing understanding of its functioning depends our progress.

In colonial days—when certain medicines were brewed from certain weeds—it was important to recognize and distinguish these weeds by name. Today, it is important to know how these same weeds reproduce in order to prevent them from running amuck in our gardens.

Yesterday the horse and buggy limited the family horizon. Today the vacation by automobile is a national habit and the summer camp an accepted institution. Both offer a new frontier for intimacy with nature. Furthermore, an awakening realization of the need for conservation demands an about-face in traditional attitudes toward our natural resources. This opens an almost untouched field of public service to the lover of the out-of-doors. Most challenging of all is the relation of the nature educator to the use of the additional leisure time created for America's millions by technological advancement in industry. The new nature education is the training of individuals in present-day outdoor recreational activities. Such nature recreation can and should be a very real contribution to society.

The fundamental movement of nature recreation to the out-of-doors had its inception in the *summer camp.* The author became deeply interested in nature recreation during his 13 summers (1914 to 1926) as director of Camp Chequesset, the nautical camp for girls, down on Cape Cod. In June, 1920, with the encouragement offered by the National Association of the Directors of Girls' Camps, he organized the Nature Lore School for the precamp training of nature leaders. His seven springs with this school were most useful in formulating the ideas that follow.

In the summer of 1927, *Nature Magazine*, acting on its conviction that nature study is the fundamental key to good camping and a vital factor in conserving forests and wild life, organized a special nature service for camps. Mrs. Vinal and the writer (and Rex) were sent on a friendly visit to 50 selected camps to give advice and assistance. The trip covered a trail of 3,209 miles through New England and New York. The adventure was most inspirational, and, because of pleasant recollections of the encouragement given by the camp directors along the way, much of this material has been assembled from this journey.

It then fell to the author's lot to organize and direct the Nature Guide School (1928). At first, this was under Western Reserve University, but it is now at Massachusetts State College.

Through these many years the idea has been steadily growing. Many organizations such as the Scouts and Camp Fire Girls and teachers' institutes have requested short-term training courses. Serving the public as ranger-naturalist in three national parks has also been both a privilege and an inspiration. During the years 1936 and 1937, the author was on the itinerant faculty of the National Recreation Association, giving work in nature recreation in various institutes throughout the nation. This was also a pioneer adventure.

From time to time the author published in various magazines the results of his experiences in all these activities. At this time the author would like to express grateful appreciation to Joan Chater Harap, who has given abundantly of her time in arranging the mechanical setup of the manuscript and to Dr. E. Laurence Palmer for critical reading of the material.

In attempting to present the idea of nature recreation, there probably has been a neglect of the formality of language that one might expect in a textbook for leaders. If such is the case, it is due to an anxiety to retain a viewpoint and to arouse enthusiasm for the nature-lore movement.

The book is intended for the uninitiated as well as for students in colleges of education. This may explain the lack of technical terms, although it is fervently hoped that scientific precision and modern pedagogical procedure have not been sacrificed.

With these apologies, the author submits the book to the thousands of nature friends who are seeking means to guidance of wayfarers along the trail.

WILLIAM GOULD VINAL.

AMHERST, MASS.,
October, 1940.

CONTENTS

Part I

THE PHILOSOPHY OF NATURE RECREATION

CHAPTER I

NATURE EXPERIENCES IN THE HOME

THE EDUCATIONAL PHILOSOPHY OF NATURE PLAY

We Are Children of the Forest. An animal in the forest has two serious occupations. One is to get food, and the other is to escape being food. He has to look forward as well as backward. An important message may come from any direction. Such a severe "life-and-death" training for ears, eyes, and nose makes for keenness. By closing the door to eye development, ear training, or even nose education, we are dwarfing our possibilities. Our closed-door policy for recent generations has resulted in our children and their pets' being less developed in outdoor keenness than the savage and wild animals.

Both the dog and his master are outdoor animals. The most carefully laid city plan will not replace the activities outlined by nature. There is no form of hunting, chasing, fishing, or climbing that surpasses that provided by the forest. Nature has a long line of provisions for the training of every physical and mental requirement. The change to the city block has been abrupt. The price of herding and fencing has been many diseases, the wasting of certain organs, and the starving of certain instincts. The grating of machines is no trumpet to the finer instincts of the ear. To the dog, the highest priced ball will not replace the free forest. Nor will the cave instincts find an adequate outlet in alley sports. Is the wild rabbit's protest so wholly unreasonable when he refuses to eat in captivity? Is the turkey so addicted to disease in his native haunts? Why does the muskrat gnaw off a leg for freedom? Is not the fact that a two-weeks-old baby can hang by his hands 2 or 3 min. a relic of going to school in the treetops?

The Lower Forms of Animal Life Never Attend School. They do not have to. They are graduate students from the start. The honeybee never goes to school. Neither does the clam or the bullfrog.

A frog can catch a fly with more precision than a schoolboy. He sees a fly and snaps at it. His stomach does not have a schooling. It goes to work on the fly and picks up the nutritive parts from the non-nourishing wings and claws. A frog's stomach at the start is better at separating the good from the bad than a baby's at 12 months. A bee does not have to learn to make a six-sided cell or to make a beeline for home. His education is ready-made. The human animal is not of this order of being. Mammals have carried the process of education to a higher level.

Man Is the First Animal to Have a Thumb Rule of Nature. Man is the first animal to have a thumb in opposition to the fingers. The monkey has five fingers, but man has four fingers and a thumb. This is not so at first. A newborn baby has five fingers like a monkey. The baby's thumb demands thumb action. Its position soon spells grasping. Man first grasped to protect himself. His thumb was in the race to throw a stone, to use a club, to pull a slingshot, and to throw a spear. He must have room—not mere elbowroom but his thumb rights.

Man's thumb soon makes him a tool-wielding animal. He craves to have tools to serve him. He wants to shape his arrow so that it will travel the farthest. He admires the cunning hand. Indian education was built up around the hand and the eye. His tools were all hand-made. They were specifications of his right to become a man. They were diplomas for graduation from infancy. Thus the viburnum became fashioned into an arrow, the ash withe into baskets, and the mellow clay into pottery.

Thumb rule is intimacy with the "feel" of nature. It is the bond of man and nature out of which come the art material of the Indian and the campcraft of the Boy Scout. It is thinking through nature materials to something constructed. It is a creative and educational process.

Modern civilization blocks this opportunity for development. The city is a desert. The stones are pavings, the trees are grilled, the gardens are fenced, the soil is lawned, and the flowers are "posted." Everywhere it is "hands off" nature material. Repression of impulses means unhappiness. Nature's laws are older than man's laws. The child who does not learn the thumb rule of nature is not living up to his possibilities.

Nature Play Is the Serious Occupation of Childhood. Climbing apple trees, chasing butterflies, hunting frogs, fishing for bullheads, gathering shagbarks, making mud pies, harnessing brooks, pushing across a pond on a raft are the serious occupations of childhood. Hunting and fishing have always been prescribed courses in nature's school. Creating or inventing was added to the program as a course of training for the human family. These courses of study are of educational significance and will continue to be a masterful factor in building up the mind.

Nature Play in Youth Is Fundamental for Nature Recreation in Later Life. Educators agree that a child can learn, with less effort than an adult, to read, to write, to speak French, and to play the piano. It is equally true about running, throwing a baseball, swimming, fishing, making things with the hands, and fighting. If the child does not learn to do these things at the right time, the chances are he has lost them for life. If a girl does not learn to throw a baseball before she is twelve years old, by the time she reaches the ripe old age of eighteen, she will not be able to throw a ball. The man who does not go fishing as a boy usually will not find any fun in it when he is old. One can grind away at business for 50 years—looking ahead to the time when he will go fishing. That time never arrives. If one does not enjoy the fields, waters, and forests in his youth, to be put in those places in old age will be punishment. It is the duty of every parent to see that his children are not robbed of the early enjoyment of nature play.

The Street Child Needs Nature Guidance. Every youth has the right to both opportunity and good leadership in nature play. We inherit impulses. We do not inherit the habit of going afield or of listening to and appreciating bird music. We can go through life and never hear the birds.

I have a class on its first bird trip. A meadowlark across the field whistles "spring of the year." The whole class listens, but only a few hear it. I hold up my hand and close it to signal that the lark is singing again. A few more hear it. Why do they not all hear it? What is lacking in their complex nervous system? Why does not this sound excite their sense of hearing? Why is it not transmitted to their whole being? Some of them have had musical training, but that makes no difference. From sensing sound to recognition of sound is a long jump in sense education.

What has been said about birds applies to the whole field of nature. No city is too urban not to have kept some opportunities for studying nature. We need a new definition of nature to include skyscrapers as well as birds and flowers. "Nature guides" are trained to make the most of what the city offers.

SOME FUNDAMENTAL CONCEPTS OF NATURE EXPERIENCES IN THE HOME

The Farm Chores Were an Early Course in Social Obligation. Once upon a time, the whole farm was home. Home meant life. We turned toward home after school or after play. At the same time, the cattle gathered at the bars, the pigeons hovered nearer to the barn loft, the chickens clustered at the hencoop, the horse dragged the plow to the barn door. It was milking time. Fragrant hay came down from the mow. The eggs had to be gathered. Nighttime meant that all life was turning home. It implied home just as much as mother at the window, a good hot supper, a crackling wood fire, and a cheery lamp on the table. Seeing the dog curling up on the braided mat and getting the cat in were correlative parts of the family life. Each animal had a name and belonged to the inner circle. We were all playmates. We had a mutual understanding. The animals had to be given their supper. They had to be protected if need arose. The home animals were responsible for the first laws of citizenship. They were the means of an unconscious understanding of social obligation.

These were the great moral influences for a farm boy. He was but one of the group. He had an obligation to care for others. It took time to do the chores, but doing them was not thought of as self-sacrifice. It was not a sacrifice. It was life. When a child is cut off from the farm, he is deprived of a very important part of his education.

The Child with Pets Is Learning Social Responsibility. We can go a great deal further than we have toward duplicating the opportunities offered by the farm. A very important part of study on the farm was animal husbandry—or better understood in the city home as "keeping pets." If we cannot bring the farm into the city, we can certainly have pets.

Timeliness is an important factor in having pets. A child and a puppy seem to understand each other. They are both growing muscles. The child gets great delight in imitating sounds. In the early days, the dog is a bow-bow; sheep, a baa-baa; and the cow, a moo-cow. The child's endless repetition of these sounds is significant of a fellowship with the animal world. Instead of being surfeited with candy, dresses, and an overabundance of toys, children should care for pets. Animal friends present a simple universe. A child cannot gain the friendship of his pet unless he observes certain laws. These are the same laws by which human friendships are attained.

The nurturing of an orphan chick, for example, is a strong lesson in humanitarianism. A home has to be provided (it may be a nail keg with a small opening); he must be kept warm (by an earthen jug full of hot water wrapped in flannel); he must be fed (grit, bread crumbs, lettuce, and mash) and given clean water. He must be protected from the cat. He can be taught to come when his master

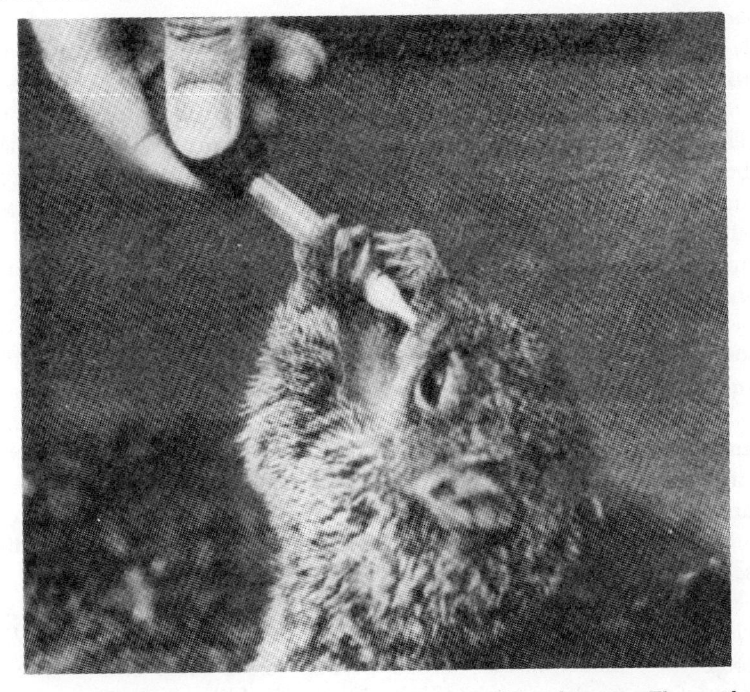

FIG. 1.—Feeding a young fox squirrel from a medicine dropper. The mother was shot, leaving four orphans. Here is one of the babies absorbing some warm milk. (*Photograph courtesy of C. M. Shipman, Willoughby, Ohio.*)

taps on the floor, to snuggle in his warm clasped hand, or to perch on a stick. A true friendship develops.

Parents Frequently Deny Children Pets Because Their Care Causes Inconvenience. Of course, caring for pets is inconvenient to most parents, but pets are for children. I realize from experience that it is inconvenient. First we had two white angora rabbits with pink eyes. They were certainly "cute." They kept growing larger and larger; and, when we went to see grandfather, we could not bring back a pumpkin, for it took our combined carrying capacity to manage suitcases and rabbits.

Then we got two Rhode Island Reds. We thought this was a grand idea, for we could eat them at camp when they were grown. On the electric car, they peeped, and everyone looked around to see the "chicken farm." I looked around too, since I didn't want to be thought guilty of anything unusual. When the chickens had grown up, no one in the family had the heart to kill them, and the thought of eating them was repulsive.

That summer, I caught two baby red squirrels. We fed them milk with a pipette. They were as cunning as could be. But, when they were grown, they would frequently show their wild nature and bite. They built a nest in the darning bag and one morning turned on the gas while playing.

Now we have Rex. He revels in auto rides. Sometimes he jumps up by the back window and braces one foot on mother's hat. The price of the hat makes no difference. His white hairs get over everything, too, mother says, but we love him just the same.

Yes, pets are inconvenient, but there is something to be said for keeping pets. The child who is starved for the lack of pets has failed to that extent in developing his own personality. His sympathies have failed to develop that much. One great source of social play has been amputated. To have animals in his environment is in his blood. Animals have been a part of family life since dog and man took to hobnobbing.

Pet Experiences Furnish an Ideal Background for Clean, Wholesome Thinking. The pet is a laboratory that permits the child to observe, to experiment, and to discover. He becomes aware of certain ideals concerning life's functions—clean cages, regular feeding, wholesome diet, and respect for body. The terms *baby*, *birth*, *nursing*, *nipples*, *navel*, *pregnant*, and *defecate* come incidentally and naturally. Not a child hesitates to clean a cage or to remove the droppings. The task is not disgusting. It is not funny. It is a part of the day's work.

Give your child experiences with pigeons, rabbits, hens, squirrels, crows, bluejays, woodchucks, rats, parrots, flying squirrels, chickens, and domestic mammals such as the calf, pig, horses, and sheep. Obtain a sitting hen or an "electric" hen. Each day, open an egg to show the wonderful development of the chick.

The facts of sex are wholesome and basic for a larger life. Each home with pets furnishes a wholesome continuous background for acquiring this knowledge, and the care of pets develops healthy habits and attitudes toward its use.

SEX EDUCATION IS A RESPONSIBILITY OF THE HOME

It is because of my faith in parents and home education that I venture to present the problem of sex-character education as a home responsibility. Homes are progressively educational. It is generally accepted that homes lend themselves to nature education and that the home is a place for vital experiences. It is also true that some parents are not tied to traditional custom and that they are not so apt to be hampered by fears and inhibitions. I am taking it for granted that parents are fully conscious of the mistakes of the past and that they recognize that the sex impulse offers not only an endowment for enrichment but an equal endowment for degradation. Sex education is one phase of nature guiding.

The Biological Background for the Story of Life. Some parents are wonderful nature guides, but they are handicapped by not possessing a fundamental biological background. The information that follows is not so much to impart knowledge as it is to guide the parent so that the life story will be a unit and finally fit into a harmonious whole.

All life begins as a cell. Seaweed, carrots, geraniums, elephants, skunks, frogs, and people start as a single cell. This cell is usually microscopic. It contains a life substance called protoplasm. In animals and in plants, the mother cell is called an *egg*, and the father cell is called a *sperm*. Life is created by union of a mother and a father cell. The union is called *fertilization*. The ovary is the organ in which the early development of the egg cell takes place.

Seeds grow from ovules found in the ovary of the flower. Mother earth is the body within which the fertile seeds continue to grow. Fish eggs are formed in the two ovaries of the female fish. Water is the medium within which eggs (cells) of most fish grow. Birds' eggs are formed in the left ovary. The ovary on the right side is not developed. Mammals develop from cells discharged from the ovarian glands of the female.

After fertilization, the egg cell divides into two cells and those two into four, and so on, until it develops the distinctive characteristics of its species. In this stage, the organism is called an *embryo*. The bird's embryo begins to grow in the egg casing before the egg is laid. It is then in the oviduct. Birds continue to keep their eggs warm by sitting on them in a nest. The hen's eggs hatch in 3 weeks. The duck's eggs hatch in 4 weeks. Baby mammals commonly have their total embryonic development in the body of the mother. The week-old embryo of the rabbit, human, and hen are difficult to tell apart.

The more highly developed the animal, the longer it is an embryo and the longer it is dependent on its parents for food and care. The mouse is an embryo 20 days, the rabbit 30 days, the human 9 months, and the elephant 20 months. After birth, baby mammals are fed milk by the mother.

In brief, this is the dramatic story of life. In itself it is neither good nor bad. It is a series of wonderful events. It is a matter of day-by-day information. The frog, the rabbit, the calf furnish this story of universality. The amount of information is not so important as an assurance of correct wholesome information when each bit of the story is sought. It is here that we need trained parents.

Practical Application in Everyday Experiences. Suppose that a group of children is asked to shell peas. Someone may discover that some of the peas are not grown. The undeveloped peas are ovules that have not been stimulated to develop. They have not received the substance of a pollen grain. They have not been fertilized. The same thing is true of a lopsided apple. The ovule on one side may not have a fertile seed.

Each spring, the sunfish can be seen laying eggs in a nest by the shore. The father sunfish makes the nest and drops the milt over the eggs and guards the nest. He puts on bright colors at mating time. Perhaps the parent has a group on a fishing trip. When cleaning the fish, he can show the roe (eggs) and the milt (sperm). He should be prepared to show some milt under the microscope. He can even show several stages of cell division.

There may be an opportunity to compare the baby partridge, which runs away as soon as it is hatched, to the helpless, naked baby robin. On each trip, the prepared parent will see a new "life story" to tell the children.

Suppose, again, some morning your little girl should find baby rats, naked and pink. Perhaps she will say, "Those are baby mice." She is told that rats have baby rats and mice have baby mice. Perhaps this is her first inkling that like begets like.

You do not announce that she has had a sex lesson. You do not mention the word *sex* any more than you do when you insist on a clean body without irritations, proper elimination, and loose clothing.

It is not necessary to go too fast or too far—the simple idea that rats have baby rats may be sufficient information for that day. It may be wise to wait until further questions are asked or further lack of understanding shown before continuing your educational campaign. Your primary aim lies in developing an uninhibited, objective relationship toward life and in providing simple, scientifically correct facts concerning reality.

If your child asks a question, he knows that his question will be respected and that he will get a correct answer. His queries are not answered as a lecture. They are not explained behind closed doors nor surrounded with hushed or whispered mystery. Every new experience challenges the child's mentality. Every turn in the trail brings new stimuli—new surroundings—new activities—new interest. We must not disappoint him.

Send for literature published by the American Social Health Association, 1790 Broadway, New York City. You will obtain much valuable help.

AMRIDGE UNIVERSITY LIBRARY

HOME ACTIVITIES REFLECT A WIDE RANGE OF NATURE INTERESTS

It would take a shrewd man to itemize and classify the ramifications of human activity and enjoyment to be found in nature in the home. They exist in the daily life of any family, even in the humblest home. The housekeeper who arranges daffodils with yellow candles to match; the father who studies about plants for the border of the walk; the girl who cuddles her puppy; the boy who is thrilled by the story of Lindbergh or Byrd, have within their innermost depths something akin to the appreciation of nature by Agassiz, Whittier, or Burroughs.

The Pocket Is the Boy's First Museum. The boy without a pocket is not a boy. The pocket is the first home of the collecting instinct. It is the child's right. A game, originated by a scout executive, consisted of each boy's emptying his pocket. The lights were turned out, and the boys were told to reclaim their treasures by feeling. They did it. This was vastly significant in its revelation of personalities. Each object was a budding interest. It stood out as making a point of contact, a foreglow of delight in what might become a lifetime satisfaction.

Attic Natural History Is an Outgrowth of the Pocket Museum. The capacity of a pocket is not unlimited. The overflow may find its way into an old bureau drawer or a homemade cabinet. It is still chiefly a junk heap of old coins, foreign curios, shells, twigs, wood, birds' nests, wild fruits, insects, stamps, and minerals. Perhaps there

Southern Christian University Library

is the beginning of a classification, or there may be an attempt to arrange the materials by size.

To prevent an outlet for the collective instinct is to cut from the child's future life one of the favorite recreations of many adults.

Nature Hobbyists. There is ample evidence that nature interest is employed for recreational purposes.

In any large city, one can find a lawyer-naturalist, teacher-naturalist, a shoemaker-naturalist, a bank clerk-naturalist, an insurance agent-naturalist, and so on. All of them are more than ordinary naturalists. Leisure yearnings in me may demand a bird hike; in you, time off to read van Loon; and, in Roosevelt, a trip to Africa. The reports of these amateurs show the advantages of nature recreation compared with other forms of recreation. (1) It is less expensive; (2) it can be enjoyed in all seasons of the year and continued throughout life; (3) it can be carried on without nerve strain; and (4) it builds good citizenship.

If the census record showed hobby growth, it would undoubtedly reveal the fact that bird hobbyists, camera fans, slow ramblers, and all the other nature specialists are increasing rapidly. This trend is a matter of opinion, but there is ample testimony for its support in the membership of nature clubs, in the attendance of nature lectures and trips, in the circulation of science books from the library, in newspaper feature stories, and in daily conversations.

THE WHOLE FAMILY CAN COOPERATE IN BACK-YARD GARDENING

Early Gardeners. There were gardens on our continent before there were people to take care of them. All the land was a garden. The ice plowed the ground, and the rivers moved the richest soil down into the valleys. The wind planted the seeds, and the feathered inhabitants and fur folks harvested the crops.

Before the white man came, the Indians had planted the native corn and squash. Whole tribes would cooperate to obtain food from mother earth. Every family knew how to plant, how to harvest, and how to prepare nature's products.

The wise pioneer settled where he was shrewd enough to see nature producing good crops. He noted that the largest trees grew in the valley. He found a spring coming from the sandstone of the valley wall, built a cabin, grubbed out a clearing, and planted seed.

Every settler carried seed. It was seed produced by grains and vegetables grown in the country of his origin and carefully brought across the sea. The pioneer knew what it meant to have a home and a garden. He knew what it meant to gain a living from the woods, the water, and the soil.

Gardening Today. There were no brick walls or pavements or ash heaps or vacant lots, until the white man came along. Then, as scientific discoveries and inventions opened new fields for exploration and industry, he was in such a hurry to make steel tracks, horseless carriages, and bricks that he didn't have any time to plant trees and flowers. Now he has made so many bricks that he is going to have a lot of spare time. A great many people who used to think that making bricks was more important than gardening realize that gardening has come into its own again, but for recreational rather than life-providing purposes. It may not be a bad idea to have to turn back to mother earth, for she still has much to offer us.

What Is a Yard For? I know what it was originally intended for: shrubs, maple sap, flowers, songbirds, aromatic herbs, root crops, fruits, berries, sunshine, and fresh air. When I go about the city, I see many yards used for things that they were not intended to be used for. Even in those yards, I see nature slipping in a few seeds, as if anxious to cover up ugliness.

Your back yard may look like a desert. If it does, it is due to someone's neglect, but you can bring nature back to the yard. The whole family should cooperate in the project. Plans should be made in advance round the family council table, with each member's ideas respected and discussed. Perhaps father will want to hide the ash heap with a trellis and vines. Son may want to plant a tree in honor of George Washington or have a fern garden in the shady corner with lilies of the valley in front. Daughter says, "May I grow lettuce and carrots?" Mother may wish that the street looked like Sycamore Road with its shade trees.

Put in a few plants that will recall the struggles of your forefathers. Plant a walnut that you brought home from camp. Build an outdoor fireplace to be the scene of many a happy outdoor meal. The family picnic, even in a back yard, is one of the best family social functions.

My Own Yard Is a Constant Source of Interest and Pleasure. Every time I go to the woods, I bring back something for the yard.

FIG. 2.—Gardening is a form of recreation that can last throughout life. *(Photograph courtesy of Paul R. Young, School Garden Department, Cleveland, Ohio.)*

I want to get on speaking terms with it. Each plant has something most interesting to teach me. If it grew in the shade, I put it on the north side of my bungalow. If it clung to a rocky hillside, I put it in my rock garden. If it had its toes in mud, I tuck it into my one-by-two swamp. On my back boundary line, I have a row of pussy willows that I cut off every spring to take to school. Of course I think that I am helping these plants to grow, but I suspect that, if the truth were known, they are helping me. They have taught me that all weather is good weather. They make me wear my old clothes, and old clothes are always the most comfortable.

There is a great deal of geography in my yard. I have a rhododendron from the Smoky Mountains; a shooting star from Evanston, Ill.; a Christmas rose from Syracuse, N. Y. (which, by the way, is a kind of buttercup instead of a rose, and blossoms in December); and a bayberry from Cape Cod. This spring, I have several seeds that I gathered last summer, including those of the alpine fir from Glacier National Park.

I enjoy my asparagus and rhubarb and dandelions, but I think that I get the greatest satisfaction from the plants given me by my friends. Those plants tell me the most. Just now I recall the red and the white peonies that my grandmother grew. Every family should have a friendship garden.

Beautiful Gardens Make Beautiful Cities. Remember, no matter what you do, it will not belong to you alone. It will give others pleasure. Today, more than ever, we want to give pleasure. If we can share joy, it will be worth while. If you make a garden and your neighbor makes a garden, and so on, your city will be a beautiful place in which to live.

Remember this, too. If you have something growing in your back yard that really interests you, something that you would like to take a friend to see, then you really have a right to take pride in your yard.

THE FAMILY PLANS FOR THE SUMMER

The Call of the Wild. The spring end of winter is the season for woodland fever. It's the time when the wilderness call plays up and down one's spine. There are pangs of restlessness for the farm and the old swimmin' hole. One hears the whisper of half-forgotten things. One longs to find one's way through the woods, perhaps to trail the honeybee or to get a whiff of new-mown hay or recently plowed ground. These symptoms need not be alarming. They are the natural periodic revolts at supercivilization. They are mental attitudes resulting from artificial lives. They are the straining of the nerve against being lulled into smug complacency, immune to stimulation by the songs, odors, and views of nature. There is nothing to do but to sign a peace contract with nature for 2 months and take to the out-of-doors. During this armistice with the city, store up a good reserve of antidisease, unadulterated sunshine, and uncontaminated sea breeze or forest air.

Gathering Vacation Literature. "Goin' natureward" has to be planned just as much as a cruise to the West Indies or a midwinter escorted tour to California. It is part of the fun. If there are boys or girls in the family, write to camps for booklets. Write to the national parks to get literature on their tourist camps. Write to the State Conservation Commission for their booklets on state parks. You may want to write to the Pennsylvania Department of Commerce, Vacation and Travel Development Bureau, Harrisburg, Pa., for their booklets on Pennsylvania nature vacations. Perhaps you would like to try out the Appalachian Mountain Club's trail-and-hut system through the White Mountains. Clear a shelf in the library for the incoming literature, and each evening get your "wilderness babies" about the fireplace for some good old-fashioned fun. This will be as much adventure for the family as equipping the covered wagon.

Choosing a Camp. Spend one evening studying the camp situation for boys and girls. You'll find the booklets very illusive. They often read like a Sunday supplement, and you may need to invite in an experienced friend to help you to put the literature through a milling process. You want whole wheat, the kind that has vitamins and proteins. If the processes of the camp have been so refined and bleached that it is simply a city school set up in the woods, the scheme is probably too stereotyped and too formal. Delegate all institutionalized literature to the wastebasket.

The more nearly the camp imitates the activities of the colonial homestead, the more nearly does it get to the root of things. There will be simplicity of dress; farm chores and dairy craft or its equivalent; manual and mechanical craft for the boys, looms and household crafts for the girls, and an abundance of woodcraft and nature lore. Community singing, dramatics, games, and water sports will also be offered under expert leadership.

When you have selected three or four camps that appeal to you, the next thing is to arrange for a personal interview with the directors.

Most directors are progressive. They are extremely enthusiastic over camp education. It is more than just a business to them. You will be better satisfied if you meet them personally, perhaps in your own home, and see them with your children. Sound out their picture of camp life and try to visualize your boy or girl in that setting. How well does it meet your child's particular interests and needs? You will wish to check up as to water supply, source of milk and fresh foods, unpolluted water for swimming, medical attention, and the type of leadership. How many counselors are there for the camp group, and what are the qualifications for counselorship?

The next thing is to study the opportunity the camp offers for real nature education. Nature education in camp should be a training for communion with the out-of-doors. This is quite a different thing from acquiring factual information about birds or trees or stars. Nature education is not botany or gardening or ornithology or animal study. It is not exposure to formal learning. It is actual living so that contact with every phase and manifestation of nature becomes a meaningful and enjoyable experience.

Select a camp at which the whole staff is interested in and enjoys the outdoor life. The leaders are those who will naturally see a beautiful sunset. They do not have to make an effort to catch the

Fig. 3.—Activities for the whole family are increasingly needed. The modern city program tends to separate families. Mother goes to the P.T.A.; father, to Rotary; Johnny, to Scouts; and Mary, to the Junior Garden Club. Following the picnic lunch, these families will be invited to go on a nature hike. (*Photograph courtesy of Tam Deering, Public Recreation Commission, Cincinnati, Ohio.*)

sound of a partridge drumming. When a camper discovers a fuzzy caterpillar walking up a coat sleeve, it is not an occasion for screaming but an opportunity for a story or an invitation to take it back to camp to rear. Counselors will not pass by fascinating legends, for example, the timekeepers of the garden—the four-o'clocks, the morning-glories, the evening primroses, or the poor-man's-weatherglass. They will be conscious of thousands of nature secrets and will be anxious to share them.

Leaders must also accept the belief that the results will vary according to the individual desires, capacities, and efforts of the campers. It is not a sin if Johnny wants to make a kite instead of reading Polaris or if Mary prefers to feed the chipmunk when a fishing trip is under way. The nature quality in the individual leader must mean more than the ability to classify flowers or to appreciate a tiger lily. It must be flexible and adaptable in all phases of camp life, in all campers, all the time. Nature education is a result of living with nature and can be acquired in no other way.

THE FAMILY CAMPING TRIP

Whether you decide to send your children to camp or not—and there is much to be said in its favor—or whether you decide on an auto camping trip for the whole family, the camp activities are somewhat the same. In each case, preparedness is the key to the success and enjoyment of the summer. This book assumes that you are a family of greenhorns. As a matter of fact, most of us are but do not like to admit it. How much do you know about the fundamental activities necessary to camping—selecting camping equipment, choosing a camp site, protecting health, building a campfire, outdoor cookery, hiking and trailmaking, and woodcraft? Preparation for each of these should be made the subject of happy family hours together before vacation comes.

Camping Equipment. Preparation for this can be played as a game on a rainy day. Perhaps you would like to have several families interested in camping participate with you. It then becomes a neighborhood gathering. The neighborhood fraternity as well as the family spirit is worth salvaging out of modern hustle and bustle. The object of the game is to see who can make the most complete list of essentials for a camping trip. First of all, make your own score card. Perhaps dad will give you 10 min. to complete a list. Someone is then called upon to read what he considers essential. If he thinks that everyone should take a casserole, fireless cooker, and washbasin, or even a piano, it may make some of you laugh. As each item is read, the group votes, and the decision of the majority determines whether or not it should be included in a list of camping necessities. The second person adds what he has on his list that has not already been given. Perhaps he remembers a waterproof matchbox and soap. The third person may think it important to carry a first-aid kit or that his blanket be marked with a name tape. Such an item as a blanket ought to arouse discussion concerning its size, warmth, and weight. You may have to call in a scoutmaster to help decide the fine points. Don't forget the ditty bag, which would contain thread, needles, wax, buttons, shoelaces, and safety pins.

The one who lists the greatest number of essential items wins and may be dubbed Daniel Boone, and the lowest scorer is the greenhorn for the day. There will be other Daniel Boones and greenhorns for different days.

Before the party breaks up, it is important that a final combined compilation of camping equipment be assembled, with specifications wherever possible, and that each family keep a copy conveniently ready for use when the actual packing for the trip begins.

A Camp Health Contest. A camp health contest may be carried on in the same way. In the Spanish-American War, there were more soldiers killed by bacteria than by bullets. The same big (or little) camp foes exist today. One should *never* drink from brooks. We should know what to use for cuts and bites and how to recognize poison ivy. All refuse should be burned. The latrine should be below and away from the spring. Flies should be kept away from the latrine pit by keeping it covered with chloride of lime. It seems as if all these things knew an inexperienced camper and jumped on him at sight. The only way to avoid them is by the armor of knowledge.

Just as soon as you can, plan a "camping site hike." It's lots of fun. The family starts at a stated place and time, presumably for an overnight trip. Dad says, however, that all hands must be back at the starting place in just 1 hr. ready to lead the group to a satisfactory camp site. All hands visit each "chosen spot." No two sites will be the same, but all good camping places must have good drinking water, good drainage, a safe fireplace, dead wood, no insects, and be off the beaten track. Vote on which is the best camping site, and cook your meal at that point. You do not stay all night. This is just practice work so that you will be safe campers to let loose in the summer.

The Campfire. The first nature lessons on a camping trip include the things upon which the whole group depends. The campfire is a good example; you will need that on the first day out. The art of fire making is not inborn, nor does it develop with memorizing lists of trees good for firewood or types of fireplace for successful fire building.

Practical nature experience must precede prescriptive nature learning. If you are to build a fire, you send out fuel gatherers. If there has been a rain, they must get pine instead of oakwood, dead instead of green wood, dry instead of wet wood, and small faggots instead of large sticks, wood safe to handle and not poison sumac. Everyone is concerned if the fire does not burn or if the meat is broiled on a poisonous stick. There is a communal condemnation if someone brings soggy wood. This is a quite different incentive from cramming facts to pass a test.

Camp Cooking. If the family does not know how to cook outdoors, they should have at least three lessons from mother. These prepara-

FIG 4.—The early pioneers were naturalists. They thatched the roof, gathered herbs for medicine, tended the corn, and made their own corn meal. What are the names of the parts of this simple handmade machinery? What did the Indians use?

tory cooking lessons can take place in the back yard. The trial-and-error method is not good enough on a camping trip. The national outdoor dish must be more digestible than a smoky "hot dog" eaten raw. Broiling is perhaps the simplest cooking method. Most beginners do not wait long enough for coals but start right in to smoke the meat. Start the fire first, and, while it is burning down to hot ashes, clean the meat, and sprinkle it with salt and pepper. Obtain a forked stick to hold the meat. Sear it on all sides, and then cook it slowly by turning. The broiled meat can be held between the halves of a split roll.

Baking is a satisfactory method and may also be tried at home "à la camp." Try a fish or a chicken. Cover it with green rhubarb leaves, pinning them together with small slivers. Cover the whole thing with a thin layer of clay and bury in red-hot ashes for an hour or more. The time will depend on the thickness of the pieces. One convenient thing about this method of baking is that, if the scales and feathers are left on, they will come off with the clay.

The camp stew is an economical dish. Use all the leftovers in the way of meat and vegetables. Put water in the kettle. Cut the meat and vegetables into small pieces. Use seasoning and allow to simmer.

The chapter on Outdoor Cookery included in the supplement will give you further advice and suggestions.

THE FAMILY TAKES A HIKE

And now for a hike. The invitation of the open road or the forest path is open to all who seek happy, wholesome adventure. How can I help you prepare for the unpredictable opportunities for enjoyable recreation that await the hiker?

Observe the Law of the Trail. Camping and hiking more than any other life develop thoughtfulness, courtesy, generosity, and comradeship. One may be well mannered in his own home and yet wear out his welcome on the trail. Ignorance of the laws of the trail is the means by which the old campaigner spots the "greenhorn" and the "tenderfoot." The code of the woods is simple. It is strict. One is on trial until he learns it.

The Trail Hog. One rule of the road is to leave it at least as beautiful as you find it. I know of trails one could follow by means of tin cans, string, eggshells, banana peelings, and paper plates that are strewn along the way. These trails are blazed by the trail hog. The path of the trail hog is most offending to the woodsman. One of the golden rules of camping is to leave no trace. All refuse is either burned or buried.

The Fire Criminals. The greenest of greenhorns is the fire criminal. He builds a big, roaring, smoking fire that he cannot get near. He fails to clean up and burn the leaves around the fire and does not put the fire out when leaving. Different states have different fire laws, and many do not allow the building of a fire without a permit. Campers disregarding these laws are subject to arrest. Fire building is an art, and the quickest way to size up a woodsman is to look at his fire.

The Ignoramus on the Farm. It is not in good form to romp in a hayfield, to cut up fence rails for fire, to leave the gate open or bars down, to throw stones in the grass, to pull hay from a stack to make a bed, to steal apples that fall by the roadside, to troop across the lawn for a drink, to steal the farmer's blueberries, to take a short cut across the plowed ground. The farmer's latchstring is always out. He is proud to have you drink from his well. He may be glad to give you some apples. He does not enjoy having you let his herd of cattle loose to run through his cornfield. Let us adopt the old law of neighborliness. Give a word of kind greeting when you meet the farmer on

FIG. 5.—A native orchid that is becoming all too rare. How many flowers are there to one plant? How many leaves? How many flower stems to a plant? Why is this correctly called the stemless lady's-slipper? Which is the best name: pink lady's-slipper, pink orchid, or Indian moccasin? (*Photograph by Robert Coffin.*)

the road. Pay a compliment to the water from his well and enjoy the view from his porch.

Hands Off Cached Property. A cache is an outdoor storage of food or supplies. Arctic explorers cache their supplies for the return trip. To disturb these goods might cause death. If you find a canoe hidden by a lake, leave it there. A thoroughbred woodsman never disturbs cached property. A greenhorn usually does, not because he is dishonest, but because he does not know the ways of the woods.

Protection of Native Plants. Woodsmen know that there is great danger of extermination of many of our most interesting plants. This is because they are torn up by the roots. The arbutus, ground pine, sabbatia, gentian, columbine, orchid, fern, and jack-in-the-pulpit need protection. If collected, these plants should be cut sparingly with a knife. It is better taste to cut a few sprays than to gather a bunch. Protect rather than destroy. Leave them for others to enjoy.

Tree Butchers. Inexperienced naturalists, boys with new knives, curio gatherers, and tree butchers cut bark from the birch trees and leave the scars for all future visitors to see. It would be better form to cut down one white birch and use the bark from its trunk rather than to ring many trees, leaving them to mar the landscape.

The American holly, mountain laurel, pussy willow, and black alder are subject to wood vandalism. Many people break off the branches and leave an ugly-shaped shrub. Use the knife rather than mutilate the tree.

There is the custom of carving one's initials on a beech tree. Have a soft poplar stake at hand for everyone to carve upon rather than have the whole forest a series of totem poles.

The Garrulous Member. Every group usually has someone who talks much and says little. He sees nothing in the surroundings and hears less. He may be full of garrulity and giggles, but the remainder of the group may wish to see the lake or hear the wood thrush. A woodsman sees and hears and is a man of few words. "A wise old owl lived in an oak, the more he heard the less he spoke; the more he spoke the less he heard. Why aren't we all more like that bird?"

Water Wailers. Greenhorns on the trail are continually wailing for a drink of water. They have always had water at their demand. To wait for a drink of water is a lesson in self-denial that they have never learned. An old scout may be as thirsty as you, but he never complains. You may never guess that he is thirsty. He is a patient waiter.

Courtesies en Route. It is wood etiquette to pass the word back, as: "Low bridge" when you are going under something; "All to the left" when an auto is coming; "Look out for poison ivy"; "See the Turk's-cap lily"; "Drinking water on the right."

"Freeze." This term—"pipe down" on shipboard, "'tenshun" in the army, "silence" in the courtroom—one of the first laws in

tenderfooting, means to freeze immediately when the signal is given.

Camp Chores. In camp, no one is exempt from camp chores. There are no bosses. Everyone shares in the tasks. I know of a party of campers who went away and left their dirty dishes for the guide to wash. This breach of wood etiquette was unpardonable. It meant a new guide for the next trip.

Fig. 6.—The house of the jug wasp. On every trip one student would discover the house of the jug wasp. No other student did. How do you explain this curious fact? (*Photograph by Robert Coffin.*)

Retracing the Trail. Perhaps the next step in this preliminary training camp is to play the game of retrace. Three people go wandering through the woods. They walk in single file, with the leader ahead. After having gone far enough to make it somewhat of a problem to retrace the exact route, the members of the party about-face. It is now up to the one who was in the rear to show the way. He will look for broken twigs, leaves that have been recently disturbed, and "striking things" that he saw on the way. He starts with a score of 50, but a point is taken off if he halts or hesitates at one point for a minute. Two points are taken off if he strikes off in the wrong direction. The two taking the test take turns retracing. Every camper should walk with his eyes as well as with his feet. This game is a training in observation.

Hike to Collect Something. On your family camping trip, you will have a great time if you decide to collect something. I once took a rustic candleholder trip.

I know a man who always collected stones for his fireplace. He can now tell you just where each came from. His son, when he was in

FIG. 7.—Pioneer girls were amateur chemists. This one is making soap, a very necessary article after a morning in the garden. This young lady suggests that soapmaking may be recreation.

the first World War, wrote and asked what he should bring home. The father asked him to bring a stone from France. Many interesting stories have gathered around this fireplace.

Another friend always comes home with a new walking stick. He keeps a sharp lookout on all his hikes and, in the course of years, has made a unique collection. The roots often take a grotesque form that may be carved into a head. Sticks around which the bittersweet has twined are often oddities for canes.

A trip to stock the family aquarium is full of interest. You get a wire hoop or make one out of stout wire; a mosquito-netting bag is fastened over the wire, and the hoop is then fastened to a broom handle. This is called a *dip net* and may be used to catch minnows and tadpoles. Clean sand, an aquatic plant or two, and irregular rocks are used for the aquarium. Small fish are better than large ones, and they should be kept clean and cool.

Handcraft. After dinner, you may wish to take a nap and then to make a necessary piece of tent furniture. Perhaps you do not have a chair. It is a rare privilege to be able to go out into the woods with father to get hickory sticks for the framework and then down to the meadow to gather cattails for weaving the back and the seat. Later you might enjoy carving or burning a design on the chair back.

Fig. 8.—One of nature's compasses. Study the rock cap on the pinnacle of ice. Which direction is south? Which way did the camera face? This picture was taken on top of Sexton Glacier, Glacier National Park. How does a compass plant work? Lactuca is the compass plant in the Northeastern states.

Go for a Swim. To make your trip completely successful, you will want to take a swim. Numerous varieties of nature experiences await you. Perhaps you'll discover some shiners. Since they make good pickerel bait, dad may invite you to go on a trawling expedition. Someone may note that shiners always hang around the shore and want to know why. If there is a nature guide handy, he will tell you that they keep in shallow water to escape the larger fish. Perhaps he cannot answer the question, "Where are the ears?" You make a note of that in your diary so that you can look it up at the library. When you prepare the fish for dinner you find fish roe. Father may tell you that they are eggs and that some fish lay 8,000,000 eggs. Such a contribution to your knowledge of science may lead up a dozen pathways. It may lead to a straightforward talk on being born, to a discussion on why some fish are protected by law, to an explanation of what is meant by a school of fish, or to speculation as to how the cave man caught fish.

Learn to Read Nature Like a Book. Every locality has its local color, its own geology, its own historic trees, and its special springs. The nature guide—whether he be parent or camp director—must be able to recognize and interpret such nature phenomena. He must be able to answer many questions simply and intelligently. Why is there a whirlpool there? What made that rock shiny? What causes that cliff to be red? How could the Indians cook in baskets? Is it too late to get a picture of this orchid? Do I smell peat burning? What is "red snow"?

Carry a tiny magnifying glass with you when you go walking. Nature will often surprise you when you examine her closely.

Take a pocket guidebook for unfamiliar birds, flowers, butterflies, or stars. The ten-cent stores and drugstores handle many handbooks for naturalists. Use them whenever a new experience whets your curiosity about nature's children.

With Emerson, we can define the royal man as "he who knows what sweets and virtues are in the ground, the waters, the plants, the heavens, and how to come at these enchantments." Such a status is not reached after one hike or after one summer spent outdoors, but, if one has an ear for nature's secrets and an eye for her beauty each time he walks in her ways, it will not be long before he can claim kinship with Emerson's ideal.

CHAPTER II

NATURE ACTIVITIES IN THE COMMUNITY

Educators Must Assume Leadership in Community Nature Activities. A large body of nature activities, which have appeared in every community within the last generation, can no longer be ignored in the education of every citizen. These are of two kinds: (1) those that concern the preservation or betterment of the community and demand a knowledge of natural science and (2) those that serve recreational purposes for leisure-time enjoyment. The pioneer child sought to understand nature in its relation to the needs of his family. He had to trap for furs, gather herbs for medicine, and "do the chores" that he might live. There was, as yet, no necessity for interpreting natural laws as they might affect groups, communities, or nations. Conservation of soil, trees, or birds was unthought of. European weeds and rats, the English sparrow and starling, the San José scale, the gypsy and brown-tail moths, and a horde of other pests had not arrived. Folks were not rubbing elbows so closely that a knowledge of bacteria, sanitation, pure air, pure food, and clean communities was vital.

Where to find leisure, not what to do with it, was the problem of the pioneer. Later, when the pressure of time-consuming labor slackened, the use of free time was ignored as an important educational factor contributing to satisfaction in life. Originally, the summer was left free so that the boys could help with the crops. Through "urbanizing," it became a lost summer, so far as child development was concerned, until the camp was originated. Scouting and the 4-H Clubs were organized, if not in a spirit of revolt, at least because the schools had not appreciated or supplied the needs for which they stand.

Through years of trial and error, parks and playgrounds have proved worth while. Hiking, nature clubs, and pets are here to stay.

These nature activities prevail in every community. They permeate the school program as warp to woof. The whole fabric of recreation is spun by the community, of which the school should be the educational headquarters. Recreational activities must be nurtured, safeguarded, and coordinated.

Many principals have already assumed this responsibility. It may not be amiss to think through the line of reasoning by which a school principal arrives at the point where he decides to work out a program of nature activities for his community.

A Brief for a School-community Program

I. *General Assumptions.*

A. *Education* is life rather than a preparation for life. The educational period is therefore 7 days a week, 12 months a year.

B. The *school* is a work-play-study unit rather than a building. It exists for the welfare of the child, not for the presentation of subject matter.

C. The *community* is a nature-study classroom, with resources more powerful than the school building. Nature opportunities are becoming less and less in the schoolroom and more and more in the community.

D. The *principal* is the educational guide for the community.

II. *Analysis of the Elements in the Situation.*

A. The Child.

1. There are some children who cannot succeed in a school building who can find a corner in the community in which they can succeed. Edison and a host of others succeeded in spite of the formalized curriculum. The child is a vital part of the community.
2. Children should be judged by their contribution to and cooperation in the community rather than by competition against others in the acquisition of factual knowledge.
   a. The community has the child four times as long as the school.
   b. The community educates the child.
   c. The community provides a wider range of nature opportunities than does the school.
3. Children benefit from organized extracurricular nature activities.
   a. The average scout gets more nature activities and a richer experience in nature study than as a public school pupil.
   b. The summer camp that has the child for 24 hr. a day for 8 weeks has more influence over him than the school that simply has him for 5 hr. a day for 40 weeks.

B. The Community.

1. The community should provide equal nature opportunities for all.
   a. The family is the basic institution of the community. Many nature activities are most worth while in the home. Successful

home activities need guidance. The vital curriculum meets these needs.

b. The nursery school is a community of nature interests of the first 6 years of life. Educationally, it may be more important than the remaining years.

c. Someone must be responsible for the education of boys and girls up to eighteen, whether they are in school or out.

d. Many adults spend their leisure time in some form of nature recreation.

e. Machines have reduced the working period to 6 hr. a day for 5 days a week. This means more leisure time for industrial workers. The community must make provision for its use.

2. Education and crime in a community have a relationship. In our communities as a whole, we spend more than three times as much for crime as for education. In communities where education costs more than crime, we find parks, playgrounds, home gardens, beautiful yards, scout troops, and other natural opportunities.
3. Communities with a complete schedule of nature activities have eliminated idleness for both children and adults.
4. City communities have paid a high price for industrialization. Within a generation, most communities have substituted overcrowding, noise, smoke, apartment houses, factories, electric cars, speeding, movies, audiences, pavements, gasoline, and rapid transits for farms, fields, woods, ocean, hills, sunshine, clear streams, and fresh air. Our education must be so organized that we may bring back to the community those things that the community took away from us.
5. Communities must plan for recreational improvement in all phases of their outdoor life.
6. The ideal community has beautiful homes and school surroundings consisting of lawns and flowers, adequate playgrounds, and parks with trees and swimming pools; scout troops with competent leaders and satisfactory meeting places; camps, nature clubs, museums, lecture courses, and exhibitions.

C. The Principal.

1. The principal should recognize that work-leisure nature activities not only have educational possibilities but need supervision.
2. The principal should be able to analyze the nature needs of a community for scouting, playgrounds, recreation leaders, and should have the initiative to promulgate the ideas and also the executive ability to set the ideas into action.
3. The principal who is an interested, intelligent, active supporter of desirable community nature activities does the most for the children of that community.

4. The principal who brings to his school the worth-while nature activities of other communities and of other schools is providing opportunities that are advancing all communities.

The Argument: A Community Nature Program Meets Seven Objectives of Education. *Protection of Health.* Sickness means the disobedience of one of nature's laws. The knowledge of certain nature facts is necessary for the welfare of human society. One ignorant person in a community may be responsible for the houseflies that exist in that locality. One housefly can carry enough typhoid organisms to inoculate the entire population. Sanitation in a community depends upon the membership of that group and can be safeguarded only by universal education.

In the case of forests, the appalling loss from preventable fires and the economic distress from the lack of conservation are striking examples of the need of a nature education that emphasizes scientific information.

The community way of thinking means the working together on such problems as mosquito control, the elm-leaf beetle, protecting the bobwhite, forest-fire laws, destroying poison ivy, pleasant landscapes, and clean milk. The gifts of nature—sunshine, fresh air, mountains, and sea—cannot be disassociated from health. Hiking, camping, gardening, and the care of pets mean positive rather than negative habits. The speed of tomorrow requires maintained physical, mental, and emotional recreation. Community nature activities provide all of these.

Cooperation with the Home. The home is the basic social unit of the community. The well-being of a community is built upon the foundation of homes. The family nature-study life is a basic element in the understanding of sex, health habits, and hygiene. Biology commences at home. Home planting and landscaping, feeding the birds, preventing flies, the warfare against rats, preventing molds and mildews, keeping a hive of bees, and caring for pets are nature activities that concern the home. Children and their parents need guidance and individual counseling in such home nature activities. The school recognizes this need and stimulates home nature activity in the classroom, whereas the community program carries it further through a home nature service. This includes opportunities and guidance in gardening, ornamentation of grounds, care of house plants, the fun of having pets, the family outing, and automobile camping.

Dissemination of Knowledge. The community nature program provides an educational center for general nature information and for the solution of specific community nature problems. The number of facts it has at its command is not so important, however, as the guidance it offers in knowing how and where to get necessary information and the best use to make of it. Obviously, the nature problems in an Italian settlement with vineyards are very different from the problem of a commuters' neighborhood. The nature educators must be familiar with whatever types of problems occur in the lives of ordinary citizens of the community so that they may help solve them adequately.

FIG. 9.—A boy scout is prepared. Scouts of Troop 27, Providence, R.I., clearing away a fallen tree from grounds of the Rhode Island College of Education after the hurricane of Sept. 21, 1938. (*Photograph courtesy of J. Harold Williams, Chief Scout Executive, Narragansett Council, Boy Scouts of America.*)

Citizenship. Scouting, hiking, and camping usually are done in groups. Such organization usually means teamwork, which, in turn, means citizenship. Neighborhood garden and bird clubs give rise to neighborhood consciousness, neighborhood pride, neighborhood beautification, parks and playgrounds. The citizen of today who enjoys the open spaces, the shaded highways, landscaped grounds, and areas for hiking will be the citizen of tomorrow who will carry the responsibility of trusteeship and loyalty.

By introducing children to interests in nature literature, by developing appreciations of the landscape, by launching natural science clubs, leaders are adapting their school courses to a training for future responsibility. In the community itself, the nature program fulfills its civic obligations by setting up a community nature service to include such activities as the development and enjoyment of parks, the beautifying of the streets and commons by the village improvement society, the planting and conserving of shade trees, the encouragement of beautiful school grounds, the distribution of shrubs and plants by the chamber of commerce, horticultural exhibitions and flower shows, nature guides for field trips and outings, scouting, planning and equipping a camping park.

Vocational Stimulation. Many vocations are opened to the youth whose hobby is nature study. He or she may become an artist, an astronomer, a beekeeper, a camp director, a conservationist, a dairyman, a farmer, a forester, a fruit culturist, an entomologist, a nature writer, a nature photographer, a scout naturalist, a ranger-naturalist, a taxidermist, a weatherman, a government biologist, a landscape engineer, a tree surgeon, an ornithologist, a geologist, a nature teacher, or some other "ist" or "er" in the great host of nature lovers.

Worthy Use of Leisure. Our educational training must provide for complete living and for the enjoyment of the increased leisure. The monotony of the machine age must be compensated for by leisure-time activities that take one into the open and provide a maximum of satisfaction and recreation. Until recently, the school never grasped the idea that here was an opportunity for education. As a result, we have been caught unprepared for the amount of leisure that has been thrust upon us. Many of us find ourselves in the peculiar position of having time off and no knowledge or training for the wise use of it. Curbstone idling exists because a vast army of the unemployed cannot turn toward nature recreation. They are hangers-on-to-the-curbstone because they are not conscious that there is anything interesting just beyond the curbstone.

In contrast, there is a much smaller body of folks trained and equipped for leisure who, in their early youth, developed nature interests and are not now "killing time." One person will grow dahlias, his neighbor will make a rock garden, another breed trout, another sketch vistas, and another is a collector of mushrooms. Many hit the trail. Life is not one minute's boredom after another.

A progressive community nature program provides a wide variety of recreational activities. Progressive nature-study leaders realize that the curriculum for instruction is the sum total of the leisure-time activities that already exist in the community. They see to it that children are habituated in the enjoyment of parks, museums, camps, forests, fields, gardens, and streams in school days. Whatever the form of nature recreation, it can endure into later life.

Character Development. Today educators believe that character education calls for interesting opportunities to act and react. The

FIG. 10.—A boy scout is reverent. A scene in the Outdoor Cathedral, Camp Yawgoog, Narragansett Council, Boy Scouts of America. (*Photograph courtesy of J. Harold Williams, Chief Scout Executive, Narragansett Council.*)

activity must be so interesting that the participant will accept the annoyance of sharing, or cooperating, in order to take part. Scouting, camping, and allied activities provide living situations for personal development. What will the individual do when swimming, building a fire, tramping in the vicinity of a private orchard, carrying an ax, when on a camping trip, or when sailing a boat, each of which activities calls for self-direction? It is practice, not theory; attitude, not knowledge that counts in such situations. Provide an organized outdoor program with good leadership, and there will be a continuity of situations that call for self-control, purposeful striving, recognition of the dignity of work, orderliness in everyday life, health, and leadership.

The First Step in Organizing a Community Nature Program Is to Make a Survey. Before the principal plans, he must have a clear-cut picture of what the community is already doing. Do the schools have nature study? Who is the supervisor, or who are the enthusiastic nature teachers? What is the relation of the teaching of science to enjoyment of outdoor activities? What has been accomplished in playground development, shade trees, and parks? What is being done by the library? Is there a community museum? Who are the most successful nature leaders in scouting? What are the nature activities at the Y.M.C.A. and the Y.W.C.A.? Has the community a hiking club? An Audubon Society? A garden club? Who are its leaders? What individuals have collections? Who are the village enthusiasts in trees, wild flowers, insects, minerals?

An analysis of all these factors will give the organizer a working knowledge of the wealth or dearth of nature activities in the community and will forestall oversight or duplication of community projects. Moreover, it should provide a list of leaders who will later become the executive committee for the program.

SCHOOLTEACHING AND COMMUNITY RECREATION

Leadership in the Schools. Responsibility for an intelligent understanding of the world we live in rests on the teacher of elementary and natural science. The teacher who is to produce enthusiasm for recreational activities in that world must possess a knowledge of and an enthusiasm for those activities. Often teachers are masters of scientific knowledge, when it is in a book, but have no time for science, when it is outdoors. The leisure-time advocate must be one who has had experience, satisfaction, and enjoyment in the field. Nature recreation requires skilled leadership. Most people who go into the woods do not know what to see, what to hear, or what to think. That is why the government has ranger-naturalist service in our national parks. Through years of patient effort there have likewise been teachers who have stood for those types of nature activity that satisfy diversified human wants. That kind of interpretation of the outdoors has become an increasingly important service.

Educating for Leisure Is an Aim of Science Teaching. Courses of study in science are unanimous in listing the wise use of leisure time as one of the aims. The content of these courses, however, presents very little evidence on training for leisure. The topics themselves would indicate that those responsible are hardly conscious of leisure-time activities. This inconsistency between aim and content would indicate that courses of study and textbooks in general science have not caught up with the approved aim of preparing for a wiser use of leisure time.

The old-fashioned laboratory education dealing with bones and muscles to be learned affords no time for hikes, vistas, a nature picnic, early-morning bird walks, nature photography, national-park tours, fishing, and the great wealth of leisure-time offerings. When Jack is memorizing laws of invisible radiation, wave motion, resonance, transmission of heat, vaporization, calorimetry, induced currents, polarization, or learning that force (in absolute units) equals mass times acceleration, he may well be taught that a wee bit of his energy can also be used to stalk birds, to get a "kick" out of fishing, or, with equal profit, he may be urged to start a life interest in collecting rocks. Instead of labeling diagrams, classifying plants, outlining leaves, naming bones, and chanting principles, he may just as profitably hike to a mountaintop. There is too great a gulf between what science can contribute and what it does to contemporary life.

Where Does Factual Material Fit into the Picture? Recently a letter came to my desk which read in part as follows: "Many teachers are having rabbits for pets in their kindergartens and nursery schools. One teacher has run into this problem. The little animals which this teacher has called rabbits must be hares. What should one do in trying to give accurate information to parents and children? Any help that you can give us will be greatly appreciated." I suspect that many teachers and camp directors are straining for gnats when they should be swallowing a camel.

When a boy, I discovered a bobwhite's nest. I made a daily trip to the nest with the hope of obtaining a young chick for a pet. One day, to my surprise, the little ones had hatched and gone. A few years later, I met a bobwhite hen with her young, and she led me away from her children by acting as if she had a broken wing. Such experiences are everlasting in one's memory. They were much more important to me than whether the animal should be called bobwhite, quail, or partridge.

In more recent years, I have learned that most birds hatched on the ground have down and can run the first day. Robins and other birds hatched at a safer height are naked and blind. And so with rabbits. Rabbits are born in burrows, naked and blind. Hares are born in a "form" on top of the ground, with fur and open eyes. Perhaps the rabbit is a weak runner and has a constant color because he can retreat to a hole. Perhaps the hare is quick and alert, feeds at night, and often changes color because he is in the open. These ever-widening acquaintances are much more interesting than quibbling with words.

And how confusing our English language can become. The dragonfly is neither dragon nor fly. The crayfish is not a fish. Scientifically speaking, the "grasshopper" is a locust and the "locust" is a cicada. The Car-*rib*-ean Sea is preferred and is so pronounced by the natives of that region, yet it is known to us as the Carri-*be*-ean. The Belgian hare is a large rabbit, and the cottontail rabbit is a hare. When do these facts become important?

In one word, the key to the situation may be most simply expressed by the word *need*. The mother rabbit must be treated carefully and must be given proper food. Very soon the young must have space for exercise. The mother rabbit is sick and needs immediate attention. By caring for the rabbits, the child's mind is occupied with appropriate problems. If an individual child in his reading has his curiosity aroused as to whether the pet is a rabbit or hare, his need should be satisfied. He will be growing by his individual needs.

Similarly, the occasion may arise when one would be glad to know that the American hare is wrongly called a rabbit. The name rabbit originally belonged to a European burrowing species which was ancestor to the domestic rabbit and Belgian "hare." The domestic rabbit is correctly so called, as it descended from the European rabbit. If a boy or teacher is going into the rabbit business, it is important to know that a rabbit can "burrow out." If the camp director comes into possession of a wild hare, he would be interested to know that there are no wild rabbits native to North America but that there are 20 species of wild hares. The hare is better at jumping than digging; therefore his pen would be built accordingly.

A hunter in Massachusetts is allowed a bag limit or possession of two hares and five rabbits a day, and there is no closed season for European hares and rabbits.* The large gaunt hares of the plains with their immense ears have always been called "jack rabbits," and, in

*1940 statistics.

spite of schoolteachers, the farmer will insist in putting up "rabbit-proof" fences. He deems it more important to know that these animals do not burrow under the fence than to say "Jack Hare." The "Br'er Rabbit" of the South is the cottontail. These names have been fixed by current usage and should be accepted as such.

Whether we possess a rabbit or hare is relatively unimportant, but it is extremely important whether our experience leads us to:

Scientific doubt. Questioning whether a rabbit's foot brings good luck. Can a rabbit jump into a brier patch and not get scratched?

Readiness to accept good proof. What one thought was a rabbit is a hare.

The use of reason. The rabbit's long ears are for hearing and not for lifting.

Direct observation. The rabbit nurses her young. How many upper front teeth? Are the young born blind or with eyes open?

Discovery. That cabbage used as food causes strong odors in the cage.

PLAYGROUNDS ARE NEIGHBORHOOD CENTERS FOR NATURE RECREATION

What Is a Natural Playground? We must distinguish then between the artificial playground and the natural playground. An artificial playground has ladders to climb instead of birches, awnings instead of shade trees, a dust-laying preparation instead of shrubs, an Italian tiled wading pool instead of a frog pond. Up to this point, the artificial playground might just as well be in a shed or basement. The artificial playground is a very uninspiring place for the enjoyment of nature. Nature study as a form of play does not mean clearing the field for action, but quite the contrary—keeping the wild places wild for nature activities. We cannot play checkers until we get the checkerboard. In other words, we cannot utilize this form of playground activity unless we prepare the way by setting aside natural areas.

A natural playground is an outdoor neighborhood area with which are associated fresh air and sunshine, trees, flowers, animal life, and play apparatus. There may be too many swings and too much apparatus. When nature's furnishings are removed, the playground becomes an outdoor gymnasium. A natural playground is an outdoor schoolroom and should supplement but not duplicate school activities. Birds and flowers are as essentially a part of the playground equipment as graveled areas and artificial equipment. All the resources of the area are utilized for playground activities. The playground that has been fortunate enough to have had its trees and weeds tolerated has therein a great natural resource in a crude state. The development and utilization of this resource is a pioneer adventure in nature education.

The Playground Leader Should Be a Trained Nature Guide. It is just as essential to train leaders for the outdoor schoolroom as for the four-walled room, and the playground that counts most is going to reflect that educational background.

It is not necessary to push someone in a swing. Children will play on apparatus without leadership. Give the boys a bat and ball, and they will organize at once. Oftentimes, they know more about it than the leader. The playground director must be much more than a supervisor for this form of physical activity. The effective leader is going to give children an ability to see and to do. He is going to teach them to protect life. He is going to develop habits that will make for enrichment of leisure time. He is going to bring out the best that is in them.

The Playground Leader Must Be a Good Child Psychologist. He must not only recognize and sympathize with the individual interests of his group but be able to direct their energies into constructive channels.

Every child at the age of six is passing through the "mud dauber" stage. It will be natural for some to carry a snake in the pocket. (That may be the boy's' first test for the playground leader.) Then there will be the collector of shells and rocks; the laboratory botanist type who is willing to dissect the daisy to the chant of "eeny, meeny, mo"; the entomologist who is ready to experiment with grasshoppers to see them spit molasses, caterpillars to see them walk tightrope, and possibly bumblebees to see which end stings; the young physicist who likes to build water wheels and kites; the "big, brave boy" who dares to pick up toads, or tries out "the snake dying before sunset" doctrine. Pulling legs off a fly and the sport of shooting them with a popgun is an early delight. But, when a lad knows that the fly has nonskid feet, eats through a sieve, and "sings" with his wings, he ceases torturing him. When he learns later that flies are more dangerous than bears, he does not return to torturing. Instead, he plans a campaign to prevent them. This is education at its best. It is the playground director's responsibility.

Objectives. It is essential that leaders formulate their objectives for a nature program before the opening of the playground. Otherwise, it will be nothing but a vague experience with mere guessing as to results. Having listed the aims, the next thing is to plan a program to give the children experience in meeting these ideals.

Suppose that the aim is neatness. There was a time when the leader would put a proverb before the child. In this case, it would probably be, "Cleanliness is indeed next to godliness." In some mysterious way, this was supposed to make him clean. This method was in vogue for generations before anyone even suspected that maxims did not make him clean. A lecture on neatness does not carry much more weight. Ideals are abstract principles. One does not keep the roadway and countryside neat in general. He performs a thousand acts of neatness. He cleans up after a picnic. He washes his hands before mixing the bread. He puts out his campfire so that it will not blacken the forests. He refrains from breaking glass. He burns his shavings. He buries his tin cans. He respects pure springs. He comprehends the smoke nuisance. He votes against the pollution of streams. Profiting by these experiences, he becomes a person who stands for neatness in the out-of-doors. Now the ideal of neatness becomes vitally important. The playground affords opportunities for concrete personal experiences in hundreds of nature situations that make for high ideals. If there are no nature experiences, there can be no development of nature ideals.

Nature Experiences Mean Materials. Every child must have material, but not the expensive, nondestructible kind. He would much rather have a brook and good, rich mud oozing up between his toes. He must handle and dissect the material. Guide him from mud pies to clay modeling. Play a game in which he interprets tracks in the sand. At the Playground Leaders' School on Long Island, we went to a clay bed and experimented in making various models. Some youngsters near by joined in. It caught like measles. Spread your nature interests by contagion.

As another illustration of nature play growing out of nature materials, we carried on imaginary horse trading. We used sticks for horses, a red osier dogwood stick for a red horse, an ash-colored viburnum for the gray mare, and the shoots of the kinnikinnick for a good roan horse. (How many of you know what color a roan horse is?) We were more serious with our horse trading than David Harum —and I am not sure but that David Harum's work was his play. Horse trading to him was a game or a sport. Give youngsters a chance to explore and dissect. Guide their experimenting into the acquiring of knowledge culled from a rich background of natural resources found on the playground. Give them material, and they will furnish the imagination to put it to use. There is no danger that the child who plays with imaginary horses is to become a horse jockey! Imagination, invention, discovery, and contest in games are recreational play. We must develop in the child a lively imagination and a spirit of discovery so that throughout life he will always have the spirit of play. First-hand nature materials are the medium for this development.

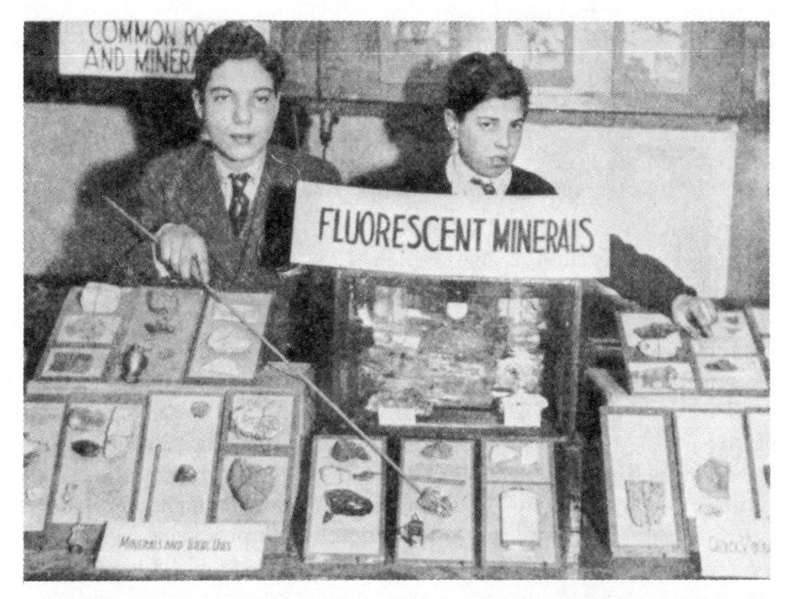

Fig. 11.—Fluorescence in minerals. Melvin Berger and Nicholar Peters, age twelve, explain their mineral collection and demonstrate their homemade box to show fluorescence in minerals at a science fair of the Elizabeth Peabody House, 84 Broadway, E. Somerville, Mass. This fair has been held annually since 1935. Over 150 boys and girls from 15 clubs exhibit such things as model coal mines, homemade incubators, and a petroleum well that really gushes. Each chooses his own subject, studies about it, and works out his exhibit. Who can deny that "science makes the world of tomorrow"? (*Photograph courtesy of H. Henry Platt.*)

The Library. Every well-regulated playground should possess or have access to a good nature library, which includes both fiction and the actual facts that are literally stranger than fiction. There will be all kinds of book about early man, caves, dogs, cabins, fire, canoes, pets, history, and biography. As far as possible, the child should be stimulated to observe and, secondly, to read and find out for himself. Therefore, alongside the storybook, there should be books for information.

A Museum. And we must not neglect the playground museum. Every forward-looking city has a natural-history museum rich in materials. Many now have a Burroughs or Roosevelt Club where children are given priceless nature experiences under leadership. The child who misses such an opportunity is neglecting an important phase of growth. The parent, too, is neglecting an opportunity if he does not find in museum and library a very real stimulant. He may go to them to refresh his knowledge. Or he may discover them in the company of children to whom these things, whether books or museum exhibits, may become adventures. The playground museum may start in an orange crate, in the toolhouse, or in an honest-to-goodness room.

THE PLAYGROUND GROUP WILL NEED TO GET BEYOND THE PLAYGROUND

Nature study in the city is a field distinct from nature study in the country, yet, with trained nature guides, much of value can be accomplished in it. Concepts of the physical world, of an orderly universe, of evolution itself may grow out of experiences resulting from playground activity. They often transcend playground limits.

The Earth Story. We need a broad general knowledge of the story of the earth. Near community playgrounds, there are always new excavations for buildings and new streets. Make an excursion to one of these a starting point. Let the group collect water-made and fire-made rocks. They will not collect long before problems set in. One may ask, "How did that rock get into layers?" If you are a wise guide, you will not tell him directly. You may take some gravel and shake it in a quart jar of water. He will observe that it settles in layers. It was in the same way that layered rock was deposited on a larger scale on the ocean floor. If the group is alert, they will ask with wonder, "Was the ocean here once?"

Frequently a fossil is discovered in excavated limestone, sandstone, or shale. It may be the impression of a shell or of a foot. Even ripple marks and raindrop autographs may be disclosed. To think that these records were made 100,000 years ago stirs the imagination. You hear that a new public library is going up. You get a permit to visit it and gather samples. You note that one block is a deeper red, and, upon inquiry from an observant youth, you explain rusting. Everyone has to have a piece of slate that is being used for the roofing. Johnny finds a specimen of granite. It is a dandy, with a beautiful polish on one side. There are enough fragments of marble from the blocks used for stairways to take back for the whole group and their families.

The group returns to the playground and discovers that it has a large and varied assortment. They pool their experiences and new knowledge of the stones. There is information enough in where each specimen came from and how it was formed and what particular use was being made of it to give any child a sound elementary understanding of geology.

Sky Study. Gather the group on the playground some clear starry night or take them across the ferry if your city is near water. Perhaps you point to the North Star and tell them to imagine that they are pilots steering their courses by that star. Find the stars of the Great Dipper. Perhaps your group will see a shooting star. Perhaps you can tell the youngsters that all suns are stars or that all stars are suns. Try to remember all the questions they ask you. Or better yet, keep a list of those that you cannot answer. Children have an unquenchable thirst for star knowledge.

The Story of Life. What child does not turn with eager curiosity to the beginnings of life? What miracles there are in the story of the green moss and the gray lichen that cling to the tree trunks in the city park! From where did they come? How did they come? Whither will they go? Sit with the group on a park bench and identify big dogs and little dogs, queer-shaped dogs and hairless dogs with the help of *The Book of Dogs* by the National Geographic Society. This tells the story of the domestication of dogs. Each boy and girl not only will learn to appreciate anew man's first animal friend but will have spread before him the panorama of evolution. It is not preached or told. He sees it right there in the park.

"Them's porcupine eggs," ventured an urchin when shown some chestnut burrs. He took the chestnuts home and planted them in a coffee tin. He also planted beans and corn. He went to the movies and saw the evolution of a chick from an egg. A true conception of the whole picture of evolution was in the process of being built.

When young minds ask wholesome questions about babies growing to manhood, give straightforward answers. Show the group the thrilling story of life on your library table. Start a green moss garden this spring. Have polliwogs and frogs' eggs in a sanded aquarium, place budding twigs in bottles of water, sprout some acorns, bring in cocoons and bursting pine cones. Every one of these is a serial in a thrilling story. Since children are going to learn the story anyway, it makes a tremendous difference *how* they learn it.

Trailing. The playground is the hub from which the nature guide leads his group on numberless trails of nature discovery and adventure. When once we start to look for the wilderness in the city, it is astonishing what can be found. In Rochester, I once had a group of Girl Scout leaders on a trip in the city park. We discovered a fox den with a steel trap set in it. In Youngstown, we found mink tracks in Mill Creek Park. The mink had circled the edge of a pond and caught a fish. In the center of Cleveland, we saw a covey of quail. There are myriads of nature experiences in any city that are waiting to stir the imagination of red-blooded boys and girls.

COMMUNITY ATTITUDES TOWARD LOCAL NATURAL RESOURCES

There Are Community Patterns in Nature Appreciation. If hordes of people in a community can find no better thing to do outdoors than to sulk on a park bench, it is a sad reflection on their education. If the minds of public-square dwellers lie dormant when tulip bulbs are pushing through the warm earth, their childhood teachers failed to show them the pulse of spring. The question whether a community is more interested in the exploitation of nature than in the resources may be answered in a drive around it. If the congested district takes it for granted that a valley is a convenient place for ashes and tin cans or that the only beautiful waterfall or lake can be subjugated for water power; if the last wilderness area can be taken over for road building; if a geological treasure can be scrapped for crushed stone without a murmur or protest, the community, so far as nature appreciation is concerned, is "bankrupt." The widespread lethargy of the public toward nature challenges the nature educator. What can be done to stimulate appreciation of nature and an active, satisfying participation in the nature activities that exist in every community?

Standards of Outdoor Tastes. Some standards of outdoor taste have been set up in our midst without some of us being conscious of them. I refer to the great development of camps, boulevards, county parks, trailside museums, and nature trails. They are storehouses of artistic achievement. Their arrangements are distinctly American. There are naturalistic bridges of glacial boulders in a glacial terrain or sandstone bridges arranged in harmony with sandstone outcrops. The profusion of tree and shrub beauty is so great that the enjoyment of the scenery depends on the ability to "frame" a curve in the trail for contemplation.

These haunts of nature are popular and destined to be more so. The people who visit them are consumers of the beauties of nature and are on the way to applying the same tastes at home. They want their home grounds in "period style." This esthetic taste, which once belonged to the wealthy, has become a cultural resource of democracy. The physical possession of beautiful areas is no longer a mark of social

FIG. 12.—Great Hall, Camp Edith Macey, Briar Cliff, N. Y. Note the hand-hewn timbers. Why did the hewing have to be done by one artisan? Why is the native rock of Westchester County more fitting than polished marble from abroad? How does the furniture match the room? How many different widths of board can you discover in the floor? This is known as tavern flooring. Why use pegs in the flooring? (*Photograph by Mattie Edwards Hewitt.*)

prestige. Naturalistic planting then is a public utility that sets a standard for the community.

The Outdoors Needs Interpreters. Increased gadgets or streamlining an automobile does not mean increased man power to handle the automobile. Park improvement has outdistanced an understanding of that development by the masses. Between opportunities resulting from conservation, nature recreation, winter sports, camping, and all the other items of outdoor skills and the use of these resources by the public there is an immense lag. The scientist and schoolteacher are too absorbed to notice; politicians are too predatory; and statesmen, apparently, are too involved.

The setting up of parks as outdoor schoolrooms does not guarantee their appreciation. The parks are there. They have their hangings and trimmings of native vines, trees, and rock. The public goes increasingly to the parks. There may be no partnership.

It rests on nature leaders to connect the outdoors and society. Seeing an interesting boulder and understanding its history are two

FIG. 13.—Scientific words must be translated into simple terms. The scientific name of this attractive fungus is *Polyporus versicolor*. Translated, it means "the many-colored fungus that has many pores." It has no common name, since it is not commonly talked about. It has a beautiful velvet texture with growth rings that have led some leaders to nickname it "turkey tail." The "velvet fungus" and the "many-colored fungus" are other suitable names. Which do you prefer? (*Photograph by Robert Coffin.*)

separate processes. A park, like a school, must be equipped to stimulate the intellectual curiosity of its clientele. It is as much a matter of guidance as *docent* service in an art museum. In general, the larger the park the greater the variety of nature offerings and the greater the need of guidance. The mass of people looking into the abyss of the Grand Canyon may be puzzled and even discouraged at the lack of ability to comprehend it. One poor soul ventured the query to me, "Why isn't it just as reasonable to think that the Indians dug this ditch as the Colorado River?" She did not have a proper background.

Most persons' minds are unprepared. They do not comprehend valleys at home on a smaller scale. The ranger-naturalist service in our national parks is organized to make the monuments of nature intelligible to all visitors. In every community, nature, in spots at least, is rich in masterpieces of landscape not only accessible to the public but well patronized by it. There is a similar need for a nature guide service trained to interpret natural phenomena in and near each community to the untrained neighbor.

Providing Training for Nature Appreciation Is a Public Service. Some cities have organized to provide nature interpretation as an educational function. Cincinnati has a park naturalist plus a naturalist service in its department of recreation. Pittsburgh has three park naturalists and two nature leaders in its Bureau of Recreation. In this city, the combined efforts of the schools, the parks, the recreation bureau, and the public camps of the Federation of Social Agencies carry on an intensive program in nature understanding.*

Some day these budding universities of the out-of-doors will rival the classical universities. The classes will be self-organized and more cultural recreational than so-called cultural educational. There will be individual or group-chosen projects instead of assignments; they will consist of first-hand activity rather than second-hand information; they will be self-directed rather than supervised; the audience will be participants rather then benched, active rather than passive, amateurs rather than technicians, explorers rather than traditionalists, and all ages instead of 89 per cent adolescents. Such cities are destined to have a continuous program of almost dramatic interest under skilled leaders.

Wanted—A Full-time Nature Guide. Every community with a population of 25,000 or more needs a full-time nature guide. A complete nature program is a community responsibility, and it ought, therefore, to be supported by taxation. This would amount to 10 cents for each citizen in a population of 25,000. It would be the guide's duty to establish a museum, a botanic garden, a community greenhouse, flower shows, pet shows, and garden exhibits; to launch conservation campaigns; to arrange lecture programs; to organize bird clubs, field study clubs, hiking clubs, all with programs; to train scout leaders in nature; to speak to various civic organizations and to run a schedule of field trips. Every community is hungry for this kind of Americanization.

One of the early projects of the community nature guide would be to organize a nature-lore school for leaders. To be successful, it should

*1940 statistics.

be in a near-by camp and last for a week or two, or at least for a holiday week end. Local scouting organizations are usually glad to lend their camp for such a purpose. The staff should consist of nature specialists, and out-of-town naturalists give an added zest to the program. Trips, outdoor cooking, woodcraft, nature songs and stories in the evening would be the course of study. The degree of C.N.G. (Community Nature Guide) could be awarded those successfully completing the requirements. The graduates would make up the all-time resident faculty for community nature guiding.

Nature publicity would go along with the school, and the nature guide would write up all club meetings, trips, things seen, unique activities, and the election of officers. If there were a movement on foot to get rid of the flies of the community, he could write a feature story to show that "prevention" is better than "swatting" as a slogan. He might tell how one community offered a prize to the one who killed the most flies. One boy with an eye for business started raising flies.

If all nature news were accepted through his office, it would assure accuracy. It is well known that some newspapers release accounts of certain monstrosities when news is scarce. For example, news of a man-eating shark and an octopus off the New Jersey coast is released every year. The guide would be responsible for nature news when it *is* news and not natural history. Better still, he would anticipate the blooming of the rhododendrons. He would tell you when and where to look for the song sparrow. He would seize on any local nature event, such as a washout, a waterspout, a visit of black ducks, or the seventeen-year locust, and present it to the public. The overrunning of the gardens with a blight might be used to show the necessity of promoting nature knowledge. Statistics about children injured in the streets, when they should have more interests in the fields and woods, would be effective. Photographs are acceptable with all of these items.

The Community Nature Almanac. *The Community Nature Almanac* is a suggestive outline of nature activities that a nature guide may carry out in any locality. It is not a series of stunts for trained animals. It is not a market-gardening job in which the manager ships an intellectual menu for forced feeding. It is a list of seasonal opportunities that people may want to take advantage of; it provides suggestions for everyone. The mountain club of 200, the insect club of 12 members, and the hermit philosopher in his cabin each has a part to perform. The whole community is exposed to certain nature activities. The guide follows up any lead that he may get. A community nature almanac has suggestions for all for every day in the year.

GOING INTO ACTION

Interpret the Survey to Community Nature Enthusiasts. Once the survey is complete, the principal plans a tentative program for community needs. The call then goes out for a meeting of all nature enthusiasts whom the principal has discovered in his picture of nature activity. These become a temporary executive committee to criticize, approve, or amend the plan. Now follows a public meeting so that the program may swing into action.

Gather Your Community Together. The rallying point may be a stereopticon lecture, a fall flower show, a tree walk, a nature exhibit by the school children, or the planting of a tree on Arbor Day. Start with the event that will be most interesting to the people, using an outdoor fireplace, the park, the museum, the library, or some school-building as a meeting place. A banquet is sometimes more popular than other forms of social gathering in a community. Make known the facts that will win the service of as many people as possible. Have all the gathering participate in something. If it is decided to organize a field naturalists' club, the president, secretary-treasurer, and executive board should be selected at this time. They will plan the next events.

"Counting the Cost." One of the first questions will be, "What will it cost?" We have spent money on museums because we think them worth while, yet we pay no attention to the thousands who go every day into the fields and forests. The children who play there are at an impressionable age, ready to learn nature's laws. The hills, ferns, and birds have cost us nothing, yet we can achieve things there that are impossible in the museum. Although it is undoubtedly a public responsibility, in the beginning days, the work will have to be done by volunteer leadership. It has been found that 50 cents annual dues are quite satisfactory for a neighborhood nature organization. This will pay for the programs and the necessary notices that have to be sent out.

Sample announcements from the itinerary of an autumn program of the Rhode Island Field Naturalists' Club show a convenient form of announcing trips:

Sept. 11. *All-day Field Trip.* Miss Sisson, leader. Phillip Sisson, guide. Union Station, 6:15 A.M., daylight saving time. Buy tickets for Woodville, Washington County. Bring lunch and rubbers. Those having autos communicate with Fred Corp.

Sept. 18. *Fossils.* Mr. Hawksley. Crescent Park car east end of post office, 1:30 P.M. Round trip 24 cents.

Oct. 16. *Birds.* Dr. Lovewell. 8 A.M. train to Sharon. 94 cents each way. Moose Hill Bird Sanctuary. Bring lunch.

Oct. 23. *Field and Woods.* Miss Bishop. Chepachet bus, 2:15 P.M. Harvest supper at the grange, 60 cents. Telephone Angel 1608 W.

Leadership for a Community Nature Program. We may think of communities as rural, industrial, residential, and foreign. The program and consequent leadership for any of these communities must vary considerably. The principal initiates and coordinates the plan not only as a school official but as a citizen of the community. With the help of the parent-teachers' association, the principal can use his influence in obtaining approved voluntary leaders for the scout troops, the playgrounds, and the clubs. Visiting teachers and special teachers from the platoon school have a place here.

In this connection, it is the duty of the colleges of education to train leaders for field service. The nature classroom of the future will not have such frozen assets as formaldehyde, dissecting pans, fixed seats, textbooks, routine, and grades. It will not be so much concerned with subject matter as it will be the headquarters of desirable experiences. The courses will not be so much a chain of sequential subjects as a reconstruction of the same desirable attitudes, habits, and skills under new experiences. In each nature or biology course, the principles and goals will remain the same, but contact with source material will offer wider opportunities for growth. Activities for afternoons and evenings, for summer and winter, will appear on the program. The student-teacher will find joy in accomplishment. He will sign up for tasks more difficult than are suggested in the most formal laboratory manual. He will master the tools of leadership because he realizes that he must do so in order to become successful in his chosen profession. He will discover a keen fascination in leading in the playground, the garden, or the club. He will seek rich experiences rather than lectures about experiences. He will not be content with hearing that teaching is a profession or that the child is a growing animal with inborn traits. He will demand a laboratory opportunity to deal with child interests.

The introductory course in biology for teachers will be less and less an imitation of the premedical or liberal arts course. For those who have special interests, there will be a tendency toward majors and minors in them. The period of preparation will be longer. It will be intensive rather than extensive. With a change from the traditional to the vitalized, the objectives will be broader and the atmosphere freer. Units of preparation will be based on desires rather than on artificial rewards. There will be more of self-realization gained through leadership in community nature activity. Records will be kept to show what the student-teacher does in the community. Attention will be given to individual tastes, aptitudes, and desires. The activities will include more of health, moral responsibility, play, democratic spirit, citizenship, and life.

What Is the Ultimate Goal? Ultimately, every inhabitant will have his contribution to make to community enrichment. It may be a mineral collection or a knowledge of dahlias, a bird bath or a hive of bees. Whether it is Indian corn, or Italian squash, or a fruit from the Garden of Eden, the product of each individual's interest will be just as welcome to the community assets. Each one will have lost himself in interest in *his* garden with *his* birds or *his* pets. The aim will be to have every citizen an amateur naturalist each in his own way. Each neighbor will have personal responsibility for his share in preventing flies, in attracting birds, in making the city beautiful. Every nature enthusiast will be teacher, every open space a school, and every citizen a contributor.

NATURE RECREATION IN NEW YORK CITY

A few years ago, I went to New York City to introduce the idea of nature recreation to the first National Recreation School. New York City was the last place in the world that I would have chosen for such a mission, but there was some satisfaction in thinking that, if it could be demonstrated in the greatest metropolis, it could be demonstrated in any community. The group gathered in a building directly opposite Central Park, so that seemed the logical starting point in a search for what nature opportunities the city had at hand. However, even as we gazed across Fifth Avenue, we could see two signs that said, "Keep off" and a policeman strolling down the walk to interpret the signs in case they weren't read or obeyed.

Nature Enjoyment in a Community Park. Central Park is possibly the most used park in the world, yet it has a wealth of common objects worth looking at. A grasshopper was our first capture, Exhibit A. Since most grasshoppers hatch from eggs in the spring, they never see their parents. What a grasshopper is is due to his own inherent efforts. This led to a discussion of the ways in which the grasshopper is perhaps as marvelous as man and more wonderful than the elephant. Soon we discovered that the Central Park policeman interpreted his job very literally. When one of the 50 students stood on the grass, the bluecoat removed the offender to the walk. Then he listened to the proceedings for a brief time to see if it sounded like a gathering of agitators. We evidently passed inspection. The number of hangers-on to our trips would indicate that the park population is more than receptive to the idea of nature interpretation. They have a natural hunger for a knowledge of their environment. Of course, some of those who went the rounds were spurred on by curiosity. "Listening in" might have been more interesting than being a "bench hound." But they were parties to the cause. Perhaps this was their first glimmer of the fact that a dandelion is in the lawn for some other purpose than not being picked. Perhaps they were surprised to see people interested in discovering that, in September, the beech tree had buds that contained all the leaves for the next summer. Perhaps they also got a thrill from seeing the cock pheasant walk across the glaciated rock and disappear in the shrubbery without a parting stone from the mob. Perhaps the grasshopper was more than a "flying cockroach," as it was once named by an East Side urchin. Perhaps this was the beginning of a better mutual understanding between the park population and the police. We are coming to see that if we are to preserve our parks for future generations, if we are to get the educational and recreational returns on the investment, there must be an organized attempt to lead people to an understanding and appreciation of public park property. If Central Park is to be saved from its commercial enemies who would build apartment houses and from its unthinking patrons who would trample out every vestige of plant and animal life, there must be leadership and education. As I see it, the park traditions and park ideals that we want can be brought about only by the efforts of certain trained individuals who have fully grasped this conception. These leaders I have called nature guides. Other departments of outdoor recreation are already well established. There are the professor of dramatics in his outdoor theater, the professor of singing in the open park or community spaces, and the professor of outdoor play in public tennis court, baseball diamond, or athletic field. The weakest spot in the recreation field is provision for nature recreation and trained nature leadership.

A Community Greenhouse. The next move of the class was a visit to a city greenhouse to make a survey of its work. Committee reports brought out the following points. The greenhouse was for show and not for education. (The chrysanthemum house, for example, was open to the public for only about 2 months in the year. The rest of the time, workmen were making cuttings, potting, and getting ready for the exhibition.) The plants exhibited were foreign species instead of native plants. The labels had scientific names instead of common names. There was no one to explain the exhibit or make it interesting. The economic function of this particular greenhouse was to produce border plants for the various parks for the city, and there was no relation established between the greenhouse and the home, school, or playground. It was thought that, with no additional financial backing, it might be made much more useful in the life of the community. This greenhouse was typical of many city conservatories.

In contrast to this, the class visited the Brooklyn Botanic Garden greenhouse. Here they found what an urban greenhouse might offer in the way of an enriching program. Its announcements of courses, lectures, and other educational advantages offered to the general public, as published by the Department of Instruction, offer activities that would be models for any city:

1. The teaching of classes: bulb culture, plant cuttings, garden Christmas presents, potting plants, care of lawn, transplanting, seeding, care of small gardens, flower study, tree study, window boxes.
   a. Of children who come voluntarily outside of school hours.
   b. Of children who come with their teachers.
   c. Of adults.
2. Lectures at schools and at the garden.
3. Loaning lantern slides and distributing study material to schools.
4. Maintaining labeled collections, a reference library, periodicals, and a bureau of public information.
5. Providing *docents* to guide parties.

A Community Botanic Garden. The New York Botanical Garden at Bronx Park is typical of what any city might aspire to accomplish. A brief summary will help the reader to recognize the educational and recreational aspect of such an institution. The recreation school spent a most enjoyable and profitable Saturday morning viewing the garden under the direction of a resident nature guide. The reservation includes nearly 400 acres and is the home of the largest botanical museum building in the world. Its lecture hall seats 700 people, and it has a library of 30,000 volumes. In the grounds, there are plants arranged conveniently for study, and here are to be found an herb garden, economic plants, horticultural plantation, 100 Japanese cherry trees, an acre of roses, a lilac garden, a dahlia collection of several hundred, an iris garden, a water garden, and a primeval forest of about 40 acres. The exhibition of a prize back-yard garden was most interesting.

At the museum, we purchased several books. Attention was called to the *New York Walk Book*, published by the American Geographical Society, Broadway at 156th Street, New York City. The material was compiled by three outdoor men who have preceded the directions for walks with profuse notes on the scenery, geological formations, flora, and points of historical interest. The book retails for $3.50. A community nature guide should give this book more than a passing notice.

Some of the class remained over during the afternoon and went to the free public lecture at the Museum Building on Autumn Colors by Dr. A. B. Stout. They then visited the dahlia collection under the direction of Dr. Marshall A. Howe.

A Community Zoological Park. The 264 acres of Bronx Park with its natural varied contour make it possible to afford a suitable habitat for many animals. There are large special buildings equipped for each of the following: elephant, lion, primates, large birds, aquatic birds, pheasants, reptiles, small mammals, ostriches, antelope, small deer, and the zebra. The Administration Building contains a large library and meeting rooms for the members. A visitor may put in hours looking over the world-wide collection at the zoological park. It is indeed one of the nature treasure houses of New York City. It is unnecessary, of course, to mention that I am interested in the zoo and believe in its educational value. What surprises me, however, is that it has appeared in so many communities to the entire neglect of the many other possibilities. The zoo is the commonest feature of community nature recreation, but it has not gone beyond the amusement stage.

A Community Museum of Natural History. The American Museum of Natural History, with its 11 acres of floor space and a membership of over 120,000 people, is recognized throughout the country as an unexcelled medium of public nature service. It publishes the journals *Natural History* and *Junior Natural History*, gives courses of popular lectures, maintains a members' club and guide service, sends out expeditions, provides a school service that reaches annually over a million boys and girls, has a library of 175,000 volumes, and issues scientific and popular publications. The recreation leaders were given an opportunity to study this important service.

The Children's Museum of the Brooklyn Institute of Arts and Sciences is the first institution of its kind and is today the largest and best equipped children's museum in the world. It maintains a nature library, assists in the organization of clubs and societies, conducts museum games, gives service to scouting organizations, gives courses, finances and guides field trips, provides loan cases, and offers storytelling exhibits.

News outside the Door. At one of the public nature lectures, we met J. Otis Swift, writer of a daily nature story called "News Outside the Door," which was printed in the morning edition of the *New York World* and framed there with the official weather forecast. This story was syndicated throughout the country. In the Saturday paper, trips under his leadership were announced. It did not take long to discover that Mr. Swift was planning a Sunday nature trip. It was to begin at the Graystone Monument on the Hudson, just beyond Yonkers.

The day was rainy, but his enthusiasm had been contagious. To our astonishment, 56 others turned out too, and we hiked along the summit of the aqueduct in a pouring rain. But these nature philosophers forgot the rain as Mr. Swift filled their souls with mystic stories of nature and pointed out scenes of historic events.

Between times, he explained to me that the group is known as the Yosian Brotherhood. On a pleasant day, there will be 150 followers. He told me that the brotherhood is not a club, organization, or fraternity. It is a state of mind, a love of outdoors and nature. There is no membership in the formal sense, no rules, no credits, beliefs, dues, or officers.

Mr. Swift is demonstrating the great contribution that may be made by a newspaper to the nature recreation of a community. A community nature guide should be responsible for "News Outside the Door" for his own section of town or country.

I do not know what the recreation leaders got out of my 2 weeks' course, but I do know that I became humble before the nature resources of New York City. They were far beyond my fondest vision of what might be even in Utopia. Most of the nature possibilities are under professional leadership. We must realize that the six forms of nature activities I have discussed are educational and recreational. They have latent possibilities for further social participation far beyond the amusement stage. Each of these six branches has so far independently developed its own service and traditions. Nature recreation conceived as a separate activity is a new problem and has yet to find its place among established organizations. To round out its service, the social use of all institutions for community welfare must be recognized and interrelated.

LEADERSHIP TRAINING THROUGH COMMUNITY NATURE CLUBS

For several years, certain student-teachers[1] in nature education at Western Reserve University had the choice of practicing nature leadership with a club of adolescent children instead of preparing "daily assignments." They were held responsible for all tests but for no laboratory work or daily preparation. At one time, there were 42 animal clubs in greater Cleveland that were an adjunct to the course in vertebrate animal study. This meant approximately 1,000 boys and girls meeting voluntarily in afterschool hours at library centers, settlement houses, voting booths, and church basements and carrying on nature activity under student direction.

This was a radical departure from the more formal method of classroom procedure, and, though none will challenge its value as experience, many will doubt the wisdom of giving credit to students who were not held responsible for daily assignments. My answer is a listing of the demands made upon those leaders by their club members.

The leaders of clubs kept diaries. I shall quote freely from these in the analysis that follows.

Club Leadership Itself a Definite Responsibility. The leader who elected the club route knew that it was up to him to follow it through to a successful conclusion. He could not drop the club in the middle of the term, for that would mean self-admitted failure. He had to make it interesting enough to attract 15 boys or girls, and, having once set the pace, he could not afford to lower his standard, for he would then lose his club.

[1] The option of club leadership was only allowed those who had had a successful 9-week period of practice teaching. This meant that the students had reached at least the fourth semester. Such students had been rigorously checked as to general scholarship, personality, and physical vigor.

Club members were ambitious. They wanted a definite goal such as an animal fair or a garden show. They clamored for field trips. Leaders who made promises to a club were held strictly accountable. The requirements of youngsters are higher teaching standards than one could hope to exact by any other method.

Club Leadership Required Preparation. The leaders will tell you in chorus that club leadership required more preparation than course assignments. To meet a club of lively youngsters required self-assigned preparation of the broadest sort on the part of the leader who would preserve his self-respect.

But there was this difference. Club leaders prepared according to their *needs* and not according to any set curriculum. Animal study leads into unthought-of channels. An animal fair was held at the Cleveland Museum of Natural History. Each club was given the opportunity of explaining and answering questions about exhibits, the material in which might be the starting point for future collections. It so happens that the museum has a notable collection of fossil fish of Ohio. One club signed for this section of the museum. The leader studied monographs and spent 2 hr. with members of the museum's staff asking questions that she might get the proper background for training her club members. In the usual course in vertebrate zoology, the fossil fish of Ohio might easily be passed unmentioned, yet they undoubtedly were subjected to the same natural laws and principles that are stressed in the classroom analysis of the classical goldfish or the type dogfish. The latter method is one of lesson learning. If preparation is a worthy objective (and we concede that it is), even the most conservative will concede that the club method of electing the experience with fossil fish resulted not only in self-discipline but in a goodly collection of factual material. We believe, however, that the facing of a quizzical audience, the concept of the scientific method, and the growing idea of the immense age of this old earth, all of which were involved in this club leadership challenge, were much more valuable.

Club Leadership Needed a Background of Factual Information. One must not overlook the fact that the children who joined an animal club, for example, did so because they were interested in animals. They probably had pets at home. If there is any pedagogue who doubts that information is necessary, let him walk into a club meeting of 15 boys with a dish of hatching salmon eggs, or a live bat, or an alligator, or take the children to a livestock show. Club members feel free to ask questions. As one leader put it, "Children *fire* questions."

How much is included in that word *fire!* Take the bat for example: Is it a bird? Why does it have fur? Will it suck blood? Why do bats eat insects?

Another consideration was that the children who joined were apt to be those who knew the most about animals. Anita did not think that all fish breathe by gills. It is fortunate the leader knew about the lungfish at such a moment. Again Anita asked pertinent questions as to whether flying fish really fly and if there were not fish that walked on the bottom of the ocean. Intelligent questions required intelligent answers.

The informality of a club meeting tended to encourage "wild tales." The leader was constantly called upon to settle conflicting ideas within the club or to explain tactfully stock notions brought from home. To wit: "One girl said that snakes do not close their eyes until night. (This information came from her father.) As it was night I had her watch the snake to tell us when it closed its eyes. She was unsuccessful. I had a snake skin which I had taken to the meeting. I showed her how the snake sheds the skin even over the eye."

Another leader who took her club to a butcher shop wrote, "I had to admit that I did not know more often than I cared to."

A Club Leader Had to Execute Judgment and Tact. Suppose that the leader takes a white rat to the club meeting. In the meantime, a club member brings in his new alligator. The thing to do is to reserve the white rat for the next meeting. It is time for alligators.

If the conversation lags, the leader must introduce a question or "something-to-do" from up his sleeve.

HOW DID LEADERSHIP IN A CLUB DIFFER FROM PRACTICE TEACHING IN THE SCHOOLROOM?

This is a second question that a teacher in a professional training school may well raise. Contrasts are implicit in the following picture of club organization and procedure.

The Organization of the Group Was in the Hands of the Leader. This included:

Investigating a Community for a Suitable Meeting Place. Arrangements were made for the use of a library, a settlement house, a community center, a neighborhood club, a playground, a voting booth.

Securing a Local Sponsor. A librarian, a scout leader, a playground director, and so on, would agree to visit the club and report to the Department of Nature Education.

Advertising for Members. This often leads to ingenious steps. The usual way was to make a poster. One leader who had a special aptitude for art asked each candidate for membership to bring his best sketch of an animal. As a result, she had 35 candidates to select from for her animal-art club. Another student went to a settlement house and had no applicants. She took her snake to the game room where a score of boys were busily engaged in all kinds of contest. She soon had an audience. They began to ask questions. She refused to answer any questions but said that all who wanted to know about the snake might come with her to the animal club room. Some leaders went into the schools of the neighborhood and spoke to the fourth, fifth, and sixth grades. Often only one child appeared at the first meeting. Again "twenty-seven boys rushed into the room and sat on the sewing machines and window ledges as well as on the chairs." Another wrote, "We went on a brook trip to see what we could find in the way of animals. We started with seven boys, but, by the time we reached our destination, we had twelve. The original seven were so enthusiastic and beaming that they infected five more." The following was the usual report: "When I went to the library for the second meeting I happened to get there a little after 3:30, and all of the children were there. Our meetings usually begin at 4:00 P.M. There were three times as many children as at the first meeting."

Woe as well as joy often followed the membership. One leader took her boys to the animal fair. There were over 3,000 children milling around. The film was shown four times, and the promised dog performance had to be omitted. One gang of boys blamed the leader because Rex did not appear on the program. "Their spokesman, with his cap cocked over one ear, told me in any but a gentle manner that they were through. This made me feel like 'giving up the ship' but, with the vision of Perry before me, such was impossible."

Supervising Is Necessary Business. NAMING THE CLUB. To the uninitiated, the naming of a club might seem a mere trifle. Such was not the case. The tribal idea is deep in our nature, and the desire to initiate is also an ancient impulse. One leader was worried because the boys wanted to call themselves the "Pacing Mustangs." I suggested that she had possession of a powerful symbol for character building and gave her a copy of *Wild Animal Ways* by Ernest Thompson Seton, which contains a story of Coaly-bay, the outlaw horse. I suggested that that be her story for the next club meeting. Coaly-bay, just as all live boys, had red blood that every once in a while seemed to show power and the eternal love of freedom.

When I suggested that we get a name there was an awful silence. "Students of Nature" was suggested. Harold volunteered that that wouldn't do, as it sounded too much like school. "Seekers of Wisdom about Nature" was the next best offer. Where did they get these inspirations? Clarence suggested that we take the first letter of each word which would give us "Sowan." Everyone became enthusiastic. They accepted the name and decided that only the members were to know the meaning of the name.

ELECTING OFFICERS. Here, too, a leader had to follow a hands-off policy. "The boy whom I consider the best leader didn't receive an office. To my surprise, the boy whom they chose as president seems like a bully. Undoubtedly I don't know him as yet." Often the leaders were complimented as follows: "One of the boys nominated me for the honorary position of president. Before I could say a word, they all agreed. Of course I had to refuse the offer, as I was only the guide of the club."

The leader also had to sense when it was time for election. Many leaders did not have election until the second meeting.

First Meeting: Only two boys. I had a toad, but the boys called it a frog Still it was a toad. Second Meeting: I entered the club room. I felt weak. What would I see? Oh, there were five boys. What a relief. I felt better. We had our election. Philip Michael Patrick O'Dwyer was our president. The secretary was Joe Kovack. I was elected the treasurer. I was informed that no one else could be trusted. So between the toad, two charter members, and three new members, we had a successful meeting. I believe that I am going to like it.

Another leader did not have the election of officers until the eighth meeting. Here are significant items, from her dairy:

Oct. 10: I was eager to see how many people had been attracted by my signs. An eleven-year-old girl came. Oct. 17: Only Gertrude and her friend Elaine came. Oct. 24: Hurrah! Four members today. Oct. 31: By the end of the meeting, I had twenty-four children there.

Clubs almost invariably select good officers. They are just as decisive in reducing incompetent leaders to rank.

Some of the members were saying, "He's too silly. He ought to set an example for the rest of us." I then asked Moses if he knew what happened to kings when the people were dissatisfied? He said that he understood, so the matter was dropped. But it was not until the sixth meeting that Moses was deposed.

MAKING CLUB RULES. Club rules should be few and should emanate from the members as the occasion arises. In the old-time school, the need for discipline arose from the difference in points of view between the teacher and the children. We now know that, if the children are given interesting things, there will be no problem of discipline. Action rather than words is the best psychology.

Assuming Responsibility for Trips as Well as Group Activity. Nature clubs lead afield. A nature club that always meets in a room is not a real nature club. Boys and girls have come to expect that at

Fig. 14.—"Embryo scientists" studying microscopic wonders in the Childrens' Science Laboratory of the Elizabeth Peabody Settlement House, now at 84 Broadway, E. Somerville, Mass. We are just beginning to discover the magnitude of scientific enterprise of which junior scientists are capable. The crying need is for competent leaders and more leaders. Children possessing both interest and capacity are waiting. (*Photograph courtesy of H. Henry Platt.*)

least 20 per cent of the time will be given to field trips. Cleveland club members enjoy adventure and "roughing it." Observing, legitimate collecting, and taking pictures as they went were the usual activities. The all-day hike included cooking out. It was important for leaders to get the permission of the parents, to see that the children were properly clothed, and to carry a first-aid kit.

Club Membership Was Entirely Voluntary. The children felt that the club belonged to them. They had formed it. They had named it. They had elected their own officers. They kept it going. They could give it up. They had it because they were working together for a common goal.

The club was a gang, and the leader was a gang member, but of the big-sister or big-brother variety. He was thought of as a guide rather than a dictator. He helped solve problems. He had suggestions when they were sought. He knew just the place for a fine trip. He had materials in case of emergency. He saw to it that each meeting was interesting. It had to be so interesting that everyone wanted to come again. It had to be so interesting and so snappy in execution that there was no need for discipline.

Groups Were Small. The size of the group was another important factor. It was urged that the club be limited to a membership of 15. This made for comradeship and for freedom of speech and action. In the case of animal study, each one could get near enough to see the toad eat his skin, handle the turtle, or take a hand in stirring the cream.

The Club Method Was the "Doing Method." There were no lessons or grades, nor was there a curriculum or assignment from above. Each meeting was for 1 or 1½ hr. It was sufficient unto itself, although it related to the main objective of the club. The procedure was wholly informal and often developed into a heated argument. Leaders listened hard for ideas born of inner urgings. They made excellent working capital. The children were not merely entertained, they worked better as self-starters rather than by the cranking-up process.

"Last week we had two turtles. The children placed them on the floor and let them make an attempt at racing." Nothing educational about a terrapin race, you query? That would be difficult to prove. It is no longer safe to take anything for granted. At any rate, a safe rule in club work is to let the activity start with the child.

"When the boys and girls saw the toad they all wanted to see it jump. When I started to take it out of the jar, a boy asked if he could do it. Then everyone wanted to hold it. One girl was afraid of getting warts and said so. The boys laughed. The girl accepted the challenge." The leader, but not the children, recognized the handling of the toad as an experience in attitude and a step toward doing away with superstition. This is a major objective in any science.

We had our meeting in a portable school building. It had not been cleaned for months. One of the boys found a moth flitting about. It was nearly as large as the frog. We wanted to try feeding him to the frog. There was quite an argument as to whether the frog could really down it. The frog settled the question by grabbing the moth and gradually shoved it in with his chubby hands. The boys were thrilled.

The children seemed a little disappointed today for I had no animal. When they found that our discussion was to be about going to the pet show and that they could commence planning their part, they were at once interested. The meeting was earnest and businesslike. The discussion included: Why were we going? How were we going? How could we get the money? What our responsibilities were? How could we find materials for talks? Who should talk?

Another leader reported that her best meeting was when they were making fruit-jar aquariums. Her father had taken her to a pond where she obtained a number of catfish and Johnny Darters. She had a pail of sand and an abundance of water plants. Each member was to bring a fruit jar. Those who forgot them were glad to run home and get one. The leader demonstrated how to wash the sand and set up the aquarium. She answered all questions, and then each one set to work. The aquariums were to be sold at a street fair. The leader said that she was well repaid for all the time that it took to get ready.

It is true that the club method can be used in school but not equally true that school methods can always be carried into a club. Leaders of clubs soon become conscious that, if their plans were based on activity motivated by interest, they were more apt to become successful. School classes can well take their inspiration from the enthusiasm of afterschool clubs. It has also been claimed that anyone who can run a club of adolescent boys or girls can teach but that all teachers cannot run a club of boys or girls successfully.

A Club at Its Best Was the Center of Responsibility. It connected with the home and the neighborhood.

My children want to have a pet show. They have already enlisted their parents to help make cages. The idea came from the children, and it is all voluntary. In fact, I have to run to keep up with them. I learn a lot. It is really a fifty-fifty proposition. Some of them are getting talks ready for the mothers' club.

We had a special meeting today to get ready for our animal show. I found them a little impatient. They were waiting for me in the rain. Tony had been standing there a whole hour. He confided that his mother had made a special trip to the associated charities to get him some clothes so that I wouldn't be ashamed of taking him. There were many patches, but Tony was entirely presentable with an almost brand new cap two sizes too large.

I was ready to weep at the little story. Ruth told me that she had been lecturing all night on the garter snake. Her mother had awakened her several times in order to stop her. Edward had slept with his father's watch under his pillow so as to be sure of waking up in time. Soon all were busy bringing chairs down to the basement, hammering, hanging signs, roping off a center ring, and arranging homemade cages. Brothers and fathers came down in case we needed help. We put them to work too.

We made an aquarium for the library tonight. The boys donated their largest and prettiest marbles along with a few shells. Some of the boys made a chart of the aquarium so that the children would know its contents. We elected a committee to present it to the librarian, but the whole membership went with them.

Club Experiences Involved Character Education. The leader who lent a keen ear heard sentences that carried a world of goodness. One boy brought his dog to the dog show. When anyone showed interest, he would say proudly, "This is a clean-cut dog." He won first prize for having the cleanest and best taught dog. Yet, previous to this opportunity to develop an interest in animals, he had belonged to a gang that had been stealing bicycles, repainting them, and selling them for a small profit. His father had had to drag him to school and see to it that he went in the door. "A clean-cut dog." What a foundation for building right attitudes and habits!

We tried to feed our turtle but did not succeed. Alice had read a story of a little girl who had a turtle and had endeavored in every way to make it happy. She could not get it to eat and let it go. The club asked if they could let the turtle go after the meeting so that he would be happy. I was very glad to comply with their suggestion. I was not sure whether it wanted lettuce, whether it was a carnivorous species, or whether it was just natural for it to refuse to eat because hibernation days were here, but I thought that my children had gone a long way when they really wanted to take it back to its natural home. I hope that I decided wisely.

Perhaps the final test of humaneness came when several hundred club members went to a moving-picture presentation of the White-Fuller expedition to Africa. In one scene, the drivers hit the camels to get them to move across a stream. One could sense that the audience caught its breath, and a murmur of resentment swept over the young spectators. At least one objective of animal study had been accomplished.

Character Education Applied to Leaders as Well as Members. One leader recorded in her daybook:

I took a black snake to my second meeting. I had not intended to pick it up, but when I got there I mustered up all my courage and the snake curled around my hands. It wasn't half bad.

We had three new members at the last meeting. One of them walked to the street car with me. He told me that he belonged to a nature club at school, but that it was awful. All they talked about was "leaves and stuff." He said that he liked to study about snakes and real things. Of course, I did not tell him that leaves are real. I am going to double my efforts to make things interesting. Besides, I am determined that it will be the boys' club.

Furthermore, a bond of sympathy was developed among club leaders. They felt that they were pioneering and that an exchange of experiences and materials was worth while. Word quickly went the rounds that churning butter and serving animal crackers made a good meeting. The holding of the toad by each child had significant values, but the same procedure with a frog was usually disastrous, since the frog inevitably escaped. The leader who "charmed" the snake found he had a definite prestige with the club.

In conclusion, you may ask what is my feeling today concerning this experiment? Do I keep on with clubs as a means of preparing students to teach nature study in the elementary grades? Yes, I still cling to the idea that the club is an efficient way of leader training. It is not the only method. But at present it remains as a more satisfactory medium than the courses in nature education many training schools provide.

The following quotation from *The Nature Study Idea*, by Dr. L. H. Bailey, is the keynote to the nature-lore club:

I like the man who has had an incomplete course. A partial view, if truthful, is worth more than a complete course, if lifeless. If the man has acquired a power for work, a capability for initiative and investigation, an enthusiasm for the daily life, his incompleteness is his strength. How much there is before him! How eager his eye! How enthusiastic his temper! This man will see first the large and significant events; he will grasp relationships; he will correlate; later, he will consider details.

CHAPTER III

NATURE RECREATION AND THE SUMMER CAMP

CAMPING, CAMP DIRECTORS, AND THE NATURE COUNSELOR

A curiously marked box recently came to my office. On the label were "Fragile," "Perishable," "Rush," "This Side Up," "Keep Away from Steam Pipes," "Must Be Kept Very Cold, but not Exposed to Freezing Temperatures," and "See That Ice Chamber on Top Is Kept Filled with Ice." It was also marked "Value—$11.50, Express Collect, from Aberdeen, Wash." If the phrase "Live Fish Eggs" had not been evident, the package would certainly have piqued my curiosity.

Lifting the hinged cover, we observed that it was like a fireless cooker. In the center was an open box with a screened bottom full of ice. A lower box was similarly constructed, but it was 3 instead of 5 in. high. This was full of moss, and between the layers of moss were salmon eggs. Three eggs were visible on the moss.

These eggs had had a 6-day journey from Seattle to Cleveland and had been given an environment as near as possible like the cold lake in which they would normally be laid—ice-cold temperature, moisture, plenty of air, and gentle treatment. We placed the eggs in the running water of the aquarium.

What's inside a Salmon Egg? An embryo and yolk sac capable of developing into a free-swimming salmon in a few weeks. What a wonderful time clock! The young fry are predestined to remain in the mountain lake until the third spring. Then they descend the river to their ancestral home in the ocean. After 4 years they may very probably but not necessarily come back to this same river and abandon their marine life. An instinct drives them up the Columbia River for 1,000 miles or the Yukon River for over 2,000 miles to a cold mountain lake. This inner urge is so strong that it will send them up a 15-ft. waterfall. If rocks have fallen into the river and made obstructions, they go over the rapids to certain destruction. Once up the river, the fish again await nature's drive. Instinct tells the mother salmon that it is not time to deposit her eggs until the water is down to 54°F. In a salmon egg, there are principles of inborn tendencies, driving powers, and timeliness that stir our imaginations.

Children Have Instincts and Capabilities. Every summer, like the salmon, swarms of children gravitate to camps and playgrounds. They, like my package of eggs, could also be labeled "Fragile," "Perishable," "Keep Away from Steam Pipes," and "Value Unlimited." They also inherit not one but many drives to send them far afield. Their inner urges demand a world in which to stalk, to hunt, to fight, to run with the gang, to identify themselves with the world of the out-of-doors.

In this quest, some of them will be mismanaged; some may be wrecked on the rapids; others will be started on the road to more complete development. On the whole, I believe that thousands of children find in camp life a most suitable environment for happy, healthy growth.

Modern Civilization Stunts Sense Development. The forces of nature were at one time the raw stimuli that trained the human dynamo. The whole natural environment acted upon the living being —oxygen on the blood, the snap of a twig on the ear, a falling raindrop on the skin. Early man was required to use all his sense receptors. His very existence depended upon them. Indeed, until two generations ago, man's body and mind found in his childhood surroundings sufficient outdoor stimuli to develop a full quota of sense responses to the world about him.

Today, he must be sensitive to stop lights, fire sirens, telephone bells, and a host of man-invented mechanistic signals. Response to these is important, often vital, but it does not depend upon a well-rounded development of all the sense centers. Most of us have all the sense organs and a full complement of sense possibilities, yet no "nature sense" at all. To some eyes, the Big Dipper does not exist; to a neighbor, it is just stars; and to others, it is "the clock of the sky." The color-blind do not fully enjoy a sunset or rainbow. The newborn child is tone deaf; so are some adults. Many are unnecessarily color-blind and tone deaf. They never go beyond the ABC stage of response to nature. This is especially true of the man whose horizon is the city limits.

Camp Life Provides a Natural Environment for Growth. If city civilization stunts normal sense development, we are faced with the problem of widening the horizon and providing once more an environment for complete growth. We must again send the child to nature's school. This objective lies back of the whole movement. In camp life, educators see the ideal learning situation for richer and fuller sense development.

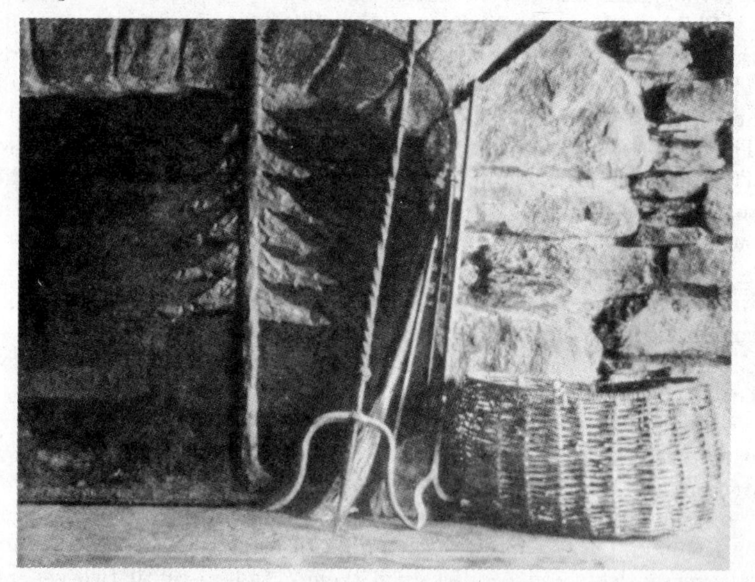

Fig. 15.—The old homestead industries should be returned. The campers who foraged for willow to make this wood basket considered the finished product more valuable than if the raw material had been purchased from a dealer. Looking at glowing embers through hammered iron fir trees was a thrill. Camp Edith Macey.

What Is Camping? With these facts before us, it may be well to ask, "What is camping?" It is, first of all, pleasant living outdoors in the forest, in the mountains, or at the seashore. It implies a camp site rich in natural resources. Areas that dwindle into baseball fields, golf courses, and graveled walks become real estate and not functional campgrounds.

Good camp directors watch their trees as mother hens watch their chickens. They seek constantly to multiply the forests, the wild flowers, and the birds. They know that the wider the range of outdoor nature experiences the campgrounds provide, the greater the opportunity for building among campers an abiding satisfaction in life in the open.

In camp, there must be people, but not too many. These people are naturally attracted to the woods. They rejoice in the primitive and unconventional. They think of camp as the place of rooted affection for the country. They have the feeling that nature is always there. Camping is joyous outdoor living.

A Camp Brings New Experiences. A new girl arrives at camp on Cape Cod. Let us say that she comes from Missouri. Everything is new—the salty air, the bay, the sailboats, the snug white colonial houses, the pitch pines, the seagulls and herons, the fog, sunsets and clear nights, the sea lavender, beach pea, and dusty miller, fishermen on the beach or in their skiffs, wharves, channel buoys, and so on.

There is much to learn. "Why does the fisherman say 'Good mornin'' when he does not know me?" She enters the village dry-goods store. "What business has that man with side whiskers to ask me where I come from? What are those red berries? Oh, yes! Cranberries. How do they taste? Can you eat them raw?" She bites one, and her face writhes at the acidity. An old camper eats a raw oyster. It is a delicacy to one—slimy, slippery "goo" to the other.

The new camper hears someone calling "Barbara." She investigates and finds that it is sheep saying, "Baa-baa." Someone else could distinguish the sound without looking. The Onondaga Indian thought that the quail said, "Koo-koo-e," and we think that it says, "Bobwhite."

A steamer in a dense fog blows its whistle. A landlubber strains her eyes to see if the boat is on shore. She cannot judge distance by new sounds. She thinks that she can throw a stone from the top of the cliff into the water. The distance is deceiving. She doesn't realize that the tide runs out persistently, on time, and she misses dinner because of a head wind or tide or no water at all.

Nature education, like charity, begins at home. It is where we are. It is knowledge through the school of experience. Omit nature experiences, and there can be no real nature knowledge.

Solitary Wildness. In this day of the turbulent mind, we should cultivate the charm of solitary wildness—an opportunity to drink at the well of imagination. We should find the solitude of lake, sea, mountain, moor, or deep woods. We should try to sense their changing moods or reflections. Take the last hour before sunset, when the animals are settling down for the night; before sunrise, when things are beginning to stir; or a drowsy hour at noon. At such times, campers may acquire the art of quietness—the magic of timeless leisure.

Plan for each camper to have "an hour of sensibility" in a quiet nook of his own choice, alone and undisturbed. Let him play a game of listing sounds—the wind, the birds, distant farm activities—or the odors that he gets—the scent of flowers, trees, and fruit—or new forms of nature that he sees from his resting place. What thoughts do these impressions stir? Can they be shared? Have him try to capture the spirit of the woodland in writing.

Camp Activities. Water sports are generally conceded by camp directors to be the most important activity. The successful camper is at home in or on the water. When he graduates, not only is he a swimmer but he is capable of lifesaving. The chances are that he can master a canoe and can be trusted to show good judgment and resourcefulness on a trip.

After water sports, what then? Most camps have a highly organized athletic program. Large boys' camps tend to make school athletics the major sport with baseball, tennis, and basketball the "big three" and volleyball, croquet, and golf the minor activities. Boys' camps are also more inclined than girls' camps to repeat city games. On the other hand, some very successful camps do not schedule formal sports.

Athletics and Camping Objectives. Camp directors should consider critically the relation of an organized athletic program to the aims of camping itself. The transplanting of the city playground or the school athletic field into the wilderness caters to the already developed physical skills of boys and girls. It overlooks the basic objective of camping education—blazing a new trail to joyous outdoor living, to nature recreation. Furthermore, too much coaching for expertness and overemphasis on the desire to win, often characteristics of camp instruction, do not foster lasting or satisfying recreational companionship—another camping ideal.

Games away from the athletic field and delights in the deep woods can be made engrossing, and training in nature play should be part of the equipment of camp leaders. Without setting up a single goal post or stepping over a camp boundary line, most directors may find within their own campgrounds endless opportunities for activity more valuable than participation in athletics.

Here are a few examples of the kind of recreational activity I have in mind: exploring, adventure, trail building, forest-fire patrolling, boatbuilding, outdoor cooking, tent pitching, building lean-tos, constructing stone fireplaces, gypsying, camp sanitation, overnight hiking, nature dens, the camp zoo, tree planting, forest nurseries, nature guiding, hare and hound, capture the flag, use of knife and ax, forest first aid, signaling, conservation, stars, whittling projects, forest judging, storm hikes, raiding, rafts, treasure hunts, birch-bark dishes, outdoor beds, physical geography, nature photography, tribal ceremonials, harmless birds and snakes, nature museum, bridge building, and fishing.

FIG. 16.—Nature Guide School students exploring a brook. Nature leaders must first of all know by personal experience the thrill of discovering water life. One should have a dip net and a sufficiency of glass jars. Thousands of children are waiting for competent leaders.

Mr. Camp Director, do you mean to say that *your campers* do not already appreciate baseball? Are you not willing to substitute these needed outdoor activities? Do you not prefer to send your campers home *knowing camping?*

CAMP DIRECTORS AND THE PROBLEM OF NATURE GUIDANCE

A $1,000,000 museum, a stereopticon lantern with an opaque projector, a radio, a mountain brook teeming with life, or the most luxuriant meadow in the world does not make a nature program. Neither does laboratory drudgery. What we need is leaders. They have to create a new job in a new field. The great outdoors constitutes a reservoir without limit for joyous living, but such a reservoir is valueless to the leader who is not constantly training himself to use it. This applies equally to directors and counselors. Trained directors can get on better with trained counselors, who, in turn, can get along better with trained campers. At present, there is the demand and the opportunity for better trained camp leaders. Unfortunately, it will be a long time before the supply will equal the demand. It may be well to consider the difficulties that all too often block a more effective and popular program in the summer camp.

One way to consider this fundamental problem of nature guidance is to glance over the correspondence of camp directors who are seeking nature counselors. Their letters have so much in common that one can almost predict the contents.

They usually start as follows: "We have never had successful nature study, and we wonder if you can suggest the right kind of a leader." They also usually make it clear that they want a leader first and a scholar second. "Send me someone who can take the children on exploring trips and give them adventure," or "I want a nature leader who knows progressive educational methods, who has attractive personality, and who knows nature." These camp directors are right in wanting such counselors, but it is a large order. They do not always appreciate the obstacles in the nature counselor's path, nor do they give their full attention and cooperation in making the nature program appeal to all campers. The following announcement, made by a director at breakfast time, is enough to cripple any spirit of adventure in nature lore: "Cap'n Nickerson will take those who prefer to sail down the sound and will leave the wharf at nine o'clock; Miss Jones plans baseball, and if there are any left who would like to go out with the Bug Lady, they may meet her on the front porch."

Let us read the camp directors' letters a little further. A next paragraph may say, "We would like a person of some training for the work but have not any funds," or "We have made it a policy not to pay any money to our first-year counselors." Perhaps it is the other extreme, "I'll pay any amount if I can get someone who can really put nature study across." An inconsistency between the requirements and the salary is immediately apparent. A trained nature counselor should receive a salary commensurate with other counselors. They do in many camps, but frequently, in planning their personnel, camp directors do not consider their nature-study program of equal importance with the more traditional sport activities. One director goes on to say that she wishes to reserve the right to drop the candidate at the end of two weeks if the leader "does not make good." It is needless to add that this prospective leader started the season with "fear and trembling." Such an attitude jeopardizes the success of leadership at the very outset.

Fortunately, most camp directors are not of the kind just mentioned. They are coworkers with the nature counselor, seeking the same ends and, with him, recognizing in nature endless opportunities for vital experiences.

It is also true that some nature counselors are sacrificed on the wheels of organization. Any director must be aware that athletics is the most popular activity for campers of high school age. Our social fabric has brought this about over a long period of years. Were nature recreation instead to have received the same expenditure, the same coaching, and an equal applause, it would be difficult to get high school students to throw a bladder full of air at an iron hoop day in and day out. I do not believe that this is a prejudiced remark, for I have coached basketball teams for years and get a lot of enjoyment out of the sport. If this premise is true, it is unfair to schedule nature lore and a basketball game at the same time and ask the campers to take their choice.

Leaders Must Decide on the Rewards in Nature Lore—Pleasure, Points, Insignia, or Medals

Camp Awards Are Frequently Used to Motivate Nature Activity. Many camps have a generosity of nature, but the interested spirits are few. From each camp may come one camper who is deeply interested. There may not be one. It is not the favorable spot that takes hold of the camper. The camper must be led to the interest. In many camps, this motivation is provided by prizes and awards. But prizes and awards for what?

In spite of all that may be said to the contrary, emphasis in camp practice continues to be on a "list" as a measure of nature interest. Whether it be the identification of trees, a collection of insects, an accumulation of facts, or within the realm of flowers or stars, an appraisal of the nature program will reveal the "list" as the ever-present requisition for camp acclaim. The camper can still earn medals and insignia with "lists." He chants the "bird list," for example, and an emblem is sewed onto the proper place. Then the "bird list" is promptly forgotten because the camper must pass on to the "bug list."

On the other hand, if the whole camp program is on a system of points and awards, it is too much of a handicap to expect nature to win a place without its honors and silver cups. However, the practice of awarding medals for accomplishments in nature has no justification. Getting any fun out of regimented nature study is akin to asking a hen to sit on boiled eggs.

How many points are you going to give for your camper's mind being in tune with the moods of the lake and mountains? Have they ever seen the purple hills and beyond? At night, do they see the shadows coming out of the forests to the lake shore? Do they see the reflections of the mountains change—reaching half across the lake at times? Do they know that the loons will have difficulty in rising out of calm water? And if not, who will tell them? Are these things conversation at breakfast? Perhaps your enthusiasm will supply just what the camper lacks. How can campers admire without an awareness of the presence of the environment? The most valuable part of naturewardness cannot be scored.

The Criticism of the Point System Is That It Does Not Deal with Feelings and Attitudes.[1] The enjoyment of nature precedes the desire for knowledge. A delight in one bird experience with a zest for other bird experiences is worth more than knowing 10 birds and having no interest in the eleventh. Camp nature should primarily be concerned with the state of mind rather than the science. Do not worry about three constellations, 15 trees, and 25 flowers. That has been the aim in some schools, and it has nearly killed any impulse to enjoy nature.

It is my suspicion that some schools, by dictatorially saying, "Learn 10 insects for tomorrow," have created the antinature feeling that is too evident among young people. The same system in camp can bring a similar reaction. It has recently come to my attention that a teacher in a Connecticut school said, "I'll take you on a nature walk tomorrow." To her chagrin, there was a protest. Upon investigation, she found that it came from those who had been to camp. They had been subjected to the point system and were tired of it.

Lead children to enjoy nature, and the knowledge of nature will follow. It is the number of experiences saturated with joy rather than the number of beasts and flowers named that counts.

Adventuring for nature's gold is too largely incidental so far as counselor consciousness is concerned. But it leads to right attitudes in the open, the recognition and obedience of nature's laws, useful and

[1] By the "point system" is meant that the whole nature program is based on the award of points. Scoring points for a game is a different matter.

necessary skills on the trails, and joyful employment of leisure time—desirable outcomes in a well-balanced program of nature education.

What Are the Objectives in Nature Leadership?

Ever since there have been standards and minimum essentials for swimming leaders—and such standards are necessary for safety along the water front—there has been a periodical call for the same in nature recreation. There are certain minimum essentials of knowledge such as knowing poison ivy, knowing the disastrous effects of a forest

Fig. 17.—The influence of leaders is no better shown than by the manner in which the leader handles snakes. The fear of snakes is passed on by the example of adults rather than as an inborn trait. (*Photograph by Amos Hoff.*)

fire, knowing the importance of washing the hands before working with food. One should have certain skills, as in transplanting a tree, handling a snake, or making a whistle. Knowledge does not guarantee habits. Along with knowledge, there must be certain attitudes in regard to the conservation of native wild flowers, the pollution of streams, and good outdoor manners. Beyond this, it is undesirable to standardize nature recreation. It is the artificiality of nature lessons that has killed the spirit.

If the leader goes to camp with the sole idea of emphasizing fact to the exclusion of body health, better thinking, and enjoyable use of leisure time, that leader will fail.

I know a music counselor, a graduate of a well-known conservatory of music, who, on the first day of camp, examined every camper as to voice and ability to sing the chromatic scale. His summer's program failed the first day. The next summer, a college trio came from Dixie. They just sang and sang. The campers caught the spirit, and the camp became known as a "singing camp." Everyone sang just for the love of singing. Singing became a tremendous power in developing the spirit of that camp.

FIG. 18.—An animal cage that has evolved through trial and error. A ¼-in. galvanized wire mesh nailed to the inside of a wooden frame is the most serviceable. If the door lowers from the top, it is convenient for cleaning out. If the bottom of the cage has a removable galvanized tray, it can be washed, sterilized, and placed in the sun. Two ring-necked doves have a home in this cage.

In most camps, there is a stream of enjoyable activities. The nature offerings must be interesting enough to compete with other activities. The camper selects but is not "assigned." The nature counselor is not a coach in subject matter. He is a red-blooded leader who is interested in children and the opportunities for their happy growth in the out-of-doors, and, seeing the challenge of this new profession, has enrolled in the camp program to do his bit in child development.

THE CAMP NATURE PROGRAM

Long before camp opens, each person responsible for a definite part in a camp program should sit down and think through his plan for the coming season. Not that the scheme will be final—it will not. It goes without saying, however, that the leader should know whither bound, the vehicle of travel, and the best procedure. Any counselor who finds himself concerned with the development of nature lore for next summer may find the following suggestions helpful. They concern four major areas of nature interests: work with animals, work with plants, the camp museum, and the use of native materials as the basis for campcrafts. Nature recreation through trips will be discussed in the following chapter.

Animal Study Is a Fundamental Activity for Junior Campers. In the rush of modern life, we do not find so many tame canaries, white mice, pet rabbits, and caterpillar cocoons in the possession of children as formerly. Our children are told that they must be sympathetic and that they should gain a sense of responsibility. But how are they to go about it? Camp seems to be one logical place to develop these desired human qualities, because the summer camp (1) provides an ideal environment for housing a goodly collection of live, tame animals, and (2) offers on every hand wild animals and birds, waiting only for kind treatment to become interesting and instructive pets.

Important Pointers for Work with Pets and the Pet House

The Animal House Is an Educational Environment. Pets make possible a fundamental program. The success of the adventure depends on leadership. The animal house is not a zoo where one merely gazes or is amused or passively entertained.

It Meets Child Aims. The child wants fun, adventure, and new friends. He wants to satisfy the parental instinct. All this can emanate from the pet house.

It Is a Place for Child Growth. You have old campers who have had considerable experience at the pet house and beginners who have had none. There is no set time for any one camper to succeed in the care of any one animal. Guinea pigs are easier to know and to care for than chicks. The object is not to graduate from guinea pigs but to be able to cope with situations that occur in guinea-pig families—to be able to meet contingencies as well as routine. To do this, one needs to know the food, ways to handle, disease, prevention, safeguards during pregnancy, and inherent traits. The same knowledge applies to chicks and dogs. In the case of dogs, however, there is the *added* responsibility of teaching. The challenge is greater. Thus the work should be progressive in ability requirements. There should be something new each day. Ruts indicate old age. Monotony spells death. The leader must plan for the bringing in of new pets, the birth of young, and closer observation that there will be a growth in interest. Think faster than the children, or you will lose them.

It Is Organized as a Democracy. Let the children elect leaders. Have them inspect animals and cages and report. Let them determine rules of conduct and make policies as problems arise. You are a guide and not a dictator.

It Calls for Necessary Routine. There can be no compromise on sufficient food or clean cages or on well-groomed animals. The children will foresee this at once. Any mistakes or slovenly conduct should be checked right from the start. Be orthodox up to this point. Beyond this, create interest and imagination.

It Is a Place to Adapt Policies. If the children feel that Mary is selfish with the baby rabbit and wants no one to touch it, they create and adopt a rule that all the animals belong to all the campers. They can coin a policy such as "one for all and all for one." In a democracy, there is a small chance for foolish rules. If reasonable, rules will be obeyed. Public opinion is usually fair.

It Is a Place for Action. A child is an animal in action. He is not a "sitting down" animal. Provide for *do* rather than *don't.* "Smooth the fur this way." "Lift the rabbit by the body like this." The child learns about the rabbits by playing with them. Provide a period for playing with each animal. This can come during feeding time. It should follow the "clean-up duties."

Time Can Be Allowed for Mental Reaction. Say, "I'll tell you a story about a rabbit, after you have put the animals back in the cages," instead of, "Put the animals back right away." Ask for one thing at a time—as, "Do all the animals have lettuce?"

One Must Know the Animals. Read all you can about them. It will stimulate your power to suggest and direct.

Everyone Takes Part in the Work. You set the standard of work by your own actions. If you have a share in the work or assign yourself a duty, they will observe how you go at it. It is your responsibility that they do not stray into the lake, that they are not struck in the eye by the heron or bitten by the rat. A scratch or bite requires care.

It is not so much a matter of being brave or not brave as of acquiring correct attitudes and habits in the prevention of infection.

The Animal House Requires Excellent Personal Qualities. *Be on Time.* If campers are to be on time, leaders must be on time. It is *just* that animals be taken care of on time.

Be Humane. If you handle baby chicks carefully—interestingly—you will have a household of like dispositions. Your actions are reflected. The cat likes "stroking," and pigeons do not. Some animals prefer to wrestle; others have the play spirit.

Be Honest. If you do not believe in the worth-whileness of the pet house, keep out. If you do not know why the bittern swallows frogs whole, say so, but do not let it stop there. Say, "We'll try to find out." Lead the child to the joy of finding out. It is *not* an assignment. It is something to be discovered, to be announced at the campfire, to be told a visiting parent.

Be Just. *A* has a clean cage, and *B* does not. Rotate duties so that everyone has a chance. Let your rotation scheme be known. Everyone has tasks.

Be Tactful. Appreciate child feats and limitations. Do not ask Mary to teach the guinea pig tricks if the guinea pig is not teachable. You are not presenting lists. You are not teaching school. You are dealing with personalities and their integration into a social community.

Be a Sympathetic Mixer. Go from group to group and help each in activity. Make comments. Do not hold aloof. You lead by action more than by voice. Actions are louder than words. You are dealing with opportunities. Your enthusiasm will be contagious. That is equally true if you "go stale."

Be Experimental. Which food does the animal prefer? Can it learn to follow a maze? Can it find "hidden food?" Will it thrive on candy?

Be Observant. Keep a record of original observations on a card attached to the cage. Have the child write down date, observation, and name. Encourage observation reports at the campfire. If campers are to be observant, you yourself cannot lag. Jot down a few observations for yourself. Always give campers first chance.

Be a Good Sport. Keep the inhabitants of the animal house happy. Be cheerful, sincere, and enthusiastic. If it is a hot day, do not dwell on the fact. Gather in the shade and tell an appropriate story—how eagles keep their young cool, for example.

FIG. 19.—A water snake swallowing a sunfish. The snake is the only animal that can swallow something larger around than it is itself.

FIG. 20.—Beaver house with entrance. This picture was taken at a low stage of water. This is legitimate photography and desirable when one wishes to show a definite point that is usually under water. (*Courtesy of Palisades Interstate Park, New York. Photograph by R. E. Logan.*)

Give Individual Opportunity. Individual choice is the right of the camper. Do not fret if a group has gone horseback riding. The horse challenges the intellect as perhaps no other animal. Encourage interest in the horse. Horseback riding is animal study.

Be Versatile. New possibilities must be suggested by the leader. Wading for frogs and playing with the ground hog are not meaningless pastimes. Turn joyful actions into educational investments. Why is it difficult to catch frogs? How does the frog protect his eyes when he goes into the mud?

Encourage Outgrowing Interests. Clay modeling, plaster casts of footprints, soap carving, trapping, and other interests may appear. The campers may wish a white-footed deer mouse, a mole, a chipmunk, or a skunk for observation. A group sets about making a box trap. Adventure may be the prime incentive.

Hide Your Objectives. Have in mind that you are to teach children health laws, humaneness, sex-character attitudes, dependability, cleanliness, and citizenship. Keep these aims under your hat. No one wants to be told to be good, to be kind, or to be dependable. Develop attitudes rather than habits. Right or wrong habits will follow right or wrong attitudes.

THE CAMP IS A WILD-LIFE SANCTUARY

Chipmunks Hold First Place as Camp Pets. Nearly every camp can boast of chipmunks, but few camps can boast of taming them so that they will sit in the hand of a camper and eat. Camp Hanoun has the right to claim that accomplishment. Immediately upon our arrival there some time ago, Mrs. Vinal was taken by the hand by two enthusiastic girls and patiently led to where two chipmunks had set up housekeeping. The children could hardly wait to tell her all about their pets—how the chipmunks had paid friendly visits back and forth, each to the home of the other, and how they had become tame. Walnuts were quickly brought forth and tapped gently on a stone as a signal to the pets. Mrs. Chippy immediately peered forth from her doorstep and came out to get her nuts. She had just begun to eat when Mr. Munk appeared and scolded so loudly that his wife went hastily down below; but her spirits soon revived, and she was back in a jiffy for more food. She had just begun to munch another nut when it slipped from her paws and rolled down the hole. Down she scurried after it, and, since the hole was very small, she had to back out carefully, holding the nut in her paws. This time she put it in her cheek pouch for safekeeping and scampered off to hide it before returning for another. One look at the gleaming eyes of the girls was enough to know that they were having unforgettably happy moments. The friendship of the chipmunks was due entirely to their own efforts, and they knew that one lapse of kindness or one misdeed on their part would put an end to the trust that the animals had placed in them.

The story of Furry, a baby red squirrel, given in Mrs. Comstock's *Handbook of Nature Study*, would be of interest in connection with squirrels or chipmunks.

The Crow Is a Mischievous Pet. Crows' nests are easily located, and a young crow need not be caged. The crow's recorded bill of fare consists of cutworms, grubs, grasshoppers, mice, snakes, frogs, all kinds of berry, and grains. Just to forage for his daily food will certainly impress some very startling facts upon his providers. Other interesting things about crows and their care may be found in Mrs. Comstock's *Pet Book*. Ernest Thompson Seton's *Story of Silver Spot* is good for a campfire story.

The Skunk Teaches Good Manners. Another black pet may be the skunk, "sachet-pussy," polecat, or civet cat, as he is often erroneously called. This animal is not as black or malodorous as he is painted. He is the stock example of what it means to get a bad reputation.

A mother skunk and her two little "skunkies" were observed nightly from the piazza at Owaissa by means of flashlights. The mother would scold and stamp with her feet, and the little fellows would hold wrestling matches and squeak with delight, accompanied by other squeals of amusement from the spectators. It is great sport to take a skunk grasshoppering. Such an expedition proves the real usefulness of a skunk to the community.

Turtles Stand the Test of the Ages. Without apparent reason, the turtle appears to be a boys' pet. A big snapping turtle at Camp Timanous was kept in a large cement aquarium made in the ground. This was a popular spot at feeding time, when he received his daily meal of raw meat. At Lanakila, the turtles were kept in a terrarium through which flowed water from the aquarium. The turtles had laid eggs that were being hatched in sand. Dallas Lore Sharp's *Turtle Eggs for Agassiz* is a story well worth telling around the fire on a rainy evening. The New York State Museum has published a handbook that is of great value in this connection—*The Amphibians and Reptiles of Allegany State Park* by Bishop.

A Brook Aquarium Provides a Variety of Wild Life. A successful type of camp aquarium was seen at Yawgoog, the camp of the Greater

Providence Council, Boy Scouts of America. This was in the form of a screened area across a brook, and near at hand was a bulletin board supplying information identifying the water life. The enclosure was on a nature trail, and running water kept the aquarium in excellent condition. The boys had great fun making a dam, clearing a pool, sanding the bottom, carpeting the banks with moss, installing a water wheel, and setting out water plants. Capturing fish with dip nets so as not to injure them, rounding up turtles, curving over the top of the

Fig. 21.—Bull snake and eggs. This photograph suggests that this snake guards the eggs and that it may even incubate them. What is the truth of the matter? (*Courtesy of Palisades Interstate Park, New York. Photograph by R. E. Logan.*)

wire to keep the snakes within bounds, and weaving greenbrier in the upper meshes to keep a new crop of boys from leaning too heavily on the wire were problems that were met and solved in turn. The brook aquarium at Yawgoog was the notable factor contributing to the summer's nature experience.

Birds Patrol the Camp Sanctuary for Insects and Rodents. Only a few camps have bird-feeding stations. It is true that summer is not the ideal time to attract birds, and food is plentiful in the woods, but a little patience will be amply rewarded. Soap shakers filled with suet will attract birds to a definite place for photography. Sunflower seeds, cracked corn, buckwheat, hemp, and wheat are enjoyed by seed-eating birds. Some Girl Scouts knit Christmas bags and fill them with seeds cooked in suet. One camp is noted for its homing pigeons that are released on trips. The fine attributes exhibited by the birds are made use of by the directors in little talks to the campers. At another camp, the boys utilized as a bird blind the upturned roots of a tree to which the earth was still clinging. Peep-holes had been made through the clay to watch the birds visiting the drinking pool gouged out by the uprooted tree. The inspiration that animal and bird photography brings to a camp will certainly encourage campers to study the wild life that is about them and will repay the camp directors who take the active trouble to preserve the camp property as a wild-life sanctuary for nature's folks.

CAMP GARDENS

Camp Gardening Must Be Interesting. Camp gardening has been on the decline ever since the days of war gardens. Why? Surely the gardens are not to blame, so I fear that we must place the blame on the leaders and their methods. Their failure can be summed up simply as neglect to recognize that this activity must not be a chore. It must be, as it easily can be, a source of pleasure and interest. For example, it is merely a lesson in mathematics to dictate that corn should be planted four grains to a hill, the hills 2½ ft. apart in rows, and the rows 3 ft. apart. Instead, the approach is made by pointing out that corn shoots out, and the bean backs out; that the blade is perfectly wind-resistant; that the leaf has a rain guard; that there are brace roots; that there is a miniature ear of corn at the base of every leaf; that there are literally hundreds of interesting things of the garden. Who wouldn't get excited with interest?

Tilling the soil is a necessary part of the work, but there are life histories, experiments, and the war with insects to be considered. Leadership is all-important, and the leader must recognize that gardening, more than any other activity, affords an opportunity for problem solving and putting the child in sympathy with common, everyday events.

Plant Crops That Mature Quickly. The short season is, of course, a handicap to camp gardening, and crops should be planted that can be harvested. Lettuce and radishes are two of these. At one camp, the campers make sandwiches from their garden produce and sell them at the annual bazaar. At another, they pot red maples and balsams in paper drinking cups and take them home to plant. At still another, the garden director is an agricultural school graduate and a high school principal. At this camp, a gypsy degree includes 8 hr. of work in the large camp garden.

Flowers Add Beauty to Camp Interiors. Camp decoration is one legitimate objective for flower gardening. Flower girls, who gather flowers for the tables and take care of the flower boxes, are a real part of a gardening program. When this is followed by conversation, announcements, and after-dinner stories, it is far better than regular flower shows, where the plants are set in mechanical rows and labeled. Rustic flower holders are attractive, and fern balls where the matrix is made of sphagnum moss, log-cabin fern dishes, and window boxes add to the charm of the room. Or use birch logs which have been bored to hold test tubes.

The Wild-flower Garden. Wild plants may be brought from the woods, a good supply of black humus along with them, and planted carefully in some moist, shady location as nearly like the former conditions as possible. If the royal and ostrich fern are native but not found in the campgrounds, they may be transplanted to add beauty to the wild garden.

Wild-flower seeds are sold by many dealers. It is much better to buy these than to risk transplanting the more delicate varieties. The wild-flower garden and the fern walk denote character for any camp.

The Bog Garden. There are those who think that only a rich man can afford a water garden. The only requirement in riches is to be a zealous lover of aquatic plants. The natural bog needs no excavator, and the plumbing is taken care of by nature's springs. If steppingstones are laid, one may enter the bog dry-shod. To change a bog is to destroy its uniqueness, and bogs are becoming so rare that it is up to camp directors to preserve those that are discovered in their vicinity.

Occasionally directors have chills or fevers at the mention of going to a swamp for enjoyment. They picture reptiles, evil insects, and other imaginary dangers. Yet some of the most interesting flowers grow in bogs. One camp has a natural bog garden 5 min. walk from headquarters. Just imagine! Five minutes to such gifts as pitcher plants, the showy orchis, sundews, and sphagnum! Jump on this bog, and huge pines some 70 ft. away will quake. What a library of stories about plants that eat insects, moss that makes coal, and the sphagnum that was used for surgical dressings during the first World War! How much better it is to have campers go to the bogs to view the rarer plants than to bring them into camp and risk their destruction or extermination.

Wild-flower Protection. A fine scheme to instruct campers as to which flowers should not be picked is to post colored pictures of these flowers. The loose-leaf edition of *The Wild Flowers of New York* is well adapted to this use. The New England Wild Flower Preservation Society, Horticultural Hall, 300 Massachusetts Avenue, Boston, Mass., produces and distributes leaflets on wild flowers and conservation in general. Post cards of our rare wild flowers can be obtained from the National Wild Flower Preservation Society, Washington, D.C. Essay competition papers are sent out by the Keystone View Company.

Soil Testing. Another interesting side of wild-flower gardening in camp is that of soil testing. It introduces the camper to soils and their variations and contains a lesson in environment. Soil-testing outfits can be obtained at a small cost now that the demand for them has increased, and two or three of these should be in every camp that appreciates the value and interest of a wild-flower garden.

CAMP MUSEUMS: OUTDOOR AND IN

The Outdoor Nature Den. Although one should first of all recognize that the campground is an outdoor museum in itself, it is often more fun to set aside some nook as a *nature den.* This area should include a pond and brook for water life, a rockery for certain ferns and lichens, a shady corner for native flowers, like the moccasin and orchids, and an open space for field plants. The nature den may be marked off with gray birch rails, but an arbor vitae or red-cedar hedge is more permanent and gives it a secluded atmosphere. Two evergreens may mark off the entrance with a rustic sign overhead or two rock piles covered with creeping vines. When one enters, one sees markers indicating The Fern Walk, The Rhododendron Path, To the Turtle Pond, The Wild-flower Garden, The Spring, Follow This Trail to the Woodpecker's Hotel, The Beaver Houses Are This Way—No Loud Talking.

If the visitor takes the rhododendron path, he may see small wooden signs along the side telling the common names of shrubs, trees, and flowers. Beneath the name is written an interesting fact about the plant: Shadbush—Blossoms When the Shad Go up the

Rivers to Spawn; Trembling Aspen—"A Weed Tree" Used with Spruce for Paper Pulp; White Ash—Useful for Basketry; Sensitive Fern—Young Shoots a Substitute for Asparagus. Attention may be called to The Ovenbird's Nest—Do Not Step on It; or Red-eyed Vireo's Nest Overhead—Young Hatching, Do Not Disturb; Dog-toothed Violets—It Took Them Seven Years to Produce Seed, Do Not Pull Out; Can You Find the Four Kinds of Ferns on This Ledge? Help Us to Protect Them; Mountain Laurel—Two Thousand People Visited This spot Last Year and Did Not Break This Shrub; This Is a White Oak Stump. How Old Was the Tree When Cut? Which Way Did It Fall?

Land Liabilities May Offer Unusual Settings. Each camp, of course, must make a survey of its grounds and see what it has that can best be made into a nature den. I once saw an amphitheater of fireplaces made in an abandoned gravel pit. A unique nature garden was in an old quarry. It was like a visit to fairyland. The seams of the rocks made natural steppingstones. The stone stairway led past seeping pockets of hanging ferns and polypody. The last descent was by ladder that took one onto the quarry floor. The whole had the effect of a room. The draperies were all sorts of vine—clematis, frost grapes, woodbine, and bittersweet—which had been trained along the walls. Here and there were white quartz with nature quotations carefully lettered in moss-green paint. A seam of talc was featured. From the mineral exhibit, it was but a step to the pool in which grew native water plants, each identified on a little map held flat under a plate-glass weight on a rock shelf. Here and there were rock chairs and fireplaces, perfectly safe, even with flying sparks. The speakers' pulpit was nearly hidden with greenery. The whole setting was the work of a master and planned to the minutest detail. It was like a great painting. What at first had been considered as a very undesirable feature of the grounds had become a gold mine instead of a lime quarry.

THE INDOOR MUSEUM

The Indoor Museum Is a Nature Headquarters. Directors of summer camps are awakening to the importance of a nature headquarters as an aid to encouraging nature interest and hence to the building of resourcefulness and satisfaction in the individual campers. There are still many directors who believe that, with the great outdoors on every hand, a museum is superfluous; but the gradual increase in the number of camp museums is testimony to its real place as part of the regular camp equipment.

The Museum Meets Many Nature Needs. *It Answers Questions of the Moment.* The indoor camp museum is a device to bring the child and nature together. Those things that the child has oppor-

FIG. 22.—A camp museum is a workshop and not a morgue. Note the glass-jar spider gardens.

tunity to see in nature do not usually need to be brought inside. The nature leader must use his judgment. If interest lies in observing a butterfly visiting a flower, the process should be watched in the fields. If the object is to see the butterfly suck up the nectar, this can best be done in the museum by feeding the insect a little honey or sugar solution on a glass plate. When the butterfly has served its purpose, it is released, and the museum is ready for the next thing that may be called upon the stage of nature experience.

It Interprets Local Physical Phenomena. The camp museum presents nature material that gives a vivid and lasting impression in order to help the campers realize better the life and processes of the environment. The geology of the locality may be the foundation.

The formation of the mountains, valleys, and lakes that surround the camp is told with specimens and models as a story so as to be readily understood by the children. The old idea of going to a museum and merely gazing is of little value. Visitors at camp usually look about the museum with idle curiosity. A camper visits the museum with a deep interest in one thing. It may be with the nature counselor who

FIG. 23.—Horned toads are not toads. These horned toads are fed by a self-operating flytrap. The flies eat the molasses and are then guided to the cage above by a fine wire screen in the shape of a cone.

uses the models to make clear just how the rocks of the quarry were put down. This may be followed by a field trip, which, in its turn, must have a single, definite aim in view.

The Museum Is an Outlet for the Collecting Instinct. The collecting age leads to exploration. This is an opportunity for lessons in conservation. Collecting excursions are opportunities to establish right nature habits. They must start as recreational and become educational. For example, the camper may collect leaves but not birds' eggs, minerals but not rare flowers and ferns.

Camp Museums Are Not Natural-history Morgues. The modern museum has long outgrown the idea of being a repository. Wild-flower morgues date back to the days of the closet botanist, when credit in courses was gained by collecting 53 specimens of wild flowers. In zoology, the same idea existed in the belief that the animal must be pickled in order to be worth looking at. It is at least a half of a century since even schools have considered that there was any merit to the plan.

Museum Material Should Be Interesting, Useful, Closely Linked to Camp Activity. These are three requisites. Keep them in mind before allowing anything to cross the museum threshold, and, when anything ceases to meet the test, exclude it. There should be no compromise possible on this regulation.

Accessibility Is Essential. Camp museums should be placed along a well-beaten track so that the campers may drop in at odd moments on the way to or from the recreation hall, the sleeping quarters, or the bathing beach. Few young people will of themselves seek out a museum in an out-of-the-way corner, but many seemingly indifferent campers will drop in with "buddies" to look around and become so interested in the work that they will soon be as enthusiastic as their more nature-inclined friends. At one camp, the museum contains the post office, while another camp has a museum in an old boathouse near the bathing beach. So successful is this latter arrangement that many of the parents pay more attention to the collections and specimens than to the swimming meets.

Comfortable Roomy Quarters Are an Asset. The museum is a workshop. It should not only be a laboratory for those busy with collections, displays, or exhibits, but it should provide adequate space for developing rainy-day projects growing out of nature lore.

A rustic shelter is ideal for a museum, as is also a log cabin. In these cabins, a fireplace is really essential, giving warmth and coziness to those retreating to the museum on a rainy day. The social significance of fire is recognized by all camp directors and, in the museum workshop, as round the council ring, may provide stimulation for individual or group effort. The triangle fireplace, which was inaugurated at the Luther Gulick Camps, is a good type. Not only is it practical but it gives an opportunity to see the entire length of the flames, the sparks, and the smoke.

The Arrangement. The size, however, is not so important as the layout. Any small room, tent, or lean-to will suffice. The walls will have art burlap. Around the border will be benches or shelves somewhat below the eye level of the children. Beneath the benches are airtight chests to store things away from mice and insects.

An Actual Camp Museum. Suppose we walk through a camp museum, tabulating its materials as we go.

On the wall we notice:

1. A set of fire pictures. If a group is assigned to a "trench fire," and they do not know how to do it, they do not ask questions but consult the picture.
2. We note a map of the region. Campers constantly refer to that when planning trips or when wishing to know the name of this lake or that mountain.
3. The weather map always appears in a frame. It has been found more useful and dependable than the words of weather prophets.
4. The knot board illustrates a skill necessary to successful camping.
5. The swimming chart records the accomplishments of the campers.
6. Paintings and sketches on trips and last week's photographic contest are a pictorial record of recent camp happenings.
7. There are pictures of last year's pageant—a reminder of former camp standards.
8. All kinds of leaf print, cattail basket, curtain pull, freshly painted door stop, and a townet represent hours of nature activity.

The front of the benches is reserved for working space. Let us glance along the back:

1. We note a model of a bubbling spring that was made after the last mountain trip to show how a spring works.
2. The material in that box is being arranged for a campfire talk. The campmaster is going to tell us about the way a glacier carries and deposits gravel.
3. Here are models of log cabins. One group is going to make a cabin out of driftwood.
4. Birdhouses are being made to take home and will be on exhibition at the camp meet. Campers still have to stain them.
5. Here is a group of animal life. There are tadpoles in these jars. They were egg masses last week. Several caterpillars are on these different potted plants. That milkweed chrysalis formed yesterday. That sign on the toad cage says, "Give me a fly." We are told that he ate 55 caterpillars for dinner.

6. There used to be an observation beehive at that window.

7. Here is a compound microscope. Campers have seen one-celled animals through it.

8. This section is reserved as a "What-is-it?" shelf. If anyone does not know the name of a flower, etc., he puts it on this shelf. Honorable mention is given to the one that names it first.

Fig. 24.—Sphagnum moss was used as a surgical dressing in the first World War. It is soft, absorbent, and cheap. Note the fruiting bodies. (*Photograph by Robert Coffin.*)

9. Yes, this is a storm window. It is cheaper than plate glass. It is kept over these Indian relics, since people were always moving them, and they got lost.

10. That box of sphagnum moss? That has been here several years. It is interesting because campers collected sphagnum for the Red Cross during the first World War. Some kinds are useless. The army used the more adaptable varieties in place of absorbent cotton.

The chests contain loan material. There are geology hammers, cyanide jars, field glasses, minerals, samples of soil, a series of models to show how camp rocks formed, a good collection of birds' nests (a talk is given once a year about those), homemade butterfly nets, fruits of trees, woods of trees from the sawmill (used when campers

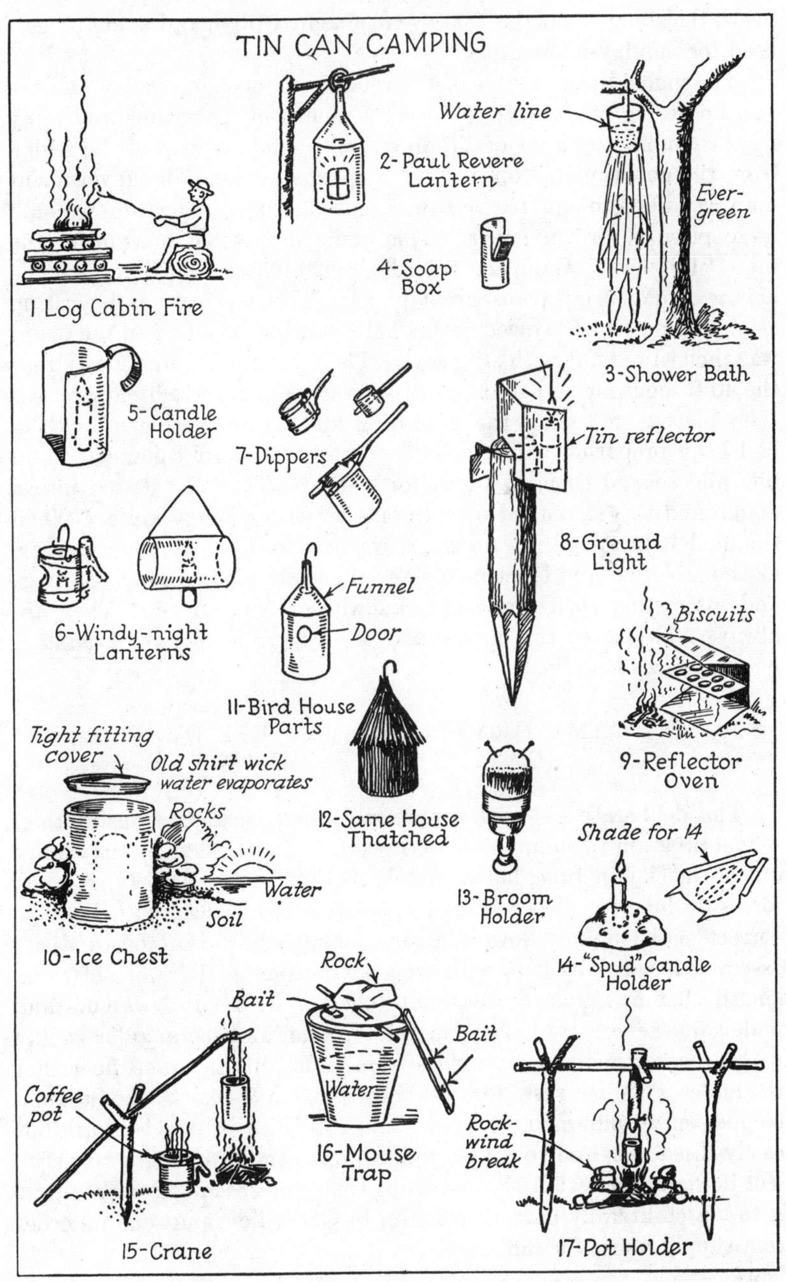

Fig. 25.—Tin-can camping.

heard the story about the 1,000-year pine by Mills), and many objects used for Sunday-night talks.

The model in the center of the room is of the camp valley and the two bordering mountains. It took a month in spare time and rainy days to make it. First of all, an enlarged contour map of the region from the government topographic map was made. The government map was lined in squares and then reproduced in larger squares on a large piece of brown paper. This made it possible to transfer the map "by eye." Campers traced the 20-ft. contour lines on the enlarged map using transparent paper. This tracing was placed on 1-in. pine board and traced with a hard pencil. The line on the board was then sawed out with a jig saw. The same steps were repeated for the 40 ft. contour and so on, until all were sawed. Each pattern was then placed on top of the preceding and in proper place. Others had been preparing papier-mâché. They tore up old newspapers in bits and soaked them in water for 3 days. This was stirred into a dough and was smoothed over the model with a putty knife. When the model resembled the region, it was left to dry. It was then varnished, colored, and labeled to show the trails, campgrounds, springs, and interesting rock formations known to the campers. They are always referring to this model and often have little talks around it before going on a trip.

CAMP CRAFT AND THE USE OF NATIVE MATERIALS

The deliberateness with which most craft leaders transfer their school program to camp invites criticism. Watch them as they move out of the city in June, laden with batik, books of design, Ivory soap, forms de luxe for electric fixtures, ready-made frames with holes in correct position and dowels assured, knockdown birdhouses easily assembled, wood baskets with wooden bottoms and frames of exact length that are guaranteed to fit together in 5 min., walnut- and mahogany-veneer tray bases in round, oval, and rectangular shapes with an assortment of butterflies from India; multicolored fiber that resembles genuine rush for weaving hanging baskets, and a hand lacquer spray pump to put on a stain furnished in powder form but easily dissolved; and so on, ad infinitum, to the extent of a trunkful. Yet it would seem that the last thing that a craft counselor should do is to march literally past a thicket of basket willow and send an order to a supply house for raffia.

The camps that are true to the ideals of outdoor living do not repeat the activities of the schoolroom. They play nature games instead of basketball, enjoy nature music instead of practicing the scale, and use local raw materials instead of raffia, plasticine, and glass beads. Every camper should have a favorable opportunity to collect craft supplies out of the environment, to come in contact with a skilled leader, and to create craft material. The camper should gain an understanding of why the old industries of the homestead were so

FIG. 26.—Breaking flax. Does flax furnish thread to weave into silk, cotton, linen, or cloth that is "all wool and a yard wide"? "Indian hemp" is another name for dogbane, which also provides a good fiber. Your great-grandmother knew these plants. She was a botanist. Note the pilgrim herb garden in the background.

excellent in technique and training. He should get the feeling of how these old-fashioned gifts were expressed in craftsmanship. He should live in the atmosphere of expressing himself and his ideals in his work. Nature itself should inspire art work in camp.

Most camp directors would probably be glad to have an activity program of primitive crafts if they could get the leaders. Someday there will be a textbook on the idea. It will tell just how the Indians made their pottery. There will be hints as to how their pictorial language originated. Most of the homecraft of three generations ago consisted of simple objects made from the immediate natural environment.

The craft guidebook will go into detailed explanation of the making of such common things as soap, cornhusk mats, hooked rugs, samplers, spruce gum, horehound candy, quill pens, tanned skins, spinning, and the like. It will do more; it will point out that, in creative campcraft, the products are not the end in view. The important thing is to cultivate a love of the simple life and the outdoors through the use and appreciation of its craft materials and resources.

Nature should be used as a distinct and satisfying source of craft interest. Handmade looms, twig brooms for the hearth, birch furniture, chairs rescued from dusty attics of the village to be caned with cattail, significant stones in the chimney, flower borders that resemble animals, metal oak leaves supporting acorn inkwells made true to nature, bent growths of wood for door handles, latches lifted by a latchstring, crocks with ferns by a rustic pulpit, white birch-log flowerholders for the table are some of the things that embody the spirit of the open.

The children should be taught whittling. They should make boats, baskets out of ash splints, birch-bark boxes ornamented with porcupine quills, fire sets, sketches in the open, and plaster casts of animal tracks. They can make lacrosse sticks and adapt this fine old Indian game to the age of the campers. There should be a real harmony about the camp Tepee, the craft director carrying on a practical experiment in adapting homestead industries to modern youth.

As camp director at Camp Chequesset, I worked on the principle that craft out of the immediate natural environment is more interesting and vital than craft out of the shop; that gathering sweet grass for basketry is more alluring than sending for raffia by parcel post; that the homemade rag doll carries a sentiment that is not expressed by the "dolled up" specimen that squeaks "mama," rolls up its eyes, and exhibits coal tar dyes. The following experience is one example of how that principle worked out in practice.

One day, a camper brought in some bone carvings made by her grandfather, who was master of a fishing schooner that sailed from Provincetown. The collection consisted of two species of whale, a shark, and a Bible. Here was exhibited the handiwork of an old sea captain. His environment was limited to what came on deck. He had leisure time. He made good use of his talents. No doubt that he enjoyed this pastime and obtained immense satisfaction.

The campers found these "animals of bone" interesting. An idea had been supplied. Immediately they set to work translating their imaginings through modern materials and tools. Instead of bone, they used ivorine because it was available and easier to cut. Instead of a knife, they used a jig saw and file. In place of mere whales or sharks, they made pendants decorated with sea-life designs. In addition to fishlike forms, they imagined clouds, waves, and grasses.

FIG. 27.—This Pilgrim maiden is using the cleaver to make shingles. Handmade shingles are coming into demand. To make them takes skill. They are emblems of the back-to-nature movement. White cedar or white pine shingles are the most satisfactory.

Everywhere we find the tendency to say that our boys and girls are different. We often smile at anything that suggests old-fashioned. However, we must recognize that, if youth is different, the underlying laws are the same. Youth is still interested in doing things. Given opportunities for self-expression, they will not let those opportunities go unused. Let us not insult their intelligence.

PRACTICAL SUGGESTIONS FOR CAMPCRAFT

Firemaking. Learn about the various kinds of fires. Make a fire-by-friction set, decorating it with primitive designs. Construct stoves out of clay or stone.

Indian Craft. Read about the Indians of the locality. What did they use to make baskets, mats, ornaments, canoes, and houses? What did they use for dyes, designs?

Colonial Craft. Visit old homesteads, and discover how they spun, wove, and dyed cloth. Have them demonstrate how they made candles, chests, and tables. What did they use and how did they make

FIG. 28.—Pulling the draw shave in shinglemaking.

baskets? Get them to teach you how to cane a chair. Ask to see their samplers, hooked and braided rugs, and cornhusk mats.

The Art and Craft of the Early Fisherman. An unusual summer experience would be to study the primitive method of fishing in the locality. If a trap or weir was used, it was probably made of stakes and brush, without nails. This required thought and skill. The primitive fisherman needed to select a strategic point to build the trap. He had to discover what bark or branches to use for lashings. He had to know how to make it substantial to withstand tide or current. He had to decide how to get the fish out of the trap. The Indian and the pioneer had to carry on patient observation and experiment through the stimulus of hunger, but the camper might also be able to learn where the fish lurk and how they migrate.

A simpler form of fishing handicraft is the fishpole. Some leaders may insist on having their fishpoles from a wood grown on a South

Fig. 29.—A Puritan fish-drying ground. Why did they use rocks? Wooden racks are still used to dry codfish in Nova Scotia.

Fig. 30.—Grinding meal was extremely important to these maids of Salem town. Some scouts believe that hand-ground meal tastes enough better to warrant making a mortar and a pestle such as shown in the picture. The method looks as old-fashioned as witchcraft. An acquaintance with nature increases our happiness and betters our mode of living. The tall salt-marsh grass was used for thatching.

Sea island, or possibly a steel rod of many pieces, finely fitted. The country boy, who can catch six fish while the leader is getting one, will name the hickory, hornbeam, shadbush, or white ash as his choice, but as a last resort he knows that almost any hardwood will give good service. The leader's rod may cost $50, but the country boy's pole is harvested with a scout knife.

Tackle making follows the cutting of a pole. To scout along the river bank and find a feather, to catch an insect appreciated by a fish, to make an imitation of this insect that will pass the inspection of a fish—this is an art in its own right. If a camper carries his handicraft through to a successful conclusion—that of landing the fish—he has caught more than the fish. He has gained a sense of real independence, a secure feeling of being able to battle his own way in the wilderness through his own handiwork. This we call the height of accomplishment.

Camp Equipment. Camp furniture such as the stools and benches of the lumber camp, a birch broom, a rustic toaster, hat racks, coat hangers, pothooks, gourd cups, and cornhusk mats are useful and make the cabin attractive. The weaving of a bed from fragrant balsam boughs provides an unforgettable experience.

Musical Instruments. Make a corn fiddle, an elderberry fife, or a kettle drum. A wooden xylophone may be heard a mile away on a still night. Dead pieces of cedar were sounded with a wooden mallet until a complete range of notes was acquired. If the piece sounds too high, the end is chipped off, if too low, it is slashed off on the side. Quaker-oats boxes and other boxes of various sizes were placed under the keyboards to give resonance.

Picture Frames. A tree that has been burned by fire and then exposed to the weather for many years is antique wood. The weathering has given a rustic effect similar to that of quartersawing. Enos Mills has used such pieces for picture framing.

Place Cards. Have a contest in making place cards. Shell and pine-cone animals may be wonderful creations.

CHAPTER IV

NATURE TRIPS AND TRAILS

Trips Are Happy Opportunities for Impromptu Nature Learning. Part of the human make-up consists of the delight in "going places"—everybody enjoys an outing. Consequently, there is no happier opportunity for impromptu outdoor learning than the trip to visit the spectacular, the unusual, or the otherwise stimulating nature phenomenon. What does the country around the camp have in things of interest and charm—not the obvious things, but the ones to be sought out? What historic trees populate the neighboring forest; what flowers hide beneath it; what boulders tell stories of the past; what bogs and caves and brooks does the land afford? These are questions that the wanderlust of every true camper raises and that the maker of the nature program will answer through provision for a wide variety of experiences in nature trips. A careful study of the environs is likely to reveal admirable facilities for this kind of recreation and, if done in advance of the camp season, leads to an adaptation of the program to the specific locality and the type of camper. Such a procedure will prove far more successful than any preconceived plan for hikes in general.

Nature Trips Should Be Pleasurable Activity, Not Endurance Tests. Campers get out of trips what they can put into them. The wise leader will therefore begin with walks where the objectives are fairly near, the trip challenging but not overtiring, and the nature material rich in easily recognizable old friends. On such excursions, campers almost unconsciously develop an appreciation of the beauty in the world about them, and they gradually acquire a working knowledge of how to adapt themselves to nature's ways. This training of mind and muscle enables them to meet without undue fatigue the heavier endurance demands of the overnight hike, the several day mountain trek, or the even longer trip by horse, canoe, or auto caravan.

Instead of being a physical ordeal, a camping trip then becomes an enjoyable and memorable recreational experience.

Teaching on Nature Trips Is Highly Effective. The teaching carried on during outdoor trips is entirely impromptu, yet it results in astonishingly effective nature learning. Curiosity about the trail

FIG. 31.—The white or canoe birch on a country way in New Hampshire. Give me the beauty of thy bark, O birch tree, and for this glimpse I will leave it for others to enjoy. Living birch trees are not to be used for post cards and other souvenirs. It is against the law in some states to mutilate trees. A poem, such as the "Spirit of the Birch," appropriately placed, will often provide the desired protection. (*Photograph by Robert Coffin.*)

is uppermost in the minds of campers at such times, and questions about the squirrel chattering in the treetops, the anthill teeming with life, the contours of distant hills follow in quick succession. Where interest is deep, impressions are equally strong, and information received becomes an unforgettable body of nature knowledge.

It is encouraging to nature educators to listen to campers reliving, in reminiscence, trips they have been on together in former years. The accounts inadvertently reveal an understanding of the basic principles of nature; they are still amazingly clear in detail; and, above all, they reflect an atmosphere of satisfaction in outdoor experiences that is the essence of successful nature recreation.

A TRAIL PROGRAM FOR CAMPERS

Reaching the journey's end by paths or trails off the beaten track always adds to the excitement of a hike. However, certain hazards, both to the camper and the forest he passes through, are involved in this practice, and there should be training in uncharted woodland walking before it is practiced to any considerable extent. There are a number of suggestions about basic camping skills that may serve as a guide to the camp director or nature counselor planning a trail program.

General Prerequisite Camping Skills. Safe fire building is one of the first requisites for trailbuilders. A camper should know the fire rules, be able to select a safe place to build a fire, put a fire out properly, take the wind into account, gather the right kind of tinder, have reserve material, lay a fire correctly, light it with ease, use good judgment, and adapt himself to circumstances.

The trailers should know how to cook, because trailbuilding often leads far from camp.

First aid should be known thoroughly.

One should also know how to test drinking water and how to make it safe.

Use of the Compass. Preparedness against being lost is another step to be considered. For this, the use of the compass must be learned. An intimate acquaintance with the story its trembling needle tells is absolutely essential. This can be a fascinating experience. For example, a camper may be blindfolded and "lost" in the wilderness, equipped only with a compass, knife, sandwich, and two matches. Let him get out of his predicament, preferably with an older camper delegated to trail him without being detected. (This, incidentally, is excellent experience in trailing.) Other games that will teach the use of the compass, such as finding hidden treasures with its aid, can be devised. Campers should also be taught how to use a watch in bright weather in place of a compass.

Topographical Map Reading. Thus prepared, the next step may be to obtain a topographic map of the vicinity from the U. S. Geological Survey. This map will give contour lines and waterways, and the camp may be divided into teams to play trailing games and plan trunk trails in accordance with the map. These main trails may lead to a mountain summit, an old mine or quarry, a lake, a deserted village, or any other destination that will appeal to the wanderlust known as "the lure of the trail." Those who can use the map with the greatest ease may be given the title of *map trailers.*

Trial Trails. The camper ready and the trail planned in theory, the next move is to submit to the test of reconnaissance before it is actually adopted, and trailbuilding begins. A team should try out each trail, tying white tags at about every 50 ft. to serve as preliminary markers. Items of interest that may be discovered along the way or by detour or short side trips should be marked on the map. These may include caves, big trees, springs, polluted areas, views, minerals, rare flowers, and various trailside interests. Those who show skill in reconnoitering may be known as *pathfinders.*

Trailmaking Tools and Their Use. Actual work in the building of the trail can now be considered. For this, such tools as a crosscut saw, ax, shovel, mattock, brush hook, knife, compass, and whetstones are desirable equipment. In camp, a grindstone or emery wheel is advisable, and every camper should know how to handle and care for these common tools of the trail. Certain rules relative to handling them should be emphasized, the first being to keep them sharp and to know how to do so. It is inadvisable to plan "cutting contests" between unskilled campers, and there should be frequent demonstrations. The camper skillful in wielding trail tools may be crowned *trail artisan.*

Trailmaking. We are now ready to set about building a trail, and the best method is to divide the campers into teams of eight headed by a mature and experienced camper. Each group should be equipped with a crosscut saw, whetstone, and two each of the other trailbuilding tools. The members of the squad should work in twos and each have a chance at grading, rock building, trimming, and grubbing over the section of the trail assigned to them. The title of *trailmaker* will be voted by the members of the crew to those who do their part joyfully and cooperatively as well as effectively.

Some Pointers for Trailmakers

Do not cut trails across other people's property without written permission.

Trails should be narrow for single files.

Go around live trees.

Cut out all fallen logs, dead trees, and roots that will trip one up.

Grub out brush in the tread.

In overhead clearing, allow for wet branches hanging down. (This is most dangerous for ax users. Warn against "catching" the ax on limbs.)

Trim branches close to the main trunk without scarring the trunks. (A pruning saw is best for the less experienced.)

Pile brush where burning will not injure trees.

Burn brush on a wet day when there is no danger of forest fire.

Take out loose rocks and lay flat across wet places.

Go around swamps. Corduroys are expensive.

Fords are preferable to bridges.

When bridge building is necessary, send for Boy Scout publications for directions.

Be on the lookout for fine views.

Cut trees to open up views. Leave trees to frame the views.

Provide natural log or stone seats.

Sky-line trails should follow the crests of hills.

Trail Marking. "Blazing a trail" is a familiar expression, but painting white spots or bands on the trees is a better method than the

Fig. 32.—Trail signs help the hiker to understand his surroundings. This type of sign is used by the Society for the Protection of New Hampshire Forests on the Lost River Trail. Signs must be durable, easily read, and well placed.

ax blaze and does not seriously mar the trees. Smaller stones atop larger ones should mark the trail, also. At cross trails, rustic signs in keeping with the character of the woods at that particular spot should be erected, placed on posts at about 5 ft. from the ground and marked with the name of the trail, its destination, direction, and distance data. Along the trail, interesting things should be marked, such as trees, ant nests, rare plants, outcrops, ferns, and animal tracks. It is well to post information on trail etiquette, such as: the nonstripping of the white birch; the nonpollution of a spring; the prevention of forest fire; the leaving of a rare orchid in place; restraint in the neighborhood of a nesting wood duck; wariness of poison sumac.

Trailside Stations. Along the complete camp trail there should be many trailside stations. There can be campcraft areas, bird blinds, feeding stations, tree houses, a sugar house, and other things selected by the crews themselves. An Adirondack lean-to along the trail with a bed of boughs and a fireplace in front adds to the interest of the trail.

Trail Committees. A trail committee might be appointed by the camp director to make a thorough survey of the situation. It might be possible to have the primary trails meet other camp trails and become a part of the network of the mountain-club trails.

TESTED SUGGESTIONS FOR HIKERS

Preliminary Hints. *Be Comfortable.* You will enjoy any hike more if you put on old shoes and old clothes.

Have an Objective. To find a bee tree; to explore a deserted quarry; to inspect a stock farm; to follow sky-line trails.

Keep Off the Beaten Track. If you can reach the objective by cross-countrying and by keeping off the auto roads, so much the better. In that case, a topographic map from the U. S. Geological Survey at Washington, D. C., and a compass will make it more of a pioneer trip.

Go as a Small Group. A hike may be taken by a lone scout, but several companions add to the zest of the trip.

Take a Nature Guide. There should be a leader—a nature guide, we shall call him—who will be responsible for explaining the history and facts of the trail in an interesting way. An old-timer who does not have too many degrees is the best choice for such a guide. He will realize that it will not be possible to stop in front of every nature fact and have it explained. He has been ingrained with a pedagogy that says that the way we think about these facts is much more important than the facts themselves. He can select from the great panorama of a hike the experiences that he got when hunting, foraging, fishing, camping, cooking, or in making primitive weapons and utensils along the same trail. To get a leader who can show you how to participate in a way that is similar to that of the first settlers goes a long way toward ensuring happy hiking.

Stopping Places en Route. *The Barnyard.* Considered as a stopping place en route instead of an objective for a special trip, the barnyard provides, nevertheless, a variety of nature experiences.

COWS ARE WORTH OBSERVING. A herd of cattle may be seen at a haystack or in a barnyard. Tell your party that you have a new game to be played with cows. Say that you will give a point to whoever answers the questions correctly first. How many front upper teeth does a cow have? There will be considerable guessing, and then someone will think that it might be well to look. The result will cause considerable merriment. Offer a point to the first one who catches a cow with both eyes closed. Give a point to the one that can describe *correctly* how a cow lies down or gets up. (It is quite different from the way a horse lies down or gets up.) Observe whether a cow cuts or tears off the grass. Where is the cow's knee? Let the group vote as you point to *A*, *B*, *C*, *D*, and so on. Those who get it right get a point. Have them vote on how many toes a cow possesses—one point for each one getting the right answer. If there are calves present, see who can gather the most evidence of play. This may occupy a period of 5 min. For instance, a calf butts. This might be in anger, but the chances are that it will be a play motion. Observe a cow chewing her cud. Give a point to the one who gives the most adept word to describe the mental attitude of the cow chewing her cud. If you wish to keep up the game, offer 5 points to the one who first sees an entirely white cow, 3 points for one entirely black, and so on. Have a guessing contest on the weight of a cow; on whether the cow is giving milk; on the amount of milk given in a year compared with the weight of the cow; on its age; on the breeds.

PAY RESPECTS TO THE PIG. "As dirty as a pig," was often heard a generation ago. One might conclude that all pigs are dirty, but whether they are or not depends on the owner. There is nothing more interesting than to see a sow with a litter of a dozen piglets. See if you can understand their grunts and squeals. The pigpen is a sort of circus. Have a pig-modeling contest with clay. Give 5 min., and then have three judges look them over.

CONVERSATION AT THE HENHOUSE. Hen talk is a great deal more interesting than most people suspect. To be interesting, it has to be understood. About the first thing one hears in the morning is a rooster crowing. That is his way of saying good morning, and he is telling it to the whole world. Everyone knows that cackling is the usual way of announcing the arrival of an egg. However, cackling may also be the way of saying, "What queer visitors." In the latter case, the whole flock joins in the tumult. You may have heard of the expression "mad as a wet hen" or "as mad as a setting hen." You may see old "fuss and feathers." Listen for a defiant crower who answers a neighboring cockerel. Perhaps the old gentleman calls the ladies of the flock. Perhaps the old hen sings out, "Here's a worm" or, "A hawk!" or, "Get under mother's wing and get warm." How much of this conversation can you understand?

A Tree Biography. Not many years ago, a large Douglas fir standing by the trail that leads west from Going-to-the-Sun Chalet in Glacier Park was broken off about 8 ft. from the ground by a wind storm. Since many hikers and horseback riders passed that way, it was considered a good place to translate the autobiography of the tree so that all who went by might have the opportunity to read woodscript as the old tree itself had written it.

To open the leaves of the book, as it were, the standing trunk was sawed crosswise, about 4 ft. up, and only to the center. Beginning about a foot above the sawed surface, the wood was cut out to the cross section with an ax. This left a notch with an overhanging roof to protect interpreting labels from the rain.

A summary of the tree's life was charted on three blue cards. These were so worded and nailed to the stump that the most casual observer not only had his attention caught but had his interest stimulated and encouraged for closer investigation. The first card, facing toward the chalet to be seen by outgoing parties, gave this information:

THIS OLD DOUGLAS FIR

Was born about 1699.
Was struck by lightning about 1903.
Has been infected with timber ants for the last forty years.
Grew as much from 1881 to 1883 as it did from 1920 to 1930.
Grew to be slightly over 100 feet tall.
Was blown down this summer in a wind storm.

The second card on the incoming side bore further chronological data:

THE OLDEST LIVING SETTLER HEREABOUTS up till the time that it was blown down.
106 years old when Lewis and Clark came.
154 years old when Governor Stevens surveyed and explored this Washington Territory.
In 1885 could have seen the Blackfeet returning from their treaty.
Was an old tree when the Great Northern built through in 1891.

Had twenty years to live after President Taft signed the bill making this Glacier National Park.

IT IS NOT TOO LATE FOR THIS OLD TREE TO TEACH SOMETHING.

The third stated:

THE DOUGLAS FIR IS THE SECOND LARGEST TREE, THE SEQUOIA BEING FIRST. The biography of this tree has been deciphered by a Ranger-naturalist. If you are interested in knowing more about the outdoors why not join one of the trips afield. They start in the lobby of the Chalet at 12:50 P.M. every day except Sunday. This service is furnished free by the United States government. LEARN ABOUT THE WONDERS OF YOUR GLACIER NATIONAL PARK.

More detailed information was typed on smaller labels and fastened at salient spots where nature's handiwork could be easily traced. The age markings were indicated with especial care, for what person does not enjoy diagnosing age, whether it be of a house, a horse, a dress, or a fellow companion? When it comes to a tree, the age may be computed exactly. However, to get the true age of a tree, the cross section must be made near the base. To start the observer off on the right track, a sign with the following information was pinned to a place that gave the date most clearly: "The dark wood grew in spring, the light wood in summer. These two growths make an annual ring." Another paper volunteered the information, "These pins show ten-year growth periods."

Some of the other labels read as follows:

Dr. Woodpecker is a friend of trees. This is where the pileated woodpecker, the cock-of-the-woods, performed a successful operation.

The timber ant is an enemy of trees. The woodpecker ate the timber ants that bored here and here.

Bark is often to be found on the inside of a tree.

This imbedded limb started years ago. It is the cause of knots in lumber.

Lightning let in this fungus growth which caused the tree to decay and finally to succumb to the gale.

This is a point of infection where the old tree tried to heal.

Follow this string up and see the white fungus that was the primary cause for the downfall of the giant.

What were the results of these trailside markers? I knew they were sometimes the subject of general discussion among visitors, but, to test the actual interest in them, I once sat for half an hour at the tree's base and played the part of listener-in on trail doings. A guide with a party on horseback volunteered the information that he had always thought it to be a sound tree. Two deer came within 30 ft., peering and laying their ears forward. A lady hurried ahead of her party, saying that she wanted to learn about that Douglas fir. Hikers went by at intervals of 15 or 20 min. until seven groups had passed. Each time they stopped, and the stump furnished the starting point of conversation. All had studied the labels before, which shows that such schemes for self-instruction do not go amiss. The tree biography paid dividends as instruction, as a social center, and as a provoker of thought. May its kind be multiplied, for every woodsy path must have an old stump waiting to be interpreted to lovers of the trail.

At the End of the Trail. *Historic Landmarks Always Have Their Appeal.* BELLAMY'S KETTLE. Long, long ago, Bellamy's pirate ship was wrecked at South Wellfleet, Mass. The inhabitants of the Chequesset country harvested the plunder of old coins, flintlocks, and kettles. Each year one of these copper kettles is hidden near camp. Once the kettle was concealed at the lowest point on the campgrounds. This proved to be at the bottom of the pond by the garden. The discoverers found something worth while jingling in the kettle. They were coins found on Billingsgate Island and given to the camp by a native as mementos for the winners of this game. One year the kettle had been buried with a "big secret" on the highest summit northeast of camp. The campers were directed to find the kettle and bring it back to camp without being captured. They were further instructed to study their contour maps and work out the best method of locating and moving the trophy. For each person disturbing the camp routine, such as lateness to a meal, a point was taken off the final score of that team. The captain of each team appointed a place to meet for council and for maneuver. The success of the expedition depended upon strategy. Compasses, field glasses, pedometers, and so on, could be borrowed at the canteen.

THE KING'S HIGHWAY. The old King's Highway, Cape Cod, was once the route of the saddle horse and the stagecoach. This was before the railroad and the state road ran down the Cape. Give the campers a compass and the topographic map of the local quadrangle. This may be obtained from the U.S. Geological Survey, Washington, D.C. The roadway is pointed out on the map. Have them note that this byway is crossed by longitude 70 degrees and by latitude 42 and 55 minutes north. The campers are now told that a sector of ye old highway has been abandoned to trees and bushes that are rapidly claiming right of domain. They are to leave in squads at hour intervals to search out and follow this abandoned loop of the King's Highway.

It takes a good scout to follow this hidden trail. For a short distance, it is seen in old wagon ruts; then keener searching for hub bruises or blazes on tree trunks is necessary or just sheer luck with the compass along the valley the road must have "follered" gives the clue. The frontiersman never had a grander opportunity for a battle of wits.

Trips to the Sites of Early Industries Are Well Worth While. THE CLAY BANK. Every old settlement has its clay pit, from which the pioneer obtained clay for chinking the cabin, for making bricks, and perhaps for pottery. Sometimes this clay bank is several miles away. The first trip of the spring may be made to locate the old-time pit. It will probably be hidden by plant growth, but pieces of brick may lead to the secret. Let us pretend that we are pioneers and collect some of this stickiest of soils. The clay will first have to be dried and pounded into a powder. The sticks and stones may be removed by sifting the powder through a fine wire screen. The clay should now be thoroughly but slowly stirred into a basin of water. Let it stand a while, and pour off the water that comes to the top (*decanting*). Place the clay on an inclined board to let it drain. If it is not being used immediately, cover it with a damp cloth.

The trip may be followed by a "clay party." The clay is kneaded and slapped vigorously to remove all the air holes. This is called *wedging*. Now proceed to make a bowl, Indian fashion. Roll the clay on a flat stone into a rope. The rope of clay is then coiled into a mat built up by coiling according to the shape of bowl desired. The bowl is then smoothed on the inside and the outside until there are no cracks. This crude piece of pottery is allowed to dry for a week.

It is now time for *firing*. In the morning, make a trench 1 ft. wide, 2 ft. deep, and 2 ft. long. Line the trench with stones and build a vigorous wood fire in the hole. Keep the fire going until you get red-hot ashes. Place the bowl in a flowerpot, using the saucer for a cover. Bury this in the ashes and put on more wood. Keep the fire going for the day, and do not remove the flowerpot until the next morning. This will give it ample time for slow cooling.

THE DESERTED MINE AND RUN-OUT QUARRY. The neglect of nature's wealth in these hunting grounds is sometimes due to the danger involved. Old mines are often treacherous. Abandoned quarries that have been overgrown may be pitfalls. A camp should first of all, therefore, bring in a specialist in the geographical sciences to make a survey and report.

The passion for collecting can be satisfied in mines and old quarries. The "finds" reveal a joy that simulates the discoveries of prospectors.

To go back to camp with a pocketful of specimens is one stage in natural history. The camper-scientist, with his assortment of gems, has his curiosity aroused to more potent things. The well-informed leader will find occasion to explain the surrounding hills and valleys. The thoughts stirred on a personal adventure of this kind are a motive for the fascinating story that underlies the whole region. Most camp leaders are too immature (or perhaps too modest) to seize the opportunity. In this case, it may be wise to invite in a geologist to clarify this travail of the mind. It may require the services of two, the brother-expert to detect the successive geological changes that have gone on in the world about and the camp director to translate the scientific into a simple story that can be understood. This magnetic field remains practically unquarried, yet the countryside of the Adirondacks and the White and Green mountains—every locale, for that matter—are coigns of vantage for the young mineralogist and camp explorer.

Call on the blacksmith. The village smithy will soon be gone. For this reason, if for no other, we should not miss an opportunity to make him a call. Not long ago his shop was the village news bureau. The men sat around on nail kegs and told yarns. The affairs of the world and local politics received their share. Some of the men had corncob pipes, and others the old "T.D." or clay pipes. The heating of the iron to a red-hot temperature, the bending of it into shape, the cheerful ring of the anvil, the fitting of the iron shoe to the hoof, the burning horn, the paring of the hoof, and the cooling of the iron in the trough of water were all fascinations of the village boy. Put up an exhibit, and see who can identify the most things. Include such passé things as an ox shoe, whiffletree, bellows, and so on.

Ye old grist mill. The old grist mill and the jolly miller may have disappeared, but the chances are that the old millstones and waterfall and perhaps the hand-hewn beams are not yet decayed. Set out on a "hike of discovery." Stop at the first old-fashioned-looking farmhouse, and tell them your quest. Ask if they have a flail that they can show you. The flail was used to separate the grain from the husk. Perhaps they have an old fireplace and brick oven. They will show you how they built a fire in the oven on Saturday morning and where they stood the bean pot and the pies and the loaves of bread. Perhaps they can tell you where their ancestors took the grain to be ground. Each one will tell you something that you ought to see at neighbor Smith's or at some other homestead along the road. Your quest will lead you on and on. At each turn in the road, you will add a bit to your story. Obtain snapshots of the ruins of the grist mill. Keep abundant notes in your diary so that you can tell the story. Perhaps you can get some corn meal to take home and try out. And when you get weary, sit down by the roadside and learn a miller's song or read a story about the miller.

THE SUGAR ORCHARD. Just as our forefathers did, about Mar. 17, we should hie to the sugar orchard. Perhaps "Hi" Simons will be on hand with his mules and stone boat to collect the sap. The sirup will appeal to your palate, just as it did to your grandpap's, and there will be much barter and trade among those who wish to take specimens back to town. With the zest of the March wind urging you woodsward, there is something appealing about harking back to the making of maple sugar as it has been practiced since the days of the Indians.

At the annual sugar-bush hike, the leader may point out the work of that most methodical woodpecker, the yellow-breasted sapsucker and the lesser creatures that come to Uncle Hi's party to be partakers with his other guests. The harbinger of spring will be responding to the great diurnal changes in temperature and will show the distinguishing features by which one may tell the sugar maple when it does not have a sap spout and bucket. Perhaps a black-capped chickadee will perform overhead.

If you know the traditions of sugar bushing, you will be sure to join the annual sugaring-off supper which will be held at the village church. Aunt Hepsie will have all the "fixin's" with all the hot biscuits and maple sirup that you can eat. The husbands will have whittled out maple paddles for the stirring and making of maple candy. Who cannot afford to know the sugaring-off as the pioneer knew it? (All this for 50 cents in wampum.)

Then, just as though you had not had a day of it, someone can show colored lantern slides of the maple-sugar industry from the time that the first flow of sap hits the galvanized pails to the big festival in the village church. It is then that you will have a complete understanding of one of the gifts of the Great Spirit and why it is made an annual occasion of nature worship.

Visit Your Naturalist Neighbors. CHARLES E. GERE, A SCRANTON FARMER-NATURALIST. There is a little road winding from the Scranton Girl Scout Camp, and at the top of the next hill is a gray-shingled cottage with windows that face the wide rolling fields and the forests beyond. Almost beneath its southern windows, the farm land drops steeply down to the scout camp and the opal waters of Ely Pond.

It is a beautiful and a simple place. There are many of them to be found among the hills of the Lackawanna Trail.

In this particular cottage, Charles E. Gere, farmer-naturalist, has spent most of his days. We drew up beneath the apple tree in the front yard. Presently the figure of a man with a white moustache, clad in overalls and high boots, came to the front door, and I knew that Mr. Gere, the kindly-eyed naturalist, was approaching. Both he and Mrs. Gere gave us a gracious welcome.

"I feel that we all have to have something to be interested in." They sound like the indisputable words of a recreation leader, but they were uttered by Mr. Gere sitting in his front room, fingering the pages of Gray's *Botany*. Then he added, "I do not believe that the young people who go to dances have a better time than I do with my plants and birds."

"How did you first get interested in nature, Mr. Gere?"

"I was about fourteen years old and was attending the village school. Schools weren't graded in those days. One time the teacher asked me to make a list of birds. I must have been interested in some way for the teacher to come to me instead of someone else. That was the first work in nature that I ever attempted. It did more to help me and make me interested in nature than any teacher ever did.

"I used to look at the false Solomon's-seal and the bellworts and wonder if they were lilies. One day I was fishing on the lake with a friend, Willis T. Lee. We were farmer boy friends. He used to boil sap on one side of the fence and I on the other. Well, I told him I wished that I had a book that would tell me the names of the flowers. Willis was a student at Wesleyan and said that he could get me one cheap. I paid just $2 for this book. I never had much schooling, and, when I opened it up and looked at it, I said, 'This is wonderful if I can handle it.' But I never thought I could. I worked at it all winter and, after I got one flower through, I felt that I could do it." (Gray's *New Lessons and Manual of Botany*, Revised Lessons, 1887, is still Mr. Gere's main source of information.)

"I used to take a basket and go to the woods and bring in what mother said were the prettiest flowers she ever saw. I would go upstairs and work up the names of those that I did not know. I mounted some, but not a quarter of them, as I didn't have the mounts, and I was alone and couldn't talk with anyone about them.

"Then I got married and did not have so much time. I was awfully poor and had to work. I have four daughters and one son, but I have managed to keep things financially evened up. We are all interested in and talk about outdoor things. My daughter, who is at the state college, used to hunt with me for moths. When I heard her holler, 'Oh, daddy, here is a Polyphemus,' I knew that she had the same thrill. She is now a counselor in a summer camp and is under people with college degrees. She was rather timid about her work until she heard one of them call a field of timothy a wheat field, and then she felt a little different.

"Then this camp came along. I have been interested for 40 years and never could find anyone that I could talk with about it. That is why I am interested in the Girl Scouts.

"Not long ago a visitor came and wanted me to help him make a collection. When he packed the box, he put my name on it. This started a correspondence with Dr. E. M. Grees, and after 2 or 3 years I joined the Harrisburg Natural History Society. This society gave me a new start. They send out monthly bulletins. They have made a list of ferns, but I can start in any afternoon and find a larger list. They do not have as good a section for ferns as this is.

"When did I get the greatest thrill?" repeated Mr. Gere. "Oh, I don't know. I have had so many of them. I have often been all of a tremble finding the name of a new plant. There is no better day for me than when I can get off somewhere in a new territory and find something new. When I go off to a presbytery I always try to get out a little. Over at Bald Mountain I saw a new hickory, a wild phlox I had never seen, and the black cohosh. Yes, I can recognize them on sight now. I never saw the flowering dogwood until 4 years ago, and I knew it. I don't use the key much now. I recognize the family.

"When a neighbor brought in the yellow floating heart the other day, I was stumped. It had a perfect water-lily leaf. It was probably 20 years since I had used a key. This was the first time that I had used Britton and Brown. I ran it down to the floating heart, which is given as the Gentian family in Gray. I went to bed disgusted with myself. Then I got to thinking it over and thought perhaps it did resemble a gentian. I got up again and decided that it was the yellow floating heart which was introduced from Europe. Britton says that it blooms from May to July, but this was October. I would probably put in a day's study now to put a flower through this Gray's Key again. But I was really glad that I had that puzzler the other day and really enjoyed putting it through. I get a real thrill if the flower is plain enough so that I can really see it and put it through. My eyesight is getting poor."

Now came the most inspiring part of our visit. Trailing Mr. Gere across the highway, we turned into a little winding shady path which led beneath large hemlocks and past rhododendrons. What a revealing place is a naturalist's retreat! Here was our friend displayed like a book. Here were the things that he liked to do, the little nooks where he had lived and worked, the plants that he had traveled miles to bring to his wild-flower gardens.

What rare ferns and orchids he showed me! No one but a real enthusiast would know them.

"This holly fern," he pointed out, "came from the North Mountain, and it is the only place in Pennsylvania that I know where it grows. I found this walking fern in Springville forming a perfect mat on a rounded rock. How I wanted a camera. The blue lobelia came from the river near 'Meahoopenie.' This showy orchid was found on the home place. I had not seen it before for 30 years and transplanted it to this garden. I was probably 4 years finding the ostrich fern. I walked all the way to North Mountain (60 miles) and back to find it. That was the first time I ever saw the flowering dogwood in blossom. It was wonderful. Finally, on a creek at Far View Mountain, I found the ostrich fern. Since then I have found it within a mile of my home. Yes, it was probably here, but I didn't distinguish it from cinnamon fern."

Across from the fernery was a small plot protected from the inroads of mice by stone slabs set on end. Beneath a cone of chicken wire, Mr. Gere had recently set out three species of sundew and the seven-angled pipewort. Some animal had insisted on nibbling the thread-leaved sundew to the ground, and he had made a wire protection. Whatever the beast was, it had trampled the wire to get at this apparently favorite morsel. "Strange," said Mr. Gere, "that with this whole thicket this animal should select this one plant." A steel trap bids fair to be the deciding factor in determining the pest. Mr. Gere declared that he picked up a great deal of information in his cultivation of the wild flowers, and an onlooker could have no doubt as to the veracity of the statement.

Soon we passed out into a clearing that proved to be a tree nursery. There was the Japanese larch, the Japanese red pine, and the short-leaved yellow pine. He said that he had obtained these from the state forestry department. He pointed out that the jack pine was outgrowing the Scotch pine and the white spruce. When asked why he was growing these trees, he gave the answer of the true investigator, "Just for the pleasure of seeing them grow. It is a good thing to find out which variety is the best to plant. This year I bought the Colorado blue spruce and the Douglas fir. I could not get them at the state property."

He then wanted to know if I had ever seen the work of the pileated woodpecker on hemlocks. I replied that I had at Bear Mountain last spring and that I had inquired of entomologists and college professors but could not find out what the woodpecker was after. My farmer-naturalist knew the answer. They were timber ants.

"They honeycomb the center of trees from the ground up. They do the same thing in the chestnut and the beech. I took a specimen of the beech to the museum at Scranton. The pileated had gone through at least 4 in. of wood. The work is done in the winter when the ants are frozen solid."

I asked him how the woodpecker knew they were there, for most bird students say that woodpeckers hear the grubs in trees. He said that he had often wondered about that, too, since the outside of the tree always looked sound. Then he went on to say, "Old woodsmen eat them. I had a New England man working for me once who had been born rich but turned out a hobo. He was working in Maine, and the men came out of the woods tipsy. The prohibition agents thought that there might be a still hidden in the woods and investigated. They discovered that the men were eating these ants.

"I have sometimes found a quart of these big black fellows in a tree. They got into the timbers of my house once. I made an opening and poured in kerosene. I bother my wife sometimes by threatening to bring home some timber ants. One winter, when I was in the woods cutting down beech, the chickadees came and fed on these ants."

He then pointed out the footprints of the ring-necked pheasant and of a skunk. He had already shown me some plaster-of-Paris casts that he had made of the racoon's tracks.

"How did you find the names of the birds?"

"Well, it is just this way. These girls come down here and expect to learn in a week what it has taken me 50 years to find out. I was down there once and asked if they believed in fairies. I used to scold my little girls for reading fairy books. Now how did I know the loon? I used to read stories about them in the north woods. How I longed to hear them! One day I was going from the house to the barn—that was over to the other place—when I heard a tremolo call from the air. I looked and saw a black-and-white bird circling around. I thought it was a buzzard from the south. Another time I heard the same call when I was in the woods. I hustled out and saw six of them and not the black-and-white bird at all. Then one day I got a close look at one and saw that it was a loon. I recognized him, as I had seen so many stuffed ones in the offices of doctors and lawyers. I don't doubt that it took me 10 years to learn the loon. That bird circling around wasn't the loon at all, as he doesn't soar.

"One time I told the parent-teachers that I had just seen a new bird and that I was going to call it 'Squealer' until I could find out its real name. It was probably 4 years before I found out that it was a killdeer. You may have heard them squeal just as they are settling

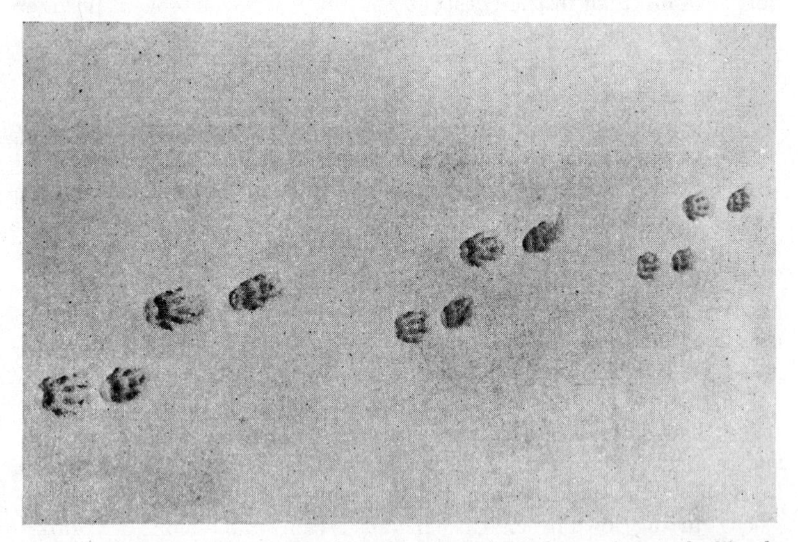

Fig. 33.—Tracking. The skunk is the only animal that makes tracks like the ones shown above. Describe them. How many toes does he have on his front feet? On his hind feet? (*Photograph by Robert Coffin.*)

onto the ground. Since last Christmas I have had the National Geographic bird book. When my children went to the village school, the library used to loan me books and told me that I could keep them as long as I wanted to.

"No, I am not interested in pets. I prefer to see them as they are. I went by a mourning dove's nest once and frightened it off, but I didn't stop to see the eggs, as I didn't want to disturb her. Another time I heard a peculiar note and worked around until I found that it was the evening grosbeak. One year a rose-breasted grosbeak had a peculiar ending, and we used to laugh at his singing 'paregoric.' Then we had an unusual robin who used to close up his song with 'chewink.' I never heard him again. Yes, I know the towhee, but he says it different. It used to seem as though that robin would sing himself to death.

"If you can lead one person to get one-half as much enjoyment out of nature as I am getting you will be doing some good in the world," said Mr. Gere, "but probably there is no other man in Brooklyn who would go for half a day in the woods to see what he can find in nature."

We departed down the road. The genial October sunshine set me thinking. These hills will be here for years to come, but that which draws appreciative people to the brow of this hill is not alone the open fields and the forests or the clear air and blue water; it is the simplicity and craftsmanship in nature of our lone naturalist. It is the sort of atmosphere and spirit that we must preserve. These things we must perpetuate that our children and children for generations to come may enjoy the spirit of nature study. As leaders, we must set up a stewardship founded on the fact that the most enduring thing is spirit.

CAPE COD HERMITAGE. Every bailiwick has its hermit. Camp Chequesset's was a grizzly sea dog who had taken to land some 2 miles from the coast. He was a Thoreau-like individual, reminding one considerably of that famous naturalist who walked the length of the Cape some three-quarters of a century ago. He had squatted on the site of his great-grandsire's claim, and his tract reached unto the shores of the same pond. From the cedar swamp in back he had in turn lugged, dragged, and rolled the logs for the framework of his hut. The adz, an heirloom, had again played its part in cabin construction, and timbers had been slowly hewn into shape for the sills and rafters. A clump of lilac marked the east bedroom of the old homestead—long since tumbled and gone. Of the old days, naught remained to suggest ancestral fortitude or thrift but scraggly apple trees, decrepit, gnarled, wind-blown, and a few belichened fence rails.

Our equipment for this trip was the notebook with a map, two pages of drawing paper, two pages for notes, colored crayons, a reverence for the crudities of pioneer days, an eagerness to hear and understand a backwoods language, a woodsy speech that has all but disappeared, and a desire to express the experience in writing and in sketch with an understanding heart. The habit of keeping a record of nature experiences, whether it be in story, sketch, song, or diary, is well worth cultivating and should be encouraged by all nature leaders. Mrs. Comstock says in her *Handbook of Nature Study*, "These books, of whatever quality, are precious beyond price to their owners. And why not? For they represent what cannot be bought or sold, personal experience in the happy world of out-of-doors."

The following description of Mr. Dyer, the hermit visited, is taken from the field book of "Bumps," age eleven, the youngest girl at Chequesset when the trip was made:

> His grandfather settled here years ago. The pond was named for him. The lilac bushes and the fruit trees indicate the great age of the place. The Hermit has planted boughs on the north side of his corn to protect it from the cold. He also made a wheelbarrow with much patience and care. He has made a little birdhouse on the top of a stick driven into an old stump which has been there for many years. He has some timbers left from those used to build his house. Back of his house he has made a chicken coop of pine boughs. He has placed boards on either side to weigh the boughs down and keep them together. He shows his interest in flowers and trees by planting them and taking care of both. Around his garden is a fence to prevent the deer (they are seen frequently in this region) from eating all the beans over night as they did one year. Years ago the house used to be almost up to the water's edge but the new house which Mr. Dyer made himself is back much farther. Mr. Dyer seems to take an interest in camp girls and is not a bit timid about answering questions.

Wild-life Colonies Present a Nature Challenge: A Trip to the Heron Rookery. A CHALLENGE. The particular excursion that I am about to describe was introduced by the following challenge: "On Great Island, just across the bay from camp, is a black-crowned night heron rookery. The rookery is of such a character that it offends the five senses. Mosquitoes infest the pines, the day is hot and these pine wood thickets are sultry, the dead fish are unsightly and have a strong odor, and the herons often throw their last meal at you. Their cry has been likened to the Indian war whoop. The interesting feature of the trip is that this particular colony is the farthest out on Cape Cod and the object of the trip is to band the grown-up birds. These bands are furnished by the Fish and Wildlife Service at Washington and whoever finds one of these banded birds, no matter where, is supposed to report to the government. There are some indications that herons go to the coast of Maine before going south for the winter. It requires a great deal of skill and bravery to run down one of these birds. Whoever catches one can have the honor of having the bird named after him. How many wish to go on this excursion?" It is needless to say that a full quota accepted the challenge.

EQUIPPING THE EXPEDITION. The next step was to equip the expedition. It was decided to have goulash for food. This meant that arithmetic for a party of 12 had to function. The individual equipment consisted simply of a tin dipper and spoon. With many helping hands, the Cap'n packed the goods in the boat. Dinner was cooked and served on the shore of the island before diving into the forest.

THE ADVENTURE. At the rookery, we did just what one would expect from the challenge. There were much scurrying through the underbrush and loud peals of laughter as the herons bluffed their pursuers by a loud "squak" or by a wide-open defiant mouth. The hiding of the heron's head under a sweater put a quietus on the bird, and he peacefully succumbed to being banded. Then followed a regular "gym" exhibition, when he was placed on a lower limb of the tree. He would balance with his wings, grab hold with his beak, and clutch with his dangling legs. By such trapeze performances, he finally gained the uppermost branches, where he again felt safe and secure. Thousands (so it seemed) of questions were shot at the leader of the party. Many were answered, and many could not be.

WHAT SENT US TO THE LIBRARY? What bookwork was connected with this trip? I can hear this unspoken query. My answer is *none* concerning the black-crowned night heron. Not that there might not have been many occasions for it, but on this expedition the thing that excited our curiosity enough for a little research in the camp library was the appearance of the lighthouse and buildings on Billingsgate Island. On the way across the bay, someone noticed that Billingsgate was unusually clear and that the houses seemed to stand up out of the water. The appearance was pronounced a *mirage*. A girl from Alabama remembered that the mirage on the Sahara Desert made things seem to be bottom side up. Much discussion followed, but it was not settled until arriving back at camp. A book was finally found that described what we had seen as a *looming*. Everyone then knew the difference and the cause of a looming and of a mirage. This part was not planned and is one of those incidents that make every nature-lore experience different.

AN OUTBURST OF SONG. The enthusiasm of the trip culminated in the composing of an original song, which was given before the "stay-at-camp" people.

DID THE TRIP MEET THE AIMS OF NATURE LORE? As we look back over this experience, what is there in it that we have asked for as the ideals of nature lore? First, there is the nature service for the Fish and Wildlife Service. The benefits of such a service need not be gone into at the present writing. There is the realization of the necessity of bird protection and bird reservations—a very essential conservation principle when it comes to appropriations to save some of our disappearing species. It was a lesson in having a good time under difficulties, which is excellent training for sportsmanship. And who is there that shall say that the information was any less valuable or that the experience was less rich than an assignment to be chanted within the four walls of the classroom? As for the outdoor cooking, singing for enjoyment, knowledge of the tides, and the hundred and one things that are a part of the trip—how shall we value them? Those who have tried it have unlimited faith in the outdoor nature-learning method.

Explore Local Geographic Wonderlands. THE CAVE TRIP. Caves have a universal appeal. The leader should know the location of the nearest and most interesting cave. When the party assembles, the chief guide takes a stick and draws a map in the sand to show the trails to be followed to reach it. Different routes may be used. In any case, the party is sent off in small groups. Since no artificial dishes will be used on this trip, each group is given some special thing to obtain en route for the cooking at the cave. It may be to get materials to light the fire by friction. This would include a bow to be made from hickory, a spindle from elm, and a string from a hemlock root or from the silk on the stem of the swamp milkweed. Another party skirmishes for dishes, such as a gourd for a dipper. A third group might like to make a stone hammer to remove the marrow from the bones for a soup. Others might explore for a spring that they will clean out and set aright.

After the supper, cave-man style, a story would be in order. This might be the contribution of those who had to come later in the day. They should remember that it was the fire at the mouth of a cave that made it safe for man to come down out of the trees and sleep on the ground. Early man could not make a fire in the cave, for there was no way for smoke to come out. Any library will be able to furnish a story for the occasion. How caves are formed, paintings on the caves in France, Mammoth Cave, underground rivers, and sinkhole country are suggestions.

BOG TROTTING. Throughout the glacial region, where swamps and ponds remain as geographic relics of the ice days, nearly every town has its fearsome bog, where, according to legend and tradition, spooks and will-o'-the-wisps hold sway, and a slow shuddering death in the bottomless depths of the mire awaits the human or lesser animal who strays off the beaten path or loses his way near by in the mists of evening. These are not merely local superstitions; they are repeated wherever bogs are found and, no doubt, are rooted in truth. Mastodons have been preserved in peat. The young mastodon on exhibition at the Cleveland, Ohio, Museum of Natural History had been wounded and evidently didn't have strength to pull out. But, for every animal actually mired beyond redemption, there are probably 100 mythically bogged. It is also actual fact that every ditch, pond, or bog must have "hard pan" or a bottom in order to hold water.

It is high time we freed hundreds of folk from their inbred fear of bogs, from their prejudiced belief that such lands breathe mystery and wickedness. It is time we took them bog trotting in these unexplored corners of nature's outdoor wonderland where they may find anew the infinite variety of nature's forms and see in process the evolution and adaptation of plant life from one botanic and geologic era to the next.

A trip to the Vlei, a bog on top of Franklin Mountain just outside of Oneonta, N. Y., will serve as an introduction to what bogland can offer.

The name "the Vlei" challenges one immediately. Its meaning and its pronunciation are as obscured by usage and tradition as the nature of the bog itself. The dictionary intimates that "vlei" is a contraction of the Dutch *vallie* but gives as a secondary meaning "a low place where water is found." From a study of old maps on this New York section, the term here is probably more correctly applied to a shallow morass found on hilltops. Such a bog may have water during the spring months or the rainy season, and become dry and parched during late summer.

How did the bog form? Some 50,000 years ago, this region was covered by an ice sheet. As the glacier melted, it left its load of gravel, which contained granite and flint pebbles. We have sandstone, limestone, and shale as native bedrocks, but never granite. When one picks up granite and flint pebbles on the top of Franklin Mountain, he has a right to a little thrill, because these pebbles were brought from Canada by the glacier. Not only did the glacier leave rocks, it smoothed off the bedrocks exposed on the surface. One walks over these glaciated rock pavements as one climbs to the Vlei.

Immediately following the glacial period, there was a shallow lake left where the Vlei now stands. It had pickerelweed, cow lily, and the iris or fleur-de-lis in its open black water, and several submerged aquatic plants, like nitella and bladderwort. There were bullheads in its muddy depths, and, no doubt, water fowl broke its glassy surface.

Just how long ago this was is a moot question. A close observer of plant life says that he doubts if there has been a pond there for

300 years. One townsman visited the Vlei 39 years ago and remembers no open water. Another saw it 56 years ago and is sure there was no pond.

There are many stories handed down that support the "open water within the memory of man" theory. Each person sticks to his side of the question as though it were a matter of religion. A collection of Vlei folk tales would make an interesting contribution to local literature.

Now the Vlei may be thought of as approaching the dry, shady peat-bog stage, a peat tundra presenting the scenery of Labrador. Sphagnum, the greatest peat former in existence, is king at the Vlei. Obtain it 8 ft. down, and you have the peat moss that you put on your lawn. Give it time and pressure enough, and it will eventually become bituminous and next anthracite coal. It is the same moss that was used as a substitute for absorbent cotton during the first World War. Because of the antiseptic qualities of sphagnum moss, the drinking water for the long voyages of whaling boats was obtained from peat bogs.

The Vlei is Oneonta's plant-refrigeration spot. Here the plants stand with their roots in ice water longer than at any other locality. They cannot get away because their kind will not grow in other situations. They remain as testimony to the time when most of the vegetation was of the Klondike variety. The Vlei is the home of the wild cranberry, the picturesque cotton grass, and the far-famed azalea, the haunt of the pitcher plant and the sundew. It is a garden of wild orchids that the foot of man seldom tramples.

The bog is a natural bird sanctuary. Here the towhee greets you with his "drink your tea," the junco flits busily about, and the liquid notes of the veery and the hermit thrush, most melodic of songbirds, rise and fall through the silence.

A few black spruces and many white pines may be discovered along the wooded borders of the Vlei. One may stand 30 ft. away and shake one of these trees by "jouncing the bog." When bogs are less secure, they are sometimes known as "quaking bogs." The encircling evergreens have sent winged seeds into the bog and consequently have a considerable number of children under way. The changing of the shrubby bog to a forest will be the next epoch. This may be a matter of three or four centuries. As it is seen now, the Vlei is a place that still remains as the Algonquin Indians knew it. Protected from exploitation and wild-life destruction, it will remain a treasure trove for the nature lover for many a decade to come. Every year, the students of the Oneonta Normal School make a pilgrimage there. Many remember the trip when classroom lessons have been dimmed by the years. It would be no small advantage if every school had a Vlei where all its students could go bog trotting.

National Parks Are Outdoor Schoolrooms. The utilization of our national forests and parks as retreats from heat and dust has long been in vogue, but a consideration of them as outdoor schoolrooms for nature education is fast gaining favor. More and more summer vacation plans include a trip to explore one of the great national parks of the west. Yellowstone, Yosemite, Sequoia, Crater Lake, Glacier—these or another of the as yet less known outdoor wonderlands may be the objective. As a foretaste of what a summer session in a park nature school may hold in store, suppose we sketch a course at Glacier National Park, where one of the globe's best outdoor curriculums is presented. There, in the "Land of Shining Mountains," as the Blackfeet Indians call it, of northwestern Montana, you and your family and your spyglass will find a whole university awaiting your enrollment. Glacial mysteries and virgin timber, alpine flowers and vanishing big game, a wide variety of subjects for open-air study may all be found in this one paradise. Headquarters are rustic hostelries tucked away high up some mountain valley. These are patterned after Swiss chalet villages, replicas of log cabins that have stood in the Alps for years. You may choose to stay at Two Medicine, Many Glacier, Sperry Chalets, or perhaps you are bound for Red Eagle Camp. If you like a boat ride, Going-to-the-Sun may be your destination. Going-to-the-Sun Chalet in the St. Mary's Lake country of Glacier Park is the dormitory address for this particular imaginary schooling. Wherever you are, comfortable mountain cabins on the edge of clear, deep mountain lakes that mirror the surrounding mountain peaks will be there, and every evening, as the darkness comes out of the evergreens, there will be the magic of campfires, under whose spell you and your companions will indulge in mountain reveries or dream of forthcoming nature mysteries.

Every school must have its teachers. Who is there in this unusual educational enterprise to direct your energies? Mere seeing does not signify understanding the 4,000-ft. garden walls with their red and green tints, and the remarkable blue lakes will not pay the least attention to the pryings of the uninitiated, nor, stoical as a sphinx, will one of the 60 glaciers divulge its ice-locked history under their scrutiny. A first-rate faculty has been carefully chosen and appointed by the government at Washington for the very purpose of leading you to these breath-taking wonders and explaining their whys and wherefores. These guides make up the Ranger-naturalist Service. They represent the best in nature leadership. Each knows there is a delight in the freedom of the mountains that cannot be denied. Each realizes, too, that you must catch it when you are young or inbreed it in your bone and marrow over a period of years before callousness to nature beauty sets in. But, once you get the mountain habit, you will cling to it as these Western rangers do, returning to it year after year as a sign of what the country means to them.

Perhaps we had better look over the entrance examinations to the Glacier Park School. First of all, our student must have the right attitude toward wild life. He must regard it, not as so much wild game but as woodland friends interesting to see and to study. Second, our visitor must have a philosophy of conservation and the balance of life. He must realize that mountain lions are quite as important as golden-mantled ground squirrels. Third, he must be free from city conventionality. He must long to foot it along winding mountain trails rather than straightaway cement sidewalks. He must be willing to replace movie excitement and radio blare with the wisdom that comes from the soil and the forest.

Only the question of fees remains before we are off. There is none. Imagine attending a university without paying tuition. But this institution is public property; the ranger-naturalist service is free. Uncle Sam is most anxious for you to benefit from his outdoor schoolroom. All you have to do is present yourself for matriculation at the park gateway.

EDUCATION: GLACIER PARK STYLE

Whether your approach is from the east or the west, you run smack into the continental divide. On the east, your train glides through the Blackfeet Reservation, where you will see bands of restless Indians who once dominated the rich buffalo plains. The red man is still stalwart and strong, and his clothing is ornamented with dyed porcupine quills, eagle feathers, and bear claws. The Blackfeet still live in tepees.

If you leave the Empire Builder at the Glacier Park station, as you probably will, the Blackfeet Indians will be there to welcome you. If you have made previous arrangements, a genial ranger-naturalist will also step up and greet you with a "howdy."

You will rapidly pass from the fir log station to the Glacier Park Hotel, with its architecture of giant firs. Your eyes will sweep from the 45-ft. fir columns to woodsy lamp stands and drinking fountains. After a pause to catch your breath, you leave the Glacier Park Hotel at the eastern gateway of the park and are whisked by bus past mountain crags, dashing waters, and clear lakes to the land of eternal snow. You leave the lowlands and the depression for a new world. Nestled in the valleys will be groves of quaking aspen quivering in the brilliant sunshine. In the Two Medicine country you will see the charred remains of a forest fire—a mute testimony to carelessness. Late that afternoon you will get a whiff of the evergreen-scented forests of the Rockies, forests as they were when the whole continent was wild. The soil was plowed for the forests by the glaciers, the relics of which you will spy nestled in the amphitheaters high up toward the peaks. You are going through the most stupendous scenery of the world. A final curve in the road, at the right, a cobalt lake. To the left—great heavens! We have arrived with breath-taking suddenness at St. Mary's Lake.

For a considerable extent of time, you'll stand gaping at the backdrop of snow-patched peaks and glaciers and the blue water of the lake in the foreground. Ribbonlike waterfalls will appear through the dark green forests. You may be hearing for the first time the call of the mountains. It is urging to you to throw off the veneer of civilization. It is saying, "You are here, relax, and take a deep breath." It is a real call, and you succumb.

Suppose you enter the park from the west. You travel along the middle fork of the swift-running Flathead River to Belton Station, the western park gateway; thence you will be frisked along the shores of the never-to-be-forgotten Lake McDonald over the Transmountain Highway to Logan Pass, at the top of the continental divide. Flanking the highway are dizzy peaks reaching into fleecy clouds. The pass at the summit is like an open door. You gaze through it to the great crags that tower from the eastern slopes of the Rockies. Somewhere out there is your journey's end—Going-to-the-Sun Camp. What new experiences await you at this strange wild-life gathering place?

On the boat from St. Mary's the next morning, there are some 75 individuals without rod or gun, leaving auto dust far behind as they head for the hinterland—a country of saddles and hiking. Representing a diversity of nature interests, they peer mountainward for adventure, recreation, and enjoyment. Red Eagle, Little Chief, Citadel, and Gun Site loom larger in turn. Lake, sunshine, peaks, mountain streams, forests, timber line, and finally Going-to-the-Sun Chalets crowd into the moving panorama.

Going-to-the-Sun University—what is the origin of this unusual name? It is taken from the peak that projects about a mile above St. Mary's Lake and is translated from the Indian name "Mah-tah-pee-o-stock-sis-meh-stuk," meaning "the mountain with the face of Sour Spirit who has gone to the Sun." According to the legend, the Sun Father sent Chief Sour Spirit to help the Blackfeet and the Pikuni. They were exceedingly poor, and they were starving. Sour Spirit taught them how to make a tepee, how to tan the hide of the buffalo, and how to make moccasins. He showed them how to make bows and arrows that they might have food. The Blackfeet became happy and prosperous.

Finally, the time came when Sour Spirit was called to the lodge of his father in the sun. In order that his children would not forget him, he caused the likeness of his face to remain on the side of the mountain in the form of snow. And there his face may be seen today, complete even to the war bonnet. Ever since that time, the Indians have called it Going-to-the-Sun Mountain.

You have hunger, too. You have back-to-nature hunger, and you have come to find riches, not in buffalo hides and moccasins, but in mighty rivers and grinding glaciers, in Montana sun and forest shade. You come to learn about incredible rock stories and the birth of the Rockies. You do not aim to kill the wolf and the mountain sheep, but you long to see them alive. And so the White Father at Washington has sent his representatives, the park naturalist in chief and his staff, to teach you, his children, the useful art of saving your starving soul, the art of relaxing your tightened nerves. And these mountains will get you. And you will become happy and prosperous. And the profile of glaciers and snow banks will remain in your memory forever.

By this time, the boat has docked, and you enter the Swiss Chalet, constructed of logs and rough stone. Once inside, you find congenial groups, family style. Hikers, mountain climbers, trail riders, fishermen, horse guides, and fine-looking college boys and girls doing the chores. You spend what is left of the day settling in and getting acquainted.

Suddenly that evening, you awaken to the fact that everyone is pulling his chair up to the fireplace. A husky ranger takes his place in front of the glowing embers. You sit agog as he tells about mountain lions and how to find lost people. Then he announces that there will be a saddle trip in the morning to Sexton glacier. The guide says that the distance to the glacier is 6 miles (it looks as if you could skip up there and back before breakfast). He says that the trail leads up Baring Creek past red argillite rock that was put down in the sea aeons ago. He says that the upper valley is the haunt of Rocky Mountain sheep and goats. With the hope of seeing one of these timid creatures, you sign up for the trip.

You linger by the fire with fellow tourists. Gathering in front of the fireplace seems like a relic of the childhood of the world. But who shall say just what thoughts, even in the few years of the existence of national parks, have crystallized around the campfire. Cornelius Hedges said that the geysers, the boiling mud pots, the hot springs, and the waterfalls ought to be set aside so that all people for all time could enjoy them. In less than 2 years, Mar. 1, 1872, to be explicit, Congress created Yellowstone National Park "for the benefit and enjoyment of the people forever." The fireplace has a magic that is not to be meddled with lightly. But you have signed up for a riding trip, and you must off to bed.

The cloud shadows are still on the lake when you arise. You see an empty trail. Then along comes a Bar X six-horse train. The man ahead has a broad-brimmed Stetson and a red bandana. The ranger-naturalist brings up the rear. You are given a dark-bay saddle pony. You fall in line with other dudes. You note that old-timers in the saddle blend in the background. The love of the trail survives in these horse guides. Every spring they return. It would be strange if they did not. It is second home to them. The ways of life at Glacier make them aware of the independent life along the trail to Sexton Glacier.

When the horse guide becomes enthusiastic about a water ouzel or when he stops to have you listen to the call of the coyote, you need not feel that he is performing a service especially for your benefit. It is the old trail law of stop, look, and listen. If you stop, you may learn. If you look, you may see. If you listen, you may hear. Only so may you sense the enchantment of the first gleam of the bear grass under a forest of Engelmann's spruce and Douglas fir or revel in the abundant growth of the sweet-scented balsam. Only so will you learn to respond to nature from the day you find the first Mariposa lily in the spring sunshine until you see the fruiting of the mountain ash long after the fall air has frosted the mountainsides.

Soon the trail zigzags out of the deep forest to where the white-bark pine predominates. It is worth a trip to see these wind-twisted, snow-bent heroes of timber line. Queer, isn't it, that presidential proclamation was necessary to set aside these Western fairylands? I hope you didn't forget your camera on this trip. As you ride up the

Sexton Trail, these picturesque trees are to play an important role in photography. They frame heather meadows and alpine valleys. Almost every timber-line picture has one of these trees for a frame.

Suddenly the ranger points out a hoary-mantled marmot high up on a snowbank. You get excited and ask if it is a bear. By this time, the animal has melted away among the boulders that crowd his pasture. One has to travel a sky-line trail to see a marmot. When he whistles, every mountain goat on the cliff wall looks up, every mule deer feeding aloft in a mountain meadow hesitates, the ptarmigan foraging for the berries of the kinnikinnick freezes into the landscape, every ear for acres around gives heed. Even the golden eagle wheeling over the crags with his eagle eye alert for a ground squirrel dinner comes to attention. Animal sentry is not a new thing. It is a natural law. You are seeing the law at work. In the light of such learning, is there anyone to say that hearing the "whistler" is less educative than disemboweling a dogfish in some urban university?

Now the naturalist shows you where a grizzly literally threw shovelfuls of dirt to dig out a fat marmot. What a track that boulder made down the mountain slope! It hardly seems possible that old Ephraim could roll away such boulders for a dozen pounds of marmot. This four-footed Hercules is as ambitious as that, for he loves marmots. The marmot converts mountain herbage and lush vegetation into good meat for grizzlies. You happen along with a ranger-naturalist detective and work out the struggle on the spot. The evidence is before you. What a story to relate to the folks back home!

Here indeed are riches. As you ascend, the nature guide has frequent huddles to point out ripple marks that were once in the bed of the ocean, or he wants you to stand at a focal point where you may look down on St. Mary's Lake and let your fancy run unrestrained. Perhaps the sun is doing tricks on yonder gale-swept cascade. Only once in a lifetime does one's mind run riot with such utter abandon. Even the children are enthusiastic. You are now a rooter for old Going-to-the-Sun. You can't see why anyone should be denied the privilege. In one day, you have literally changed food, clothes, interests, philosophy, soul, and body.

You come to a fork in the trail. The right fork goes to Siyeh Pass, the left fork to Sexton Glacier. You would love to see a mountain pass, but that experience will have to wait until another time. In this daily elective course of study, you have chosen the Sexton Glacier course for this trip.

The glacier is in a pocket, surrounded by almost perpendicular walls on three sides. The guide explains that such an amphitheater is called a cirque. It is ablaze with color. Vivid fireweeds, yellow St.-John's-wort, dwarf lupines, here and there great patches of red heather, and nodding horsemints add their artistic touches. Near low-growing arctic willows, you may find a bunch of gentians carrying the sky in their hearts. With their toes in the stream, as if dodging the ragged-edged rocks, you discover mats of yellow and red mimulus.

To stand by a timber-line garden fires the imagination. It is as if one had at last captured the rainbow. No wonder that some visitors find it difficult to believe that nature and not the government planted these brilliantly colored flower gardens right next to the glaciers, 8,000 ft. above the sea. Another amazing fact is that there is not one cirque garden backed by a garden wall 1,000 ft. high, but hundreds of them.

The horses are turned loose to try mountain herbage. The horse guide is searching for dead timber to make hot coffee. The women are gazing down the U-shaped Baring basin through which the party has just wound its way. The ranger cautions you not to venture on the ice alone, but he promises crevasses, ice caves, and glacial thunder after lunch. You linger around the coffeepot to hear the story of Louis Agassiz's descent into a crevasse, called by his mother "Louis' Descent into Hades." Soon you are off to class again. You never were so anxious to get to class before.

Nature carries out her work in Glacier Park with highhandedness. Here are outdoor enigmas for the special benefit of the most inquisitive traveler. The most cherished secrets are highest. You are hot on the trail of the cold ice, as it were. It is queer how these ice cakes grow and groan cheek by jowl with dainty alpine phlox gardens 7,000 to 8,000 ft. above the sea.

Fortunately the glacier is one brand of scenery that the souvenir hunter cannot get away with. He can carve his name in the ice or start home with a good-sized chip, but it just disappears before he has gone any distance at all. As you clamber out onto the glacier, you try to imagine yourself a spectator of the long-ago period when old man glacier was putting the valleys and mountains through their paces. You picture St. Mary's Lake a river of ice that received tributaries from high pockets like Sexton, Red Eagle, Little Chief, and Fusilade. You imagine this giant pushing out toward the Blackfeet country, toppling over forests and cutting a swath through loose limestone and argillite. Following this cataclysm, you try to visualize the forests creeping back to the slopes. It's going on now gradually and without noise—looking down toward timberline, you can see the trees marching up. So slow and steady is their reversal of the march of the trees that you had not noticed it before. How glad you are that you were forehanded enough to bring your camera. You are going

FIG. 34.—Famous old male eagle of Vermilion, Ohio. A male American eagle taken with a 16-in. telephoto lens from a steel tower 38 ft. from the nest. Mr. Shipman, an associate of Dr. Francis H. Herrick, spent five summers studying the American eagle at Vermilion, Ohio. There is a grave possibility that our emblem of freedom will be exterminated. We should become better acquainted with this majestic bird. (*Photograph courtesy of C. M. Shipman, naturalist, Willoughby, Ohio.*)

back home with proof in your hands that you have lived over the past 2,500 years in your 2 months' schooling.

A chill hastens you below timberline. The afternoon tints which flush the red sandstone are turning gray at last. Your trip down is much quicker than the ascent, and you find yourself "passing in review." This is an Englemann's spruce. That is the alpine fir. You murmur the tree friends, until you see the aspens coming up the valleys to meet you and to remind you of the chalets and the hot meal that waits to satisfy your wild hunger.

Later, you sit before the fire and relive your experiences. You have been on the roof of the Rockies, a thought that will fire your imagination forever. You have run the gantlet of 600 Blackfeet warriors—no hazard today, but a memory to quicken the pulse. You have seen Going-to-the-Sun Peak, rising a sheer mile above St. Mary's Lake. You have been a foreigner among horse guides and won their confidence by simplicity and honesty. You have watched wild bears and mountain goats, and you have learned the law, "Thou shalt not kill," one of the most important of national-park tenets.

You have hiked the sky-line trails as an outlet for pent-up restlessness. You have shaken off boredom by slinging a camera over your back, saddling a cow pony, and riding off to outdoor adventure. You have combined recreation and education on mountain treks with ranger-naturalists as professor-guides. You have seen prospectors, miners, and adventurers—they are all there still. You have passed by tumbled-down shacks, too, representing one-time bubbles of optimism. Glacier Park still has its bonanzas—but not of gold. They are of snow-clad peaks and sky meadows, of Western traditions and Blackfeet-ridden trails, of campfires with booted horsemen, gaping tourists, and ranger-naturalists. They are the call of the mountains and have been yours for the taking.

From this time on, your thoughts will often be employed about the mountains and the forests that you have seen. You will find yourself trying to realize the wonderful things that you have learned about the oldest living inhabitants of the continent, and you will constantly recall the picture of America as she was and is. And this is as it should be, for you have taken time to endow your being with the spirit of the great outdoors.

CHAPTER V

CONSERVATION: A CHALLENGE TO THE EDUCATOR

Natural Laws. Until 300 years ago, America was governed by natural laws. There was the law of overproduction by which the oyster laid 1,000,000 eggs to maintain the species. It is estimated that 1 forest tree out of 10,000 reached maturity. Centuries before the red man's arrow or the white man's gun played any part in our continent's history, there was the law of struggle for existence and the survival of the fittest. The American bison maintained himself on that law. There were periods of depression and of abundance. If the white owl and fox became abundant, the rabbits became scarce. Through the operation of this law, some forms of life like the saber-toothed tiger and the mastodon became extinct. The laws remain; the result of the laws is a constant change.

The Law of Diminishing Returns. Then came man, possessed with one idea of removing the forest cover to grow grain. The forests, the topsoil, the waters, the wild animals, and the abundance thereof became a thing of the past. Drought, parasites, and pestilence came. The canker worm and gipsy moth, tularemia and botulism added to the devastation. There was no longer abundance. The days of plenty, of wild blueberries, wild strawberries, wild ducks, and wild oysters came to an end. The days of "Christmas greening" and "free shooting" were over. The balance of nature had been upset. Reorganization was a vital necessity. Conservation was imperative.

A Conservation Program Is a Complicated Network. Man may want a carnivorous animal for an economic use such as fur, or for sporting purposes, to hunt him with hound, gun, camera, or field glass. In either case, he needs hunting grounds and a supply of animals. Thus grew up regulations regarding forest reserves, open seasons, bag limits, size of the catch, hunting and fishing licensing. Curiously enough, most of the group effort toward conservation so far has been made by the so-called sportsmen. The hunters, for example, are putting up money to feed the birds in winter.

Such efforts are inadequate and only temporary solutions. We must face the conservation problem as a whole if we are to assure our wild life or any other form of our vast national resources permanent preservation and protection.

The Carnivora eat the Herbivora, but the Herbivora are dependent upon air, soil, and water. To be more explicit, the fox eats the duck, which depends on wild rice, which must have a constant supply of water regulated from the forest. The sequence could be continued, but the point is this: to conserve any one species, you must conserve all the links in the chain of interdependent elements. For three centuries, we have stripped the forests from the land. Our slogan has been, "Conquer the wilderness." Now we are faced with the need for a new program: land planning, a sustained yield of forests, wild-game management, shellfish farming, development of submarginal land, and nature recreation. This thought sequence is directly opposite to our sequence of thinking since the pioneers came to America. It is a mental pattern, an attitude toward the world we live in, that must be fostered and developed among all the people of our nation through education for conservation.

What Is Conservation Education? In June, 1937, Dr. J. W. Studebaker, the U. S. Commissioner of Education, called a conference on conservation education. He said that he did not know what conservation implied. Ninety-nine per cent of the readers of this discourse—if, indeed, they read it—will have only a dim notion as to what nature conservation means or what to do about it. For over a quarter of a century, the writer has successively contributed to camp literature on nature conservation, but the movement to make the American public conservation-conscious has only recently been recognized as of educational importance. However, the writer believes that, if we don't take the call to conservation more seriously, not only camping but the nation itself will soon be history.

Conservation is not schoolroom conversation. It is not evangelism. It is not a subject or a textbook for recitation. It is a way of living, a practical treatment to be accorded the outdoor environment. The best definition thus far is that "conservation is the wise use of natural resources." Natural resources consist of nature's wealth, *i.e.*, birds, trees, minerals, flowers, insects, shellfish, and wild game. The prudent treatment of all human resources also belongs to the conservation concept and should be applied to preserving our population. Safety education is human conservation.

The Civilian Conservation Corps. The Civilian Conservation Corps was perhaps the greatest organization for human conservation that the world has ever attempted. It was created in 1933 to build men and to provide an emergency conservation program. $45,000,000 was allotted for the purchase of land. There were 500,000 men in 2,427 camps. I do not wish to belittle the accomplishments of this group, but the existence of a peacetime army of thousands of young men who were given morale, health, and self-respect was even more important than the work they were doing.

Two CCC boys once rode with me from Amherst to Sturbridge. I overheard one say, "That stand needs release cutting." I inquired if they knew the pines. They said that they did. I did not take their word for it but tested them. They knew the white pine, pitch pine, hemlock, red cedar, and spruce. I tried them on roadside trees and on distant trees. They knew them. I asked them which experience, high-school biology, scouting, or CCC, had done the most for them in an outdoor way. Before I could finish my question they said, "CCC. We live in the forest 24 hr. a day." These two boys were conservationists. They had done something to the forest, but it is of far greater significance that the forests had done something to them. The CCC was a powerful factor in social adjustment.

The Four Steps in Conservation. The four angles of conservation are research, legislation, administration, and education. All are interdependent and full of complexities. The case of the bobwhite quail illustrates the functioning or lack of functioning of each.

Research tells us that the bobwhite eats potato beetles, weed seeds, and other pests. It also shows that a mother quail averages 14 eggs to the nest. Theoretically, this makes a quail population of 16. If the environment offers water, gravel, dust baths, as well as such things as favorable cover, food, and shade, all may be well. However, predatory animals devour a few, a severe winter with crusted snow may exterminate a covey, or a hunter with a shotgun may kill one-fourth of the covey at one shot. The farmer who practices "clean farming," *i.e.*, allows no shrubs or wild plants along the fence row, makes it impossible for quail to exist. In southern Ohio, this type of agriculture has exterminated its cheery call.

Legislation in Ohio makes the bobwhite a songbird. If he steps over the state line into Indiana, he is a game bird even though he sings the same song. (The pheasant, on the other hand, is protected in

Indiana, but may be shot in Ohio.) In 1936, nine proposed laws to make the bobwhite a game bird appeared before the Ohio legislature. One of the arguments used was that shooting scatters the coveys and prevents inbreeding. Experiments by Stoddard in North Carolina have shown that what is left of a covey comes together again. Dr. S. Prentiss Baldwin, a scientist, has pertinently asked, "How did the quails get along before man shot them?" Animal breeders who raise Jersey cows or German police dogs or Rhode Island red hens know that inbreeding does not weaken the stock but on the other hand makes it possible to maintain not only a pure but a healthy breed. All this is confusing to a layman.

I sat next to a conservation commissioner at a scout banquet. I said something about the bobwhite's being a songbird in Ohio and he replied indignantly, "Huh, they'll have rabbits singing pretty soon." He was an administrator, but, because he knew little of the birds' habits, he didn't believe in the state law, and, to my knowledge, he did everything possible to prevent proper functioning of his own office. When the proposed legislation came up, it was defeated by the petitions of the school children of the state. They knew the facts of the case through education. Whether we have quail in the future, not only in Ohio but all through our land, depends on an integrated program of planning, research, legislation, administration, and education working as a unit for conservation.

Where Does Conservation Begin? It begins in the window box of the home. It either is or is not practiced in the back yard. It may be a part of a playground program, although usually a playground is a tar desert or a cement block on which human ants bask on a bench or balance on a teeter-totter. These same individuals could be taught to take care of thirsty trees and battered shrubs and help the area become a thing of beauty. Conservation could begin in a city park and make it more than a collection of "keep off the grass" signs or a succession of regimented tulip beds and policed beefsteak plants. Conservation could begin with a community awareness of landscaped homes, of shaded streets, of outdoor recreation centers. It could and should begin with teaching our children not only to take care of but to enjoy their physical environment.

The Conservation-recreation Tie-up. It is not just an accident that conservation areas are also recreation areas. Our most scenic regions are nonagricultural. They should never have been cleared for agriculture in the first place. They should have been protected by land zoning. Those states that have adopted land planning will not let a man clear steep hills, a sandy plateau, or a ledge for a farm. Their agriculturalists know that he would be unsuccessful as a farmer and soon dependent on the state. His farm would be submarginal land and have to be replanted with the forest that is its best crop. He is a child of the state and must be protected by the state.

The government is demonstrating one right use of submarginal lands by converting them into so-called recreation-demonstration areas. The Laurel Ridge Recreation Demonstration Project, for example, is about 50 miles outside of Pittsburgh in the Poconos of Somerset County. Family cabins and camps for children have been erected on this 5,000-acre tract.

Recreation Leaders Needed. The public does not yet know how to use and enjoy the out-of-doors wisely and safely. The administration of the Laurel Ridge project is under the Council of Social Agencies of Pittsburgh. Were it not supervised in some way like this, it would be very easy for hordes of the less privileged people from Pittsburgh to go into this beautiful area and "love the flowers to death." In a single summer, the waterways might be polluted through ignorance. The whole forest might be destroyed by one fire lighted through carelessness.

If the outdoor program in nature education is to be commensurate with the physical investment in these new recreation areas, there must be leaders trained in conservation principles, capable of directing enriching recreational activities.

Conservation Is an Individual Responsibility. Another phase of conservation that is not understood because of inertia or of ignorance is that of individual responsibility. Extinct civilizations, whether they be unearthed in the Gobi Desert, the African Sahara, or in Palestine, give evidence of a life of luxury in a land of plenty. To have passed into a land of want and extinction apparently was a process of centuries, but nonetheless inevitable. Sections of northern China once traversed with boats laden with rich merchandise are now traversed by caravans along dry stream beds. Veteran trees in the temple gardens suggest that such a drastic turn of affairs was not due to a change in climate.

Up to the present time, most people seem to think that this thing called conservation applies to the other fellow. That is what the Chinaman thought. That is a sad mistake. Conservation applies to every citizen who sleeps, eats, keeps warm, plays, works, and finds shelter and raiment. We are certainly aware that farms are not permanent. By the same token, communities are not permanent.

America is made up of communities. History repeats itself. It can repeat itself in America. Whether it does or not depends on the citizens of America.

Conservation Must Be Based on Ethical Laws. No man-made law can bring about conservation. It must be based on understanding and ethical law. It is immoral to shoot the last duck to make a profit. The world is a place to save, not to kill. The natural law of universal brotherhood—we are brothers of the wild—is a tremendous force. This is the challenge of conservation. It is an American ideal.

A PROGRAM FOR CONSERVATION EDUCATION

The Spirit of the Birch

I am the dancer of the wood
I shimmer in the solitude;
Men call me Birch Tree, yet I know
In other days it was not so.
I am a Dryad, thin and white
Who danced too long one summer night,
And the Dawn found me and imprisoned me!

This poem appears in a rustic frame near a lovely white birch at Camp Medomak. Hundreds of boys have passed it. Yet none has removed bark for post cards. No one has thoughtlessly marred its stateliness. It stands "a thing of beauty and a joy forever."

BEGIN WITH TREES

Trees Live to Give. Living trees give happiness, health, and sometimes prosperity to the child, home dweller, camper, picknicker, fisherman, hunter, canoeist, hiker, autoist, cottager, vacationist, hotel owner, artist, poet—in fact, to all citizens. The appreciation of trees should be part of our mental make-up and the protection of trees an everyday responsibility.

Tree Planting Is an Excellent Starting Point for Child Conservation Consciousness. Tree planting offers youngsters one of the best educational opportunities that will come their way. Get them together and let them discuss the need for more trees in the garden, along the roadside, down an eroded bank, in camp, school, or community grounds. Let them ask a local landscape gardener and a tree specialist to talk with them about the problem. Let the children adopt the trees they plant and be responsible for their care.

Cultivation, watering, mulching, prevention of mechanical injury by staking, prevention of sunscald with burlap, prevention of insect pests and disease, and surgery are engrossing activities. The test of success is the health of the tree and the joy in later years of being able to say, "That is my tree." Do not let yourself or the school or camp handy man rob children of this experience.

A Tree Museum. Obtain samples of various kinds of wood. Obtain problem specimens to show blister rust, fungi, annual rings, destruction by mice and rabbits, work of engraving beetles and timber ants, things made from wood products, pictures of trees, floods, erosion, forest recreation, fire damage, tourist camps. Make plaster casts by pressing leaves into molding clay and then pouring plaster over the mold.

Work with Seeds. Have seed-collecting trips. Start a seed exchange. Start a seed museum with small bottles or Riker mounts. Demonstrate seed dispersal. Start a basket-willow plantation.

The Tree Nursery Is an Early Project in Conservation. The tree nursery is a project that one may choose for the home, school, or camp. Native shrubs and trees are most satisfactory. Obtain prices of seeds and seedlings from your nearest Forest Experiment Station. Consult commercial catalogues.

Invite a nursery man to visit. Have him demonstrate nursery propagation, transplanting, "lining out," puddling, mulching.

The Christmas-tree Plantation. This is one of the most satisfactory experiences in land utilization. It is not only productive financially since a cash crop can be obtained in from 5 to 10 years, but it does much to offset the vandalism and pilfering that goes on in our forests each winter.

The Christmas-tree grower can carry on a convincing educational campaign emphasizing the following ideas.

1. Private property is protected through the use of nursery-grown trees. Driving into the country "to get a tree" is woodland robbery.
2. Live Christmas trees can be transplanted and beautify home grounds permanently.
3. "Quality" Christmas trees, well-rounded in shape, carefully and recently dug, are assured through nursery growth.
4. Thinning a spruce plantation is legitimate harvesting.
5. The use, not abuse, of trees is the purpose of planned planting.

Sugar-maple Orchard. This pioneer industry and allied festivals should be revived. The activities connected with the "sugar bush" provide enjoyable winter recreation, and $2.50 per gallon for maple sirup is a weighty talking point for putting trees to productive use.

The Swamp. Make the most of swamplands. A white cedar swamp may offer growing material for innumerable projects—wood for fence posts and general utility; sphagnum moss for the nursery trade; Christmas greens; basket willow; cranberries; and swamp blueberries.

Trip Program. A forestry trip a week will enrich any program. Points of interest might include a tree nursery, a fire lookout tower, a town or county forest, a wood museum, a woods-product industry, a lumberyard, a farm woods, a flood-control area, a well-landscaped home.

FORESTRY AND ACTIVITY FOR YOUTH

Forestry Conservation Is the Wise Use and Management of Our Native Woodlands. It is thinking of and planning for the forest as a whole. This is a much more inclusive phase of conservation than the planting of trees about the home, school, or camp buildings or caring for trees as a group. Urban mass tree planting, for example, results in an arboretum, not a forest.

Forest development means the roads, trails, cabins, campgrounds, outdoor cooking areas, recreation areas, the opening of vistas, and so on. It means protection from fire, insects, and disease.

It means the consideration of wild life—every campground is a sanctuary for *all* native animals, including the predatory ones. The forester knows that logs and a few dead trees are not objectionable. Otherwise the woodpeckers might have to go to the next county to make a home.

Forestry Facts. Man cannot create coal, oil, or gas. The forest can. A continuous wood crop is our ultimate fuel, yet, in the United States, we are cutting timber twice as fast as we are growing it.

The golden rule of forestry is "cutting trees without destroying the woods." "Clean cutting" was once the only practice. Clean cutting is too often "slashing," which means leaving "bait" for fire, insects, and fungi.

There are millions of idle acres (submarginal land) where forests were once a permanent yield. They can be restored. The principal enemies of the forest are man (fire), tree-bark beetles, gypsy moths, and the white pine blister rust. They can be controlled.

As early as 1653, William Penn proposed an ordinance that one acre be left covered with trees for every five cleared. More than two centuries later, the "Act of 1891" provided for setting aside public forests. Now there are 186,000,000 acres in the National Forest System grouped into 155 National Forests and 18 National Grasslands. The Forest Service manages 1 out of every 11 acres. The National Forests are managed under the principle of multiple use for the balanced production of timber, watershed, forage, wildlife and recreation values, including areas dedicated to wilderness.

There are 10 forest experiment stations for research. The Northeastern Forest Experiment Station is headquartered at Upper Darby, Pa. The Forest Products Laboratory is at Madison, Wis.

FIG. 35.—Pittsburgh parks are outdoor schoolrooms. Not much escapes these junior naturalists. This forest is receiving a thorough examination. (*Courtesy of Ralph Griswold, Director of Parks.*)

Forestry Is a Profession. The forester requires as thorough training as a doctor or a lawyer. The first professional school was established at Cornell University in 1898. In 1900, the Yale Forestry School was launched. In 1960, there was a total of 8,439 undergraduates and 916 graduates enrolled in the 43 institutions giving degrees in forestry.

But foresters must know more than the scientific principles and practices of their profession. They must understand and enjoy working with people. They must be leaders. The annual number of visitors to our national forests alone is over 92,000,000. Public use of forest facilities is increasing. Furthermore, leisure-time pursuits in the forest are opening up a whole new field of opportunity for the coming generation. The responsibility for interpreting forest resources in terms of usefulness and satisfaction to the American public rests with the forestry force. Forest recreation is a public service. Good public relations with patrons are essential to its success.

National and state forests are administered for the permanent good of the whole people. A well-trained staff of foresters is the surest means by which this ideal can become reality.

Junior Forestry Activities. Forestry conservation, like health and recreation, is something that extends throughout life. It is something to be lived and practiced, rather than a subject to be studied. The only way that the great majority of our young people will get such practices and resulting attitudes is through camps and public-school forests. If our future citizens are to have sound ideas on conservation, they will have to acquire them now.

Junior forestry activity does not means a new fad for publicity. It does not mean the dedication of a wood lot plus a cheer and song. It means a forested area to be used as a working laboratory over a long period of time.

The School Forest. There are 114 school forests in Wisconsin.* The first one was started in 1928. Most schools can obtain a parcel of tax-delinquent land or permission to practice forestry in the corner of a local park. If this is done under the supervision of a state or city forester, so much the better. The technical assistance of civil engineers, landscape engineers, biologists, geologists, and archaeologists are other safeguards. The government is liberal in giving assistance.

Obtain the services of a local government forester, the state department of conservation, and the school of forestry. The Society for the Protection of New Hampshire Forests sent a forester to camps one summer. Send to the U. S. Department of Agriculture, Extension Service, for their 16-mm. color films on "This Is Your Forest," "Voice of the Forest," and "Timber Resources Review." The only cost is for transportation. Start now to make a list of those experts you might call upon.

Most Campgrounds Are Permanent Forest Communities. However, most camp directors have no forestry program either for reforestation or for systematic protection from fire, insects, or disease.

When it is realized that, of 47 camps visited during a recent summer tour, each had, on an average, nearly 200 acres of land, mostly forested, the importance of forestry is obvious. But, when it is further realized

*1940 statistics.

that less than 4 per cent have fire lines, tree nurseries, trails, or cleaning-out programs, it is disturbing and indicates that there is much to be done.

Colonel William B. Greeley, one-time chief forester of the United States, in his official statements, and the late Charles Lathrop Pack, president of the American Tree Association, in his nation-wide education work in forestry, were among those who have emphasized the vital importance of education in connection with the forestry question, present and future. If, then, the summer camp is to fulfill its promise

FIG. 36.—Keen observation and careful recording are essential in woodcraft. (*Courtesy J. Harold Williams, Chief Scout Executive, Narragansett Council, Boy Scouts of America.*)

as an educational force, it must seize the opportunities pointed out for it by our leaders in forestry activity inherent in the care of the campgrounds.

The Map Is the Background for Planning. A map drawn to scale of your school forest or campground is in order. A student engineer may help. The map will show valleys, ridges, lakes, streams, roads, bridges, trails, hardwoods, coniferous stands, gardens, pasture land, shrub areas, swamps, meadows, bogs, springs, vistas, historic sites, and buildings. The local government topographic map, which may be obtained from the U. S. Geological Survey, is invaluable for planning.

With the map, plan your activities. The suggestions that follow may help.

THE WOOD-LOT LABORATORY

The Wood Lot. This means the school forest, the campgrounds, or a community forest (municipal, town, or county). It should be the core of the local nature-recreation program for juniors. Its resources meet the age-old call of the wild, the craving of our beings for "cave-man stuff." Furthermore, projects connected with its development establish right attitudes toward the out-of-doors and foster appreciation for forest resources themselves.

About the time that the ice is breaking up in the ponds, something deep within ourselves begins to yearn. The forests are calling. The call is like an unseen magnet urging us to turn our backs on brick walls. We do not know how or why. We go to the forest mystified. If we have not been wood-trained, we come away unsatisfied. Our longing has not been allayed.

This call first comes at the wood-lot age, at about 12 years. A youth likes to think that he has outgrown the hearth-side age with its purring cat. He still claims the dog. He wants "he-man" stuff. He likes the gang. He wants a shack in the wood lot where the gang can gather. He is one of the gang. They act as a gang. They fight the yellow-tailed hornet as a gang. They eat as a gang. They like to have a common fire, the same story, and to yell as a pack.

The boon companions of the boy of this age are caves, fire, water, hunger, trees, noise, missiles, snakes, and big game. These are the creations of the forest. They are inborn demands. The cave instinct, for example, is strong. If we are being chased, we want to get behind or under. The cave offers both opportunities. It is the mother-nature protection in us. The enemy likes to steal up and surround his foe. He comes in leaping from rock to rock letting out blood-curdling yells, which echo and reecho in the immense bouldery chasm. "Smoke 'em out" is said with true satisfaction. Drowning out a woodchuck is done with true gusto. It is the age of *Robinson Crusoe* and *The Swiss Family Robinson*.

The Cabin in the Woods. The wood-lot age is the working age. Cooperate with this law of nature, and plan a cabin as headquarters for forest activities. The cabin group is the sprouting of a young democracy. The members settle whether they shall wade in the pond, whether to take turns chopping wood, building fire, or washing dishes. It is better not to have too much leadership. Leave the group alone until the pangs of hunger overcome disorganization of kitchen work. Division of labor, organization, team play, common consciousness are the great lessons of cabin life. A good citizen in the cabin is a good citizen in the larger community. The building of a cabin is the launching of a young ship of state. It needs the crew to pull and

FIG. 37.—How would you hold a snake? Why is this the correct way to hold a snake? Explain how the bite of a nonpoisonous snake, like the scratch of a fingernail, may lead to infection. (*Photograph courtesy of J. Harold Williams, Chief Scout Executive, Narragansett Council, Boy Scouts of America.*)

haul away together. The wood-lot age is one of shoving off the raft—everyone with his shoulder to the pushing. The wood-lot gang is an ideal commonwealth.

Timeliness Is the Watchword in the Cabin School. In the wood-lot age, there is the impulse to strike with an ax. Satisfaction may be sought through cutting and marring a tree that is destined to become good timber. The same satisfaction may be derived from cutting a sound dead tree for a log to be used in erecting a cabin. The functional use of tools leads to constructive, not destructive, activity.

Forestry Practice on Wood-lot Trees. Growing a healthy wood crop means selective cutting or "thinning" (forest weeding, as it is sometimes called), pruning, making of fire lines, pest control, and tending line fences. These activities also offer excellent practice in axmanship, but they render greater service in making their participators conscious of nature's need for skillful care and protection.

Wood-lot Evenings. At an evening campfire program, have stories about former wood-lot owners—Washington, Theodore Roosevelt, Coolidge, Burroughs, Thoreau, and Whitman. Whitman said that he was warmed twice, once when he cut his wood and again when he burned it.

Invite in a local trapper, timber cruiser, lumberjack, sawmill owner, or pioneer to spin forestry yarns. Try a blackboard talk about Paul Bunyan and Babe, the blue ox, or read from a Paul Bunyan book.

The safety and use of our forests depend upon foresight, broadmindedness, and public sentiment. These characteristics should have their roots in early experiences on the wood lot.

FOREST CONSERVATION FOR CAMPS

Reforestation. Reforestation is a cardinal principle of conservation. Some camps have undertaken reforestation work, usually with plantings of white or red pine. In few, however, has this planting been carried on with the assistance of the campers themselves. This may in considerable measure be due to the fact that a large-scale spring planting takes place before May 15 and well before camp opens or that a fall planting cannot generally be started until after camp closes. It does not, however, seem to be generally realized that trees may be planted successfully during the summer, if it is properly done. Planting a large number of young evergreens before the last of August would not, of course, be wise, but every camper should be given the fun of planting and caring for at least one tree. It will become a perennial source of pleasure when the camper returns to camp as a grown-up visitor.

Even though the actual reforestation work may not feasibly be done during the camping season, at least a seedbed can be started and cared for. In many states, seedlings of from 1 to 4 years' growth may be obtained from the state forester at nominal cost. More camps should investigate the possibilities of such cooperation and should undertake reforestation work on their property.

One camp plans its forestry on a financial basis—each camper making an investment of work hours and thereby owning so many shares on which he will eventually receive profit. Revenue received for firewood and taxation should also be in the account. The work is carried on under the direction of a graduate forester.

FIG. 38.—Cedar waxwings enjoy mountain-ash apples. After the first of the new year cedar waxwings come to eat the "berries" on C. M. Shipman's two mountain-ash trees. During the intense cold at the end of January on one day there were 124 birds in the tree. (*Photograph courtesy of C. M. Shipman, naturalist, Willoughby, Ohio, who adopted the orphans.*)

Fire Prevention. Camp directors are apparently unaware of the possibility of insuring the woodlands. Yet it hardly seems necessary to tell them that a forest fire would quickly roast the goose that lays the golden egg of camping. A few hours and a fire would make the camp look like a deserted lumber town or a mining camp with the vein "paid out." State foresters will be glad to advise on a fire protection plan, and there is value in having the campers feel that the protection of the forest that gives them shelter is in their hands.

One of the simplest details of fire prevention lies in cleaning up the wood lot to reduce the fire hazard. Let every camper have a hand in this with a plot of his own to care for. Let him cut out all the dead trees and the weed trees such as cherry, hornbeam, and gray birch, leaving enough partly to shade the pines. If these last are not present, they might well be planted. The waste brush should be piled and burned in a place and at a time when there is no danger from fire. A trail or a system of trails can be made to serve the dual purpose of trail and fire line.

Pest Control. Insects, also, account for the loss of many forest trees, and one instance is to be noted in which the trees were stripped of leaves by brown-tail caterpillars. The campers were so affected by the ubiquitous hairs of these insects, which cause brown-tail itch, that it became necessary to close the camp. Fire lines and insect prevention should be considered by every camp director who takes the trouble to look ahead.

A Bird Sanctuary. Raise and plant berry-bearing shrubs such as cherries, black alder, mulberry, wild grape, mountain ash, blueberry, raspberry, elderberry, sumac, and spice bush. Old pasture land should not remain idle. A steep hill or rocky land or poor soil area could be dedicated as a bird sanctuary. The encouragement of song birds is a high use of land. Birds are a forest product. They pay their board in the insects they consume. Their beauty and song are difficult to measure as an economic product, but they add immeasurably to our wealth.

Game birds such as quail, partridge, and pheasant find haven here.

Ornamental Plantings. In setting out to encourage birds by such berry crops as raspberries, elderberries, fruits such as cherries, and seeds such as the sunflowers for granivorous birds, it is well to know that European barberries are host for wheat rust, red cedar for apple rust, gooseberries and currants for white-pine blister rust, and buckthorn for oat rust. The wild cherry harbors the tent caterpillar, which also attacks the fruit orchards.

EROSION AND LAND USE

Desert Making. In May, 1934, in Cleveland, a dust storm came out of the West. When it rained, it "rained mud" from the "dust bowl." Earlier in the day, a rainstorm had washed my auto clean. Now it was muddied from the sky above. That night I left on a sleeping car for New York City. The next morning I arrived, but the dust storm was in Manhattan before me. Since that time alone, the winds have robbed 5,000,000 acres of their topsoil.* As a result, 12,000 farm families between January, 1936, and July, 1937, migrated from the "dust bowl" to the Pacific Northwest. That is desert making on a stupendous scale.

A post-mortem by archaeologists suggests that former civilizations were buried by dust storms. Dr. C. Wythe Cooke of the U. S. Geological Survey says that the "Maya civilization choked itself to death

FIG. 39.—We are keepers of the soil. Farm land should be passed on in at least as good condition as when it was received. This cannot be done on steep hillsides, as shown above. Land not suitable for farming should be kept as forest. Furs, fins, feathers, and fun are forest crops.

with mud washed from its own hillside corn patches." Gully erosion may have made that "farm of yours" cheap enough so that you could buy it to use for summer vacations or for an organized summer camp. The truth of the matter is that it should never have been stripped of its forest. Then it could have grown children from the very first instead of corn. The United States holds all speed records for man-made deserts. Sheet erosion is not so spectacular in New England as elsewhere. However, it is there. It is a part of the picture of conservation. Therefore, we should understand it.

The "Desert of Maine." Perhaps you have heard of the "Desert of Maine." That is a New England monument dedicated to the

*1940 statistics.

ignorant custom of doing away with the topsoil. Years ago as Farmer Tuttle walked over his land, he noticed a miniature sand crater and threw in some brush. It was too late. The old sand kettle kept boiling, and today there are over 100 acres of sand dunes to show for it. A few summers ago, I took 25 teachers there and had to pay a good entrance fee for them to see the corpse of what was a farm. Probably the farm is now paying better dividends than it ever paid.

FIG. 40.—The Desert of Maine. Farmer Tuttle threw a few boughs into a sand crater. The kettle kept boiling and formed the Desert of Maine. Note the top of an old apple tree in the foreground. Submarginal land should be left for forest recreation.

However, several "Deserts of Maine" can bring about the "Desert of New England" under our very noses.

Sick Air. As a convincing experiment for dust-laden air, leave a pan of water out overnight. A white porcelain pan will be best. Or just observe what happens to a new layer of snow. Now figure this out in terms of acres. Sick air is not good for plants. Some plants are called smoke indicators, since they cannot endure our monoxide-laden city air. Sick air is not good for the lungs of little children, either. That is one reason for fresh-air camps. The wind robbing the soil of dust and carrying it out to sea is akin to termites. They both work unseen.

Field Trips Where One May See for Himself. Take a group out into your forest and scratch up the leaf mold. In the valleys, it may be several feet deep. On the hilltops, it may be a matter of a few inches. In the barren hillside field, it may be gone. It may take 10 years, but it usually takes 10 centuries to build an inch of good humus. The farmer calls it topsoil. That is his wealth—his bank account. But he did not know it. He thought corn was wealth and proceeded to spend his bank account like a drunken sailor with no thought of the morrow.

He didn't know that the forest was the keeper of his bank account. To hasten the "clearing of the land" he had annual spring fires. The chances are that your grandfather did that, too. Perhaps your father did. Some are doing it even unto this generation. They burn up "the old fog"—a funny name for dead grass, but no more queer than the custom of spring burning.

Plan a field trip after the next heavy rain. You won't have to go far to find a barren slope. Have the children point out miniature canyons, gullies, silted plains, dams, litter, how far the lack of vegetative cover extends, where the topsoil has gone, and how a desert has resulted. This is the way the farmer has been "growing rocks." This is the way they prepared the "dust bowl" for wind erosion. Some people call it "land disease."

Near by, perhaps on the same slope, there is a cover crop of clover, rye, alsike, or bush clover (lespedeza) or trees. Have the children describe this "farm," using such expressions as "absorption of rain water," "porous soil," "ground water," "roots checking run-off," "saving the soil," and "fertile soil."

Now have a discussion on land use. Suppose the barren slope and the covered slope are two farms. Which farmer is robbing the land? Which farmer will have a permanent farm? Which farmer will have a wood lot, a garden, and a pasture? Which farm will have floods and drought? The stronger nation will be made up of which kind of farmers? Suppose the slopes are campgrounds. Think the story through, using the term "camp director" instead of "farmer."

This is simple thinking. It is new thinking. It is also vital thinking. Ever since the Pilgrims landed, we have been making barren hill slopes without much thinking. For the rest of the time, we must conserve our soil and waters. Not only must we be given the opportunity to think, but we must be trained to think.

Abandoned Farms. Recently I had a group of 4-H leaders on a bog-trotting trip. We came across an abandoned cellar hole. We played a game to see who could find the greatest number of evidences that this was once "home, sweet home." The group found lilacs, black-cap raspberries, black locusts, grapevines, moss-covered wagon trails, an old doorstep, belichened bricks, and gnarled tame apples gone wild.

I should like to take you on a similar trip. This will be up a valley. We shall not have to go far before we see an abandoned farm. John Greenleaf Whittier saw such a home when he wrote:

> Against the wooded hill it stands,
> Ghost of a dead home, staring through
> Its broken lights on wasted lands
> Where old-time harvests grew.

Why did the home go "with the wind"? The answer lies in a story of cultivated acres, heavy rains, and gullied hills. We can picture the first settlers discovering wooded hills, clear streams, and abundant game. The hardy pioneer cleared the land. He cut the timber and killed the wild turkey with no thought of the morrow. He assumed that the forests and wild animals would last forever. He sold his crops and was prosperous. And then came hard times. He had been robbed by wind and storm. His creek and spring dried up. His land became barren. He became bankrupt and finally moved on.

The Camp Director as Conservationist. Then along came a prospective camp director looking for cheap land. He knew that a bankrupt farm might mean a bankrupt camp. In order to have a camp, there must be water. He took a walk over the farm. He noted that the valley bottom could be turned into a lake. He felt sure that the wild berries and fruits were indicators of what could be grown for game birds as well as for humans. He could picture cranberry jam, canned blueberries, and spiced grape. An expert from the village said that gullying could be checked by cover crops and that the old spring could be restored not only for the drinking water but as a source of electricity for the camp. After a good night's sleep, he found himself planning a camp program—fishing, berrying, swimming, reforesting, winter sports, maple-sugar festivals. If states could restore and publicize submarginal land for recreation, why could not camp directors?

The project was not a pipe dream. An enthusiastic friend agreed to photograph the farm from the air. This base map was used to indicate where the camp buildings, lake, orchard, meadow, and fields should be located. The land was once more to be rich in natural resources—in water, woodland, and wild life. It would once more yield sustenance to man.

The camp director realized that soil meant plants and trees, fish and fowl, history and literature, art and recreation, or, in one word, living. He realized that soil is not merely for farmers or politicians or bankers but for all who work with the out-of-doors. When analyzed, soil is the heart of camping.

WATER CONSERVATION

When the pioneers canoed up our rivers, there was no refuse. They could land almost anywhere and drink from clear springs. Fish had not been smothered by sewage. No wild ducks were so covered with oil from bilge water that they couldn't fly. The waterways did not belong to industrial firms as a handy place to dump chemical wastes. They did not belong to summer visitors who came for a few weeks from crowded cities with no understanding of wild life. There were no 1,000 miles of typhoid, no cliff walks, and no Coney Islands. The bodies of water included more than manufacturing, more than fishing, more than sailing, more than camping. Public apathy has allowed all kinds of exploiting, but, in the beginning, the bays and lakes belonged equally to all.

Water Possessions. It is only recently that states have taken reconnaissance of their water possessions. Some states know which lakes are deep enough and cold enough for trout and which should remain for the common run of sunfish and bullheads. Some choice lakes have even been reserved as safe stopping places for migrating water fowl. A few commonwealths have had technicians counting water fleas that feed the small fry that become food for bigger fish. In this way, fishing is regulated, and the lakes have been made to produce a sustained yield just like potato patches. Such water farming is called *aquaculture*.

Close your eyes, and think of the most beautiful camp that you can imagine. Let's analyze the picture. Was there any water? Were there trees? Were there hills? Was there a pasture with cattle grazing on the hills? Was there a sailboat? Was there a fisherman? I am rather certain that all of you saw a lake with a wooded shore. Perhaps some of you saw a Lake Louise or a Loch Lomond. Practically all camps have water.

Junior Waltonians. Now will you close your eyes again and think of a young fisherman—one of your own campers. Does he care whether he catches big or little fish? Is he conscious of the life history of fish and how the future fish will be provided for? Has he any attitudes in regard to the size of the catch? Will he return any to the water? What will he do with his string of fish? Is he conscious of the state fishing laws or of conservation? Are you raising a poacher, an exploiter, or a conservationist? If everyone does as you are doing, what will be the future of fishing in your commonwealth?

Recently I observed young fishermen in Philadelphia. It was a legal holiday but not a legal fishing day. There were 50 youngsters fishing near a sewer emptying into the Schuylkill. It took a park attendant to prevent them from obtaining fishing poles from the shrubbery. When it comes to fishing, Philadelphia is raising poachers. Philadelphia is rearing lawbreakers. Philadelphia will reap what she sows.

Ralph Griswold, director of parks in Pittsburgh, has another scheme. He has stocked the lake in Schenley Park with catfish and yellow perch. He has organized a Junior Izaak Walton League. The boys are given fishing licenses for a few pennies. This gives them the benefit of club leadership and a right to fish in Schenley Lake. Before receiving a license, they must know the "bag limit." They must know a yellow perch when they see it. They must know that bullheads guard their young. They must know that, if they catch the parent fish in breeding season, there will not be so many fish next year. They must know that all boys do not know the law. They see the reasonableness of a license. They are willing to show their license. They are also acquiring knowledge, skill, and attitudes for the future.

Some camps are following the Philadelphia plan; a few, too few, are using the Pittsburgh plan. Too many have no plan. The lake is merely a body of water for swimming.

Water Fowl Are Owned by Nations and Not by Individuals or States. In the upper reaches of any lake, there may be shallow waters. There may be bays capable of producing wild rice, wild celery, pond weed, and duck potato. Such water plants are wild-duck food of high order. Wild ducks belong to the people. They belong to you and to your campers. More than that, they are an international possession. We have an international agreement with Canada and Mexico that these birds may migrate to their breeding grounds with safety.

Wild Ducks Are on the Wane. Did you ever see a child on the sea beach making a sand house? As the tide came up, he retreated up the beach making successive sand models. In the protection of wild ducks, we have been like children on the seashore. There have been innumerable restrictive controls: we have prevented oil pollution, diminished the hunting days, passed Sunday laws and sunrise and sunset rules, stopped chasing with motorboats, reduced the bag limit, recommended the stagger system, stopped baiting and the use of live decoys, and made the sale of wild ducks in the market illegal. Wood duck, canvasback, redhead, ruddy and bufflehead ducks have been added to the list of permanent protection. Unfortunately, many of the hunters do not know a wood duck from a green mallard. Policing does not solve the problem. The carnage goes on. Added to the danger of the hunter's gun is destruction by duck disease (botulism) and lead poisoning. Whether there are wild ducks in the future depends on research, education, and sanctuary. There is no other alternative.

The eider duck is protected in Iceland and has become so confident in man that it nests on the housetops. The attraction of wild ducks to many city parks is another example of what one may expect if a sanctuary is provided. Most ducks are Canadian by birth and Yankee by residence. If the black mallards can be attracted to a reservation by throwing a little grain on the water, or if the old squaw will give a demonstration in diving for food, or if the wood duck carries its young from tree to water before your eyes, you have a never-to-be-forgotten experience. When the blue goose stops on its trek from Hudson Bay to the mouth of the Mississippi and the canvasback calls on its flight from Saskatchewan to the south Atlantic coast, or when we become acquainted with the Ross snow goose, which breeds in the Arctic and winters in California, then we shall have something to brag about besides the bag limit.

What Are Camps Doing in Water Culture? An aerial photograph of camps in Northeastern United States would reveal the fact that summer camps are situated in forested lake regions ideally located for wild-life sanctuaries. Contact with the state conservation commission or other wild-life organizations in the neighborhood of the camp may result in the lakes and streams being restocked with fish and in further protection of the wild life in the vicinity. All that is needed for such a step is the desire for cooperation urgent enough to make conservation a concrete goal. The preservation of wild life is intimately linked with camp education.

Jack Miner and the Birds is a classical story. Jack Miner has demonstrated that it is possible to attract and tame wild ducks and geese so that they will come to a small sanctuary. Nearly 50 years ago, he went to Canada with his father and nine other children. They settled on a 200-acre estate at Kingsville, Ont. The average acreage of the camps is 187 acres—very similar to Jack's farm. He commenced his work in 1904 and practiced first aid on injured birds. Since then, his bird-banding work has brought useful information to the biological survey. Children who visit Jack Miner can feed robins on a white-topped table. Why not in camp? *Jack Miner and the Birds* is well worth reading for constructive suggestions on bird friendship.

Some years ago, I took 50 leaders to a Wisconsin Boy Scout camp for a week end. We couldn't sleep on Sunday morning because there were so many "volleys" from the duck hunters. That afternoon it wasn't safe to take the group on a field trip because of the rabbit hunters. No one dared to do anything about it because the hunters could retaliate by starting a forest fire, and then everyone would lose. Is your camp in this predicament?

In another Wisconsin camp, the boys and girls were shown the beaver. In the winter, they were taken across the beaver dam and shown how the muskrat provides for ventilation. They were shown the mink tracks and saw where he fished through the ice. In the fall, they helped the fish hatchery release trout. They transplanted wild celery to 6 ft. of water for the mallards and beach ducks. They put up nail kegs and hollow logs as nesting boxes for the wood duck. They gathered wild-rice seed in canoes and planted it in the muddy bottom of a slow stream. They went exploring for duck potatoes. They cooperated with the state conservation department. Their campground is a game sanctuary, and the result has been unforgettable experiences on fishing trips, in watching parent teals or the goldeneye diving for food, or listening to the loon.

Campers will harvest what their camp leaders provide. Fifty such programs will make the big difference to the state of Wisconsin. Wisconsin pays $50,000 a year to advertise its forests, lakes, fish, and water fowl.* It also spends generously to educate its children in conservation. It is not wasting its money. The investment is paying worth-while dividends.

PROTECTION OF WILD LIFE

Hawks and Owls Have Been before a Grand Jury. Perhaps the hawks and owls, more than any other wild life, show that "a little knowledge is a dangerous thing." Until recently, every hawk was a

*1940 statistics.

"hen hawk." Moreover, this idea was based on circumstantial evidence and not on facts. The Baldwin Research Laboratories of Cleveland found that poultry and game constitute less than 5 per cent of the food of hawks and owls. There may be an individual "outlaw," and he should be dealt with but only on the advice of a game warden. The "soarers" (with broad wings and tails) feed on rodents. The "darters" (Cooper's and sharp-shinned hawks) are more destructive. Owl pellets show that these birds prefer injurious rodents. At the present time, these predators have none or limited protection in some states.

Many people still insist on using man-made pole-traps, although the jaws of steel close on the just as well as the unjust. Hawk Mountain is a recent effort to protect our best natural living rattraps. Camps should be militantly active in the protection of the remnants of these interesting birds. Even though all camps start educational campaigns, "hawk and owl" mistakes will still continue. Tradition is a difficult thing to live down. Dr. John B. May's book *The Hawks of North America* will add much to your knowledge and understanding and enjoyment of bird lore.

The point of this is evident. Before you blacklist a hawk or check off a crow or kingfisher or blacksnake as "vermin," get all the facts of the case. You may decide that the ospreys eat game fish. The evidence is that they do not. You may hear that a "crow shoot" is for the purpose of "vermin control." Suppose it is sponsored directly or indirectly by an unscrupulous ammunition company? In England, the starling is a songbird. Someone has stated that it destroys the elm bark beetle. Can this be substantiated?

Shall the Muskrat Go the Way of the Beaver? If your campgrounds have not been overfarmed, a beaver meadow probably remains, even if the beaver is no longer there. The first settlers thought beaver would last forever. They thought the beaver stable enough to use for currency. Merchandise was worth so many beaver skins. It did not take long for the beaver to go the way of the wild turkey and the upland plover. The same kind of exploitation by the few can send the muskrat on his way. All these animals can be brought back. If we do not provide for them, it is inevitable that they will follow the passenger pigeon and great auk, never to be seen alive again. If you should also be sentimental enough to want to save the whistling swan and the American egret you must afford them refuge.

Provide abundantly for the muskrat, and you may reap such riches as the upland plover, wild swans, and egrets.

Diversified Campgrounds. The cottontail must have his brier patch. If we leave a winter brush heap, he appreciates the buds. The quail must also have a thorny cover such as osage orange, wild plum, prickly ash, or roses, for emergency and grassy openings or a grain field with standing grain for food. Tepees of cornstalks with unhusked corn or shocked sheafs of wheat, buckwheat, or millet are important quail foods. The pheasant thrives in grassland and marshes, but the ruffed grouse must have mixed hardwoods and evergreen, for wind breaks are acceptable. The songbirds pay their board by keeping down the insects, but they are attracted by a good clean water supply and berry-bearing shrubs. Dead trees permit squirrel dens and homes for owls, chickadees, or raccoons. It is evident that the more diversified the cover the greater the number of species to enjoy. It is also easy to see that a fire exterminates many homes and kills the foods and often the young. Diversified campgrounds and wild life go together. Camping at its best means close harmony with which to make possible the full flowering of those spiritual forces that the primitive made evident in our ancestors.

A Neighborhood Game Preserve. Wood County, Ohio, has become a cooperative game farm where hunters pay $2 to $3 for a hunting privilege. The landowners obtain revenue and protection. The hunters obtain sport. If the hunters break any law—civil or "moral"—such as leaving fences down, they are blacklisted. If they try to become mighty cave men and bag all the quail, they are off the legal list. The dividends furnish ample cash for patrols. This may be a suggestion for the "camp areas" that are abandoned during winter months. Camp directors can do a great deal to alleviate the wild-life situation not only through providing sanctuaries but by setting a standard for a game preserve for the neighborhood.

Wild-life Inventory. For several years, it has been customary for bird lovers to take a Christmas bird census. Why not go one step farther and make a wild-life inventory? It has the added attraction of being good adventure. Animal tracks are extremely interesting. In some of our national areas, there are checking stations where rangers make note of the number of each species of game killed. Such a game census makes it possible to show the curve of abundance and assemble the facts of the case for future control. Over a period of years, we could make parallel curves of drought, snow, and temperature from the weather reports and correlate them with the condition of the wild life in the area under observation. Perhaps we could get an idea of the number of hunters from the number of hunting licenses. Such a procedure is an intelligent approach to the problem of wild-life protection. When we actually know whether a species is increasing or decreasing and the probable causes, we are in a position to make recommendations for its preservation.

CONVERSATION ABOUT CONSERVATION ON THE TRAIL

Following a "trail" is one method of teaching conservation. You are about to go on a self-guided expedition. It will be "double exploration," in that you will search your minds and the fields at the same time. Today we hear a great deal of "idle chatter" about conservation. Some people believe it means sitting in an auditorium, listening to a lecture, saying "ain't it awful," and then going back to the same routine the next morning. Other people think that it is time we did something about it. "Do-nothing-ness" has got us into all kinds of difficulty—war, famine, pestilence, depressions, and so on.

This modern expedition will start at the Pine Tree Camp "Wonder House." You will stroll less than a mile, and yet you will see world-wide "examples" of conservation needs. You will go in small groups. Take your walking leisurely. If possible, be energetic in your thinking. Each stop represents a new experience. Through discussion, come to a conclusion, and then proceed according to directions to the next station.

From the "Wonder House," proceed uphill to the highroad.

Conserving Time and Energy. Thirty feet N.N.E. of cabin 9, cruise N.E. to a post and then due E. to a grave. When you arrive, after careful deliberation, explain what the implications are in the title of this paragraph. How does the use of a compass mean conservation? How does using one's head (instead of just taking it for a ride) mean conservation? What do you think conservation means?

Family Cemetery. Some years ago, there was lively discussion at a Cape Cod town meeting on whether to put a fence around a cemetery. One old fellow objected on the ground that those who were on the outside didn't want to get in, and those on the inside couldn't get out. Why was it considered necessary in olden times to have a cemetery fence? Is it conservation now? In what direction do all the graves face? Is this conservation or conservatism? There are four styles of markers here, slate__________, marble__________, granite__________, and a plaque on a boulder__________. When was each in style (use dates)? Which is the most natural?__________ Conserves most? __________ Why is there a "dark" date on Edward Bassett's grave? From here, take road E.10°N.

The White-weed Patch. At post 12, New England Telephone and Telegraph Co., look to right. This used to be a field. Number the following plants in order of succession (*i.e.*, which was the first, second, and so on): pitch pine, daisies, bracken, hay, garden crop. Why were daisies called white weed? They came from England. Did they come to the Atlantic or Pacific shore first? Were they desirable? Explain. What is a plant quarantine? Where should it begin? Continue now to another daisy field.

The "California Daisy Field" (Yellow Coreopsis). How big a bouquet should you pick here? How did these flowers escape? How many flowers are there at the top of one stem? How many so-called "petals" are there on one terminal flower? Put down the range in number. What has the law of variation to do with conservation? Which ones would you conserve for experimentation? Why? What is the order of plant succession here?

Proceed to Cloth Poster Entitled "No Trespassing—Laws of Massachusetts." What is the fine for taking a fern or rosebush from the land of another? What is the shortest time in jail for doing such a deed on Sunday? How long can you remain in jail for picking the other fellow's cranberries? Why are these laws necessary? Who makes the laws?

The White-pine Plantation. Is this a pure stand or is it mixed with hardwood? How does gypsy-moth damage compare under these conditions? What do you recommend to foresters?

G. W. Redding. What are the evidences that the Reddings enjoy beauty? Don't miss their water garden. See their dahlia farm. If Mr. Redding is "about his garden," ask him to tell you the story of his bobwhites. Who owns bobwhites in America? Who owns pheasants in England? Why the difference? This is a fundamental difference. At the crossroads take road toward "Wind-in-the-Pines." Go to the top of hill. Pause again for reflection.

A Forest-fire Zone. What evidences of forest fires do you find on the left? Was the transmission line put in before or after the fire? Proof? A forest fire starting at the foot of Long Pond about 9 A.M. in September, 1900, reached salt water at 2 P.M. Folks hereabouts gathered in the fields by Pine Tree Camp Theater and in boats on Long Pond. Old folks were rescued from homes. Could such a fire happen today? Continue downgrade to the "tumor" tree with large swellings on its limbs overhanging the roadway.

The Tumor Tree. Tumors on trees are akin to tumors on people—same cause if not same effect. This tree is a black oak. How much of the tree is infected? How damaging do you estimate this infection to be? Are other trees infected? How account for this observation? Go to "Y" and keep on the Girl Scout Training School Trail to the next "turnoff," where you will see:

The "Mystery Box" on All Fours. What is its purpose? Why on "all fours" instead of on ground? Why not in the garage? Is this conservation or safety first? Continue on upper road to next corner—until you come to view of Long Pond.

Buena Vista or Grand View Avenue. You are standing in front of the Bassett summer home. Why do they like it? Why do you like it? Follow road downhill to their winter home some 150 yards away. Let's find out some more about these "folks" without disturbing them. Why do camp people like the word "folks"?

The Bassett "City House." Find several evidences that Mr. and Mrs. Bassett care for birds. Trees. Flowers. Do you believe in signs? Continue downhill to the next "sign of the time." You may see an oriole. If you remove your smoked glasses, you may find his cradle. How does he "pay board" or rent to the Bassetts? (Think of three ways.)

"Private Beach, Please Do Not Trespass." Why is this sign necessary? Mr. and Mrs. Bassett are our friends. Why? As a friend, you have permission to enter. How may we keep this friendship? Continue on trail past black-locust grove to open field. You are about to witness a transformation from the old to the new.

Open Field. For what was this field once used? Proof (at least two evidences). For what is it now used? Proof (at least two evidences). Why is an obstruction placed on the lake trail? Continue into the pitch pines on the right—just above the shrub line, and find a luxurious growth of blackberries. Do not scratch them. They do not distinguish between the just and the unjust.

Blackberries. Are these wild tame blackberries or tame wild blackberries? How did this happen? What should be the next step in conservation? As evidence that there are two kinds, pick a leaf of each. Continue downhill until you come to first trail to lake. Go to large white oak on left. You may see the wreck of a hull. What might have prevented it?

The White Oak. What insect is making life a depression for this veteran? What use did man make of this tree? Why is that an injurious use? How was the cable fastened? Proof? What is the cure for the first? The second? Go to next "opening" or vista of the lake.

Epiphyte (*Epi*, "upon"; *phyte*, "plant"). The epiphyte does no harm to its host. Find a gray, a green, and a yellow epiphyte on the towering red maple that frames the right of the lake vista from the cove house. What are they?

Go to the "Cove House." Assemble your team around the fireplace for discussion of cases.

Case 1. Pine Tree Camp is being raided by gypsy moths. The caterpillars have defoliated the trees. In an oak forest, it sounds like rain. Mr. Bassett has hired two men to pick gypsy caterpillars from his cranberry bogs. Even flooding the bogs does not kill the egg masses. The devastation almost equals that of the prairie fire already described, except that these gypsies are here to stay, and their damage is accumulative. What is meant here by "A stitch in time saves nine"? The gypsy moth was introduced from Europe. They have several more insects, just as injurious, to send us. How would you handle the problem? Apply a little common sense in the situation.

Case 2. Campers at Pine Tree recently saw red squirrels harassing nesting robins. These "red raiders" have been known to steal robins' eggs and to eat the young. At an island camp—after a few years of study—they have decided that warblers, robins, and so on, have increased in numbers, even with the presence of red squirrels. National-park guardians no longer kill cougars just because cougars kill deer. All this comes under the balance of nature law. After careful deliberation, what do you recommend to the director of Pine Tree?

Analysis of the Morning's Experience. How does the value of a self-directed trail compare with reading Chap. 56 in a book on conservation? Why? How does studying alone compare with the group method in value? Why mix adventure in the problem? Does a mixture of humor make a smoke screen? Why? What is the comparative value of visiting neighbors? How much of a variety of problems was discovered in less than a mile? What other methods can you suggest? (This means other than the old-fashioned schoolroom cut-and-dried-memorize-recite way.)

Practical Application. Can the conservation trail be used at your home? Even downtown in a large city? Can you find such a wealth of experiences in such a short radius? Will the experiences be the same? Will all people have opportunity to go to camp and have such experiences? To what age groups does this method adapt itself? Conclusion?

Part II
APPLIED NATURE RECREATION

CHAPTER VI

THE APPROACH TO LEADERSHIP

Recreation and education at their best are one and the same. The boy who enjoys raising a puppy or constructing a radio is growing under an ideal situation. The nature program should be one of experiencing and enjoying rather than memorizing and reciting.

This manual offers suggestions for a series of worth-while experiences to help leaders in planning or rounding out nature activities that may already be under way in their communities. For the most part, these experiences stem from the immediate neighborhood, but bus and auto caravan trips must not be overlooked as real opportunities for nature adventure farther afield.

Think of These Experiences as Units. Select them according to the age level, the ability, the interest, the skill of group, material at hand, and season.

Evaluate the experiences in terms of the actual activity contribution of individuals and the group. Gazing at an anemic goldfish in a glass jar, raising guppies purchased at a store, and a field trip to gather "sticklebacks" to breed in homemade aquariums are experiences of different values.

Visualize each experience in which the group is to participate. It is a proving ground. One way to visualize it is to write it out somewhat as follows:

1. Name of unit: Our Lake.
2. Objectives: (Youth seeks fun, adventure, and romance. I must also know why I am offering this experience.)
   a. To appreciate how we obtain our water supply.
   b. To know the cause of pollution (safety education).
   c. To be willing to adapt oneself to discoveries of science.
   d. To refrain from drinking from untested water (especially on field trips).
   e. To appreciate our local lakes and rivers (scenery, boating, art).
   f. To open up new interests such as Chemcraft, photography.

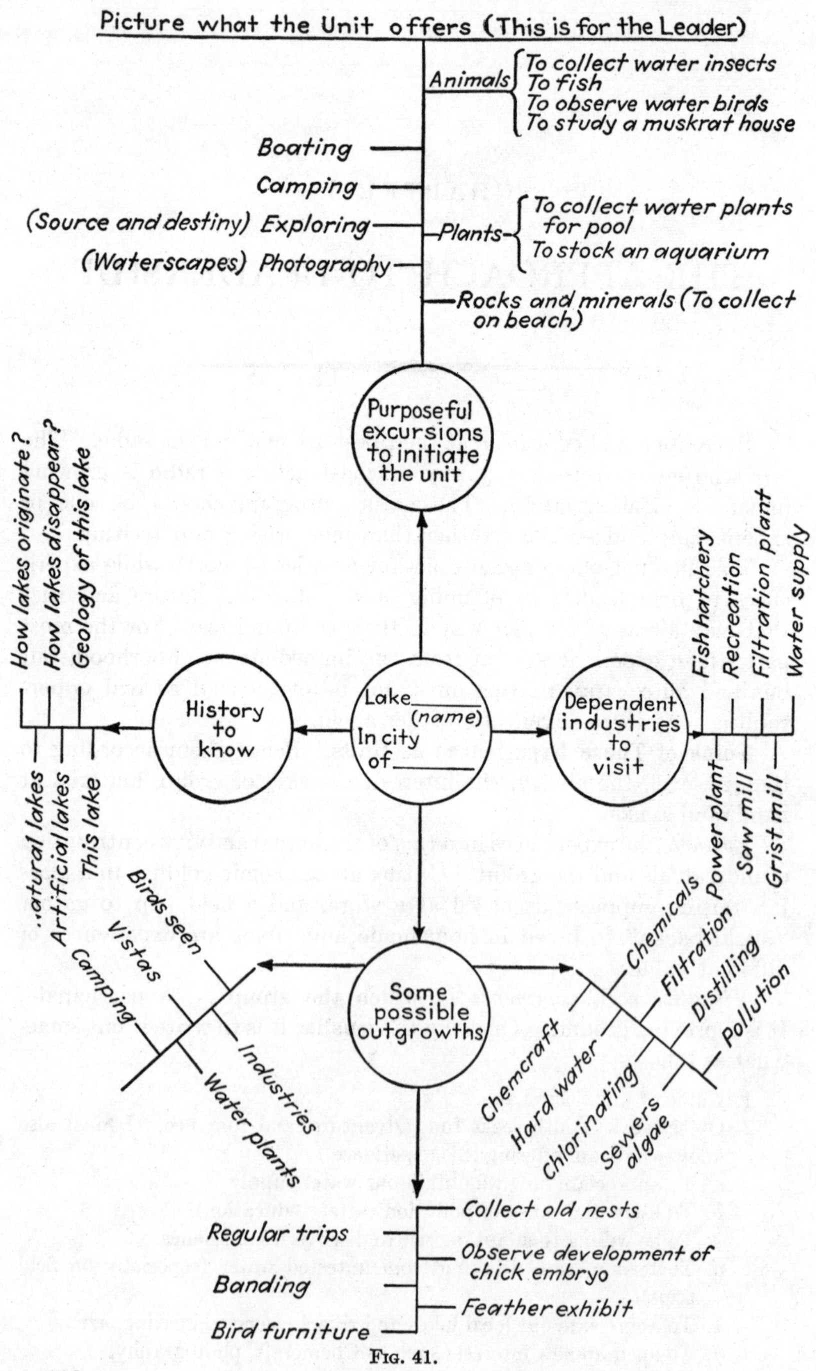
Picture what the Unit offers (This is for the Leader)
Animals
To collect water insects
To fish
To observe water birds
To study a muskrat house
Boating
Camping
(Source and destiny) Exploring
Plants
To collect water plants for pool
To stock an aquarium
(Waterscapes) Photography
Rocks and minerals (To collect on beach)
Purposeful excursions to initiate the unit
How lakes originate?
How lakes disappear?
Geology of this lake
Natural lakes
Artificial lakes
This lake
History to know
Lake (name)
In city of
Dependent industries to visit
Fish hatchery
Recreation
Filtration plant
Water supply
Power plant
Saw mill
Grist mill
Birds seen
Vistas
Camping
Industries
Water plants
Some possible outgrowths
Chemicals
Filtration
Distilling
Pollution
Chemcraft
Hard water
Chlorinating
Sewers algae
Collect old nests
Regular trips
Observe development of chick embryo
Banding
Feather exhibit
Bird furniture

FIG. 41.

Our Lake is taken as an example, for it involves things that are basic to any activity in nature recreation. It includes safety education, field trips, handwork, and appreciation. Water is involved in camping, landscaping, bird study, and all the other fields of nature interest. A recreation leader may prefer to start with the brook, water birds, camping, or the zoo. The method is the same. The only difference is in the materials. There are many routes to the North Pole. The important thing is that we arrive there. The lake route is only one way. The procedure used for Our Lake is the procedure for birds, trees, or flowers.

Out of the leader's picture will be built a program. It will center around the impulses of youngsters. If a bird club is the "outgrowth," then that should occupy the center of the stage. The chart again should picture purposeful excursions, life history to be known, dependent industries to be visited, and possible outgrowths of these experiences. By this method, a program evolves. Disciplined thinking and planning are an important function of any club.

3. Group-guidance service: Launch a project by purposeful aims such as any of the following:
   What is the source of Lake So and So?
   How many have visited the filtration plant?
   How many enjoy distilled water?
   Why shouldn't we drink water from any well?
   Would you like to make a model of our water system?
   Who would like to go fishing Saturday?
   Why do they put lakes in our parks?
   What would you like to know about our water supply? (List the questions.)
   How shall we find out? (List the suggestions, such as dates of trips, as given by the pupils.)
   How many would like to make a fruit-jar aquarium?
4. Provide working materials: Books, pictures, charts, models.
5. From suggestions, outline program for next few weeks: (Individual guidance service. This procedure opens the path to creative skills.)
   Youth should plan and make its own "good time."
   Whom Shall We Tell about Our Experiences? Shall we have an exhibit?
   Individuals volunteer according to interests.
   What experiments? Who will make a filter?
   Photographs? Who will take pictures?
   Museum? Who would like to take charge of our museum?
   Charts? Who will make a chart of the filtration plant?

Models? Who will make a model of a pump? Who will make a water wheel?
Maps? Who will make a map of our lakes?
Specimens? Who will collect water samples?
Materials? Where can we get clay? Paint?

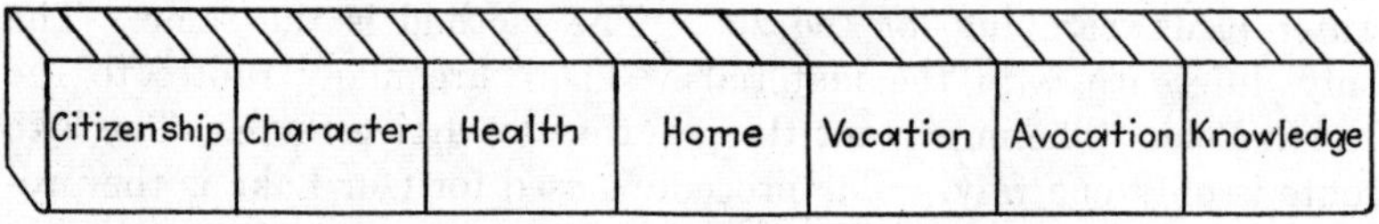

FIG. 42.—The seven objectives of education.

Outcomes. Our Lake has been written in detail to show the procedure that a leader may use in working out a program of experience. It is always important to keep your desired outcomes in mind. The National Education Association has listed seven objectives (see page 31).

You may think of these objectives as a measuring stick. If you hold this "yardstick" alongside the 3 to 6 weeks' experience with the unit of activity Our Lake, what benefit has accrued in the form of citizenship? How has the experience built character? Has it been worth while as a health experience? Has it had a favorable influence in the home? Has it been a valuable leisure-time pursuit? What has been learned? What effect has this had on the attitudes of the children?

The value of the experience can be weighed by these answers. It is a worth-while experience because it meets the seven objectives of education. Every unit of experience should be planned so as to stand this seven-point test.

CHAPTER VII

TOOLS FOR LEADERSHIP IN FIELD WORK

I. General use of tools for judging distances, heights, and sizes.

A. Individual equipment.

1. Hand.

My span is____________.

The last joint on my____________finger is 1 in.

Two hands high would be____________.

Armpit to finger tip____________.

Nose to finger tip____________.

Arms outstretched____________.

Reach in height____________.

2. Legs.

My pace is____________.

My stride is____________.

My foot measures____________.

3. My height is____________.

4. Weight____________.

B. Distances commonly known: (Try out a friend before telling him.)

1. Baseball field—home plate to first base, 90 ft.
2. Basketball—foul line to below basket, 9 ft.
3. Circle around basketball foul line, 6-ft. radius.
4. Basket is 10 ft. above floor.
5. A tennis court is 36 by 78 ft.
6. A football field is 160 by 300 ft.
7. The average American brick is 2½ by 4 by 8 in.
8. A cord of wood is 4 by 4 by 8 ft.
9. A desk is 30 in. high.
10. A chair is 18 in. high.
11. Auto tracks are about 4 ft. 4 in. apart.
12. A lath is 48 in. long.
13. The quart milk bottle, 40-qt. milk can, quart berry basket, and bushel box may be kept in mind as units of measure.
14. One acre is approximately 200 ft. square.
15. How far do you walk to school or business? What is distance in time?

C. A knowledge of the standard sizes of birds: Show some stuffed birds, as purple grackles, quickly, or point to pictures on bird chart. Good practice for field reports later. Scouts should recognize at once that a bird is larger than robin and shorter than crow. Correct answer is 13 in. Can take individual or patrol average of 10 birds.

warblers, 8 in. robin, 10 in. sparrows, 6 in. crow, 19 in.

D. Familiarity with the heights of common plants: Give a list of plants commonest to the locality, and have scouts arrange in order of height or estimate heights. This method not so exact, as heights vary.

portulaca (cultivated), 6 in.
hyacinth, 1 ft.
salvia, 2 ft.
poppy, 3 ft.
cosmos, 4 ft.
hollyhock, 4 to 5 ft.
rhododendron, 9 ft.
quince, under 15 ft.
peach, under 20 ft.
sugar maple, under 90 ft.
Carolina poplar, under 100 ft.
American elm, under 125 ft.

E. Ability to estimate tree heights:

1. Put piece of paper on tree at height you can reach. Walk away some distance, and estimate how many times this distance the tree is tall.
2. Measure off height of paper by sighting on a pencil. (Arm should be outstretched with your own shadow.) For example: If you are 6 ft. high and your shadow is 4 ft., and the shadow of the tree is 20 ft., what is the height of the tree? $6:4$ as $x:20$. $4x$ equals 120. x equals 30 ft., the height of tree.
3. Hold pencil vertically at arm's length. Sight on tree, marking height with thumb. Turn pencil horizontally, marking off an equal distance from base of tree to right or left. Pace off distance.
4. Take a right-angled isosceles triangle, and walk away from tree until you can sight along the hypotenuse. With one leg of triangle parallel to tree and the other to ground, you just barely see the top of the tree. The height of your eye plus the distance to the tree should be the height of the tree. This would have to be used on level ground.

F. City distances: Estimate to the outstanding points—such as to Central Square, to Stadium, to Monument, to University, and so on.

II. Tools for specific use on trips and trails.

A. Topographic maps are the best for field work and are now available for approximately 48 percent of the country. The price of the standard quadrangle map is 30 cents per copy, but a discount of 20 percent is allowed on orders for published maps of $10 or more, and 40 percent on orders of $60 or more, based on retail price. Prepayment is required and may be made by money order or check, payable to the Geological Survey, or in cash—the exact amount—at the sender's risk.

Maps for areas in the States west of the Mississippi River (including all of Louisiana and Minnesota) should be ordered directly from the Denver Distribution Section, Geological Survey, Federal Center, Denver, Colorado. Maps for areas east of the Mississippi River (including Puerto Rico and the Virgin Islands) should be ordered from the Washington Distribution Section, Geological Survey, Washington 25, D.C. The extent of map coverage is shown on an index which is available for each State on request. Further information concerning maps may be obtained from the Map Information Office, Geological Survey, Washington 25, D.C. The map should be mounted on cloth to protect it from rough usage in the field. If cut into small squares before mounting, it can be folded and carried in the pocket. Have an indoor "training" period prior to using the map in the field.

The following questions were prepared for a leadership class in Milwaukee and are typical of what may be used for other communities. The topographic map is a basic tool for field work. If a geological folio has been published for the locality, that also should be obtained.

1. Roads (culture, printed in black).
   a. What would lead you to suspect that the region was surveyed previous to settlement?
   b. In general, how far apart are the crossroads?
   c. What three kinds of road do you notice according to the compass?
   d. If you were hiking from West Allis to Root Creek, where would you look for the sun at noon? At 9 A.M.? At 3 P.M.? How could you get the compass points from the sun?
   e. If you were planning a hike from West Granville to Butler, in what part could you give the group an experience in cross-country hiking? Why?
   f. If you wished to pass fewer houses, would you take the country road or the road leading immediately south? Where would you first take the country road?
   g. If you went by the country road, where could you get the best coast on a bicycle?

2. The hills and valleys (relief, printed in brown).
   a. Where are the highest elevations in this quadrangle?
   b. Where is the steepest grade?
   c. How high is the cliff south of Cudahy?
   d. Do the highlands run N. and S. or E. and W.?
   e. Where is the greatest lowland next to the lake?
   f. In going from Hales Corners to Kinnikinnick River via Root Creek, tell how far you travel on level ground, downhill, uphill, and so on, commencing as follows: "For a mile we will go on level ground and then . . . "
3. Lakes, streams, and marshes (drainage, printed in blue).
   a. What is the general direction of the streams?
   b. Which way does the shore current move in Lake Michigan? Proof?

c. On which side of the piers and breakwater would you expect the greater deposit? Why?

d. A large, low object can be seen 13 miles from the Solomon Juneau monument. Why does it disappear below the horizon after that?

e. Find a pond located on a hilltop in the southern part of the quadrangle.

f. Locate a pond partly enclosed by a marsh.

g. Find an undrained marsh.

h. What is the elevation of Lake Michigan above sea level?

i. What is the elevation of Lake Park Golf Course above the lake?

j. When were the lakes and marshes formed?

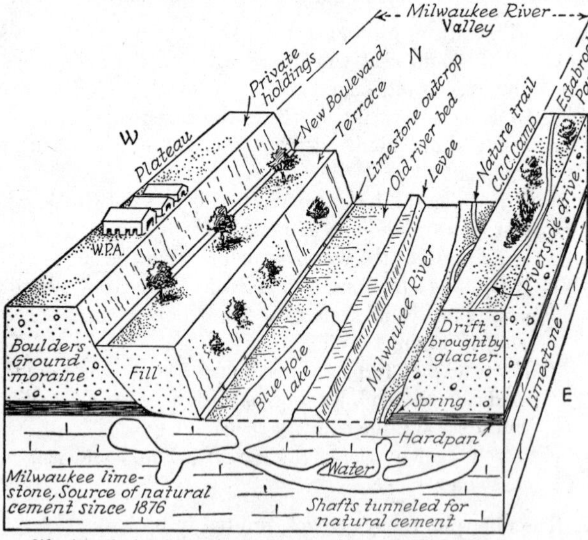

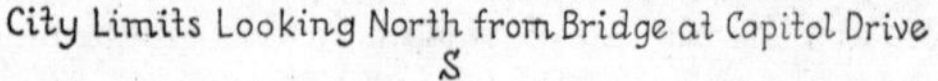

Fig. 43.—Block diagram of Milwaukee River Valley.

B. The block diagram is another basic and useful tool that is too little known. It is a sketch that represents a block of the earth's crust showing the locality in three dimensions. William Morris Davis, in his *Practical Exercises in Physical Geography* (1908), gives information on the subject. R. H. Whitbeck of the University of Wisconsin has also written about block diagrams. Figure 43 shows a block diagram and instruction sheet used for a leadership course in Milwaukee. The block diagram is more useful if the water is colored blue; vegetation, green; roadways, brown; limestone, yellow; and so on.

A trip to the Milwaukee River Projects.

Directions (as given to a group of recreation leaders for a field trip to the Milwaukee River Project).

1. By use of the block diagram, try to visualize and understand the Milwaukee River projects.
2. Hunt, in the ground moraine, for a crystalline rock brought from the northland by the great glacier. The most valuable rock will have a *facet* or smooth face, showing glacial polish and parallel scratches or striae.
3. Visit the *pinnacle of rocks* under the Chicago and Northwestern Railroad Bridge. Is this natural or artificial? What is your evidence? If a natural monument, composed of rounded stones, it is a *conglomerate* or pudding stone; if a natural monument, made of angular stones, it is *breccia;* if an artificial monument, it might have been an old bridge *abutment.* In any case, "Natural cement" was used. Explain. Should this pinnacle be demolished and removed? Why?
4. Marine days. We shall now walk around on the former sea bottom. We shall inspect the geodes (small caves filled with crystals), glance at the folded rock strata on the opposite shore to see on a small scale how mountains are formed—*anticlines* are upfolds; *synclines* are downfolds. Find the imprint of an ancient shell. These shells are called *brachiopods.* These animals are nearly extinct and exist here as *fossils.* We have harked back to the *Devonian Sea,* when fish ruled the earth. The deposit of this rock, when this was a mediterranean sea, was the last big geological event in Wisconsin. This small area in the bed of the Milwaukee River is the only Devonian rock in the state. Why is it fortunate that all of this rock has not been covered by the "dump"? Should every visitor take a souvenir? We believe it a good policy to agree that each class or club limit itself to one specimen. In olden times, the limestone was burned in kilns to make lime, which was used in plaster and mortar. There were limekilns in this part of the Milwaukee valley—only traces of which remain.
5. Make a brief survey of the landscaping of Estabrook Park.
6. Fresh-water days. Before the glacier, there were rivers. Since the glacier, there have been swamps and lakes. Fresh-water shells are abundant. They have evolved since marine days. We all have the collecting instinct. Some of us may enjoy starting a collection of fresh-water shells. Most of them do not have common names, because commonly people do not see them or talk about them. Sketches in shell books may help you to become acquainted with them.

JUNEAU PARK QUESTS
Plateau in Juneau Park
Statues
Locusts
Lincoln Mem. Drive
Tree swallow box
Miniature boat racing
Wild duck reserve
Lake shore walk
Sea wall
Milwaukee Harbor
Breakwater
W
Silt
E
Begin at Leif's, Son of Eric, statue and walk north
1- Locate everything sketched above in the panorama
2- Wet finger; Is it a lake or a land breeze?
3- How many of these words can you use?
Mains'l
Fores'l
Mast
Bowsprit
Starboard
Main sheet
Reef
Jibsail
4- Check these birds if seen
---Tree swallows - on houses
---Martins - largest swallows
---Mallards - pond ducks - in pairs
---Gulls - largest birds o'er lake
---Grackles - longtailed - by sea wall
---Robins - chestnut breast, on lawn
---Starlings - bob tailed, yellow-bills
---Terns - size of pigeons o'er lake
5- Proof that you saw them
How do ducks bank when landing?
Do male ducks (drakes) quack?
How does a swallow dip?
Where are martins feeding?
Do robins hop or walk?
How about grackles?
Which way do gulls and terns point their bills?
6- Look for mother duck and ducklings
7- Visit coast guard station
8- Get a story from a fisherman
9- Write a paragraph on back of this page on what interests you most
10- Color these sketches
Weather Record
Wind-direction
Velocity
Temperature
Sky

Fig. 44.

The pearl-button industry was introduced into the United States in 1890 by J. F. Boepple, of Hamburg, Germany. There are pearl-button factories at LaCrosse, Fremont, Stevens Point, and Prairie du Chien.

A trip of this kind would make a visit to the public museum profitable. Your children might like to see the evolution of a pearl button or might wish to identify a crystalline rock or shells or might like to see pictures of a limekiln.

7. Ice days. Our return trip will be along the east flood plain of the Milwaukee River valley. Along this trail, you will see where last winter's ice rafts scored the trees. You will see a great variety of igneous rocks from northern Wisconsin and Canada, which were brought here by the glacier. You can easily collect the following: granite, diorite, green stone, quartz, gneiss, a rock with a vein of quartz, flint, and porphyrite.

C. A pictorial direction page. "Juneau Park Quests" is suggestive of similar trips in other communities. In these days, when every office is equipped with mimeographing devices, there should be offered "pictorial trips" in which the members of the party are given a page similar to the one shown opposite. If the outline drawings are colored, they will stand out in an attractive way. It will be noted that "10 things to do" are suggested. Some of the hikers will "do all"; undoubtedly, all will visit the coast guard station, a few will try a feature story, and possibly no one will get time for the weather record. If it is the first trip, the investment will show fewer returns than if the trippers have been on many similar expeditions. Under competent leadership, these experiences will grow in richness and profit. Trips equipped with "a pictorial direction sheet" offer unlimited opportunity for progress. As soon as possible, the children should prepare the pages. Creative expression in art and story is the ultimate objective. The orientation sheet was also given the leaders. It assists the recreation leaders (who are by no means naturalists) to get a stimulating picture of the Milwaukee lake front.

It should also be noted that the trip is planned so that it can be used for an hour, a forenoon, or for a week. The opportunities are unlimited. Furthermore, it is not a bird trip or a fishing trip or a weather trip, but a general nature trip in which, in all probability, everyone will find something of interest and possibly of sufficient interest to be a challenge. The leaders were expected to be so stimulated that they, in turn, would conduct groups of children over the same terrain.

D. The model. It is but one step from a block diagram to a model. A model may be made of papier-mâché or of plaster of Paris. A model of a playground, of the city with its rivers and lakes, showing the rock layers beneath the ground, is most interesting and instructive. The

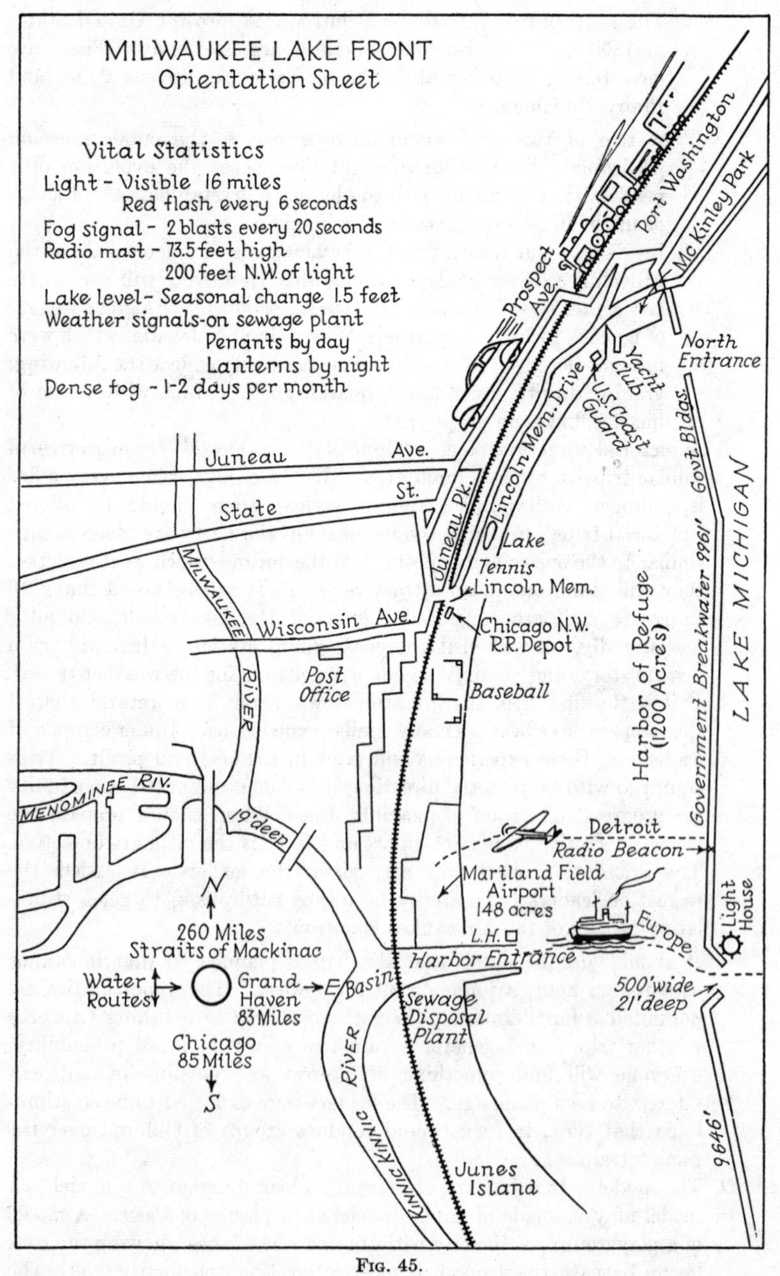
MILWAUKEE LAKE FRONT
Orientation Sheet
Vital Statistics
Light - Visible 16 miles
Red flash every 6 seconds
Fog signal - 2 blasts every 20 seconds
Radio mast - 73.5 feet high
200 feet N.W. of light
Lake level - Seasonal change 1.5 feet
Weather signals-on sewage plant
Penants by day
Lanterns by night
Dense fog - 1-2 days per month
Port Washington
Mc Kinley Park
Prospect Ave.
North Entrance
Yacht Club
U.S. Coast Guard
Lincoln Mem. Drive
Govt. Bldgs.
Juneau Ave.
State St.
Juneau Pk.
Lake
Tennis
Lincoln Mem.
MILWAUKEE RIVER
Wisconsin Ave.
Chicago N.W. R.R. Depot
Post Office
Baseball
Harbor of Refuge (1200 Acres)
Government Breakwater 9961'
LAKE MICHIGAN
MENOMINEE RIV.
19' deep
Detroit
Radio Beacon
Martland Field
Airport
148 acres
N
260 Miles
Straits of Mackinac
Light House
Europe
L.H.
Harbor Entrance
Water Routes
Grand Haven
83 Miles
E
Basin
Sewage Disposal Plant
500' wide
21' deep
Chicago
85 Miles
S
KINNIC KINNIC RIVER
9646'
Junes Island

FIG. 45.

model should be in a special room at headquarters and can serve as a starting point for an instructive trip or for summing up a trip. To visualize salt or coal coming from a mile under the city, to know that a certain valley was formed in preglacial days, to see that a certain section of the city is an old lake bed, to know that Ridge Road is an old lake shore challenges the imagination (see page 168).

E. The compass.

1. A trail for training and testing in the use of the compass. One may name the points of the compass and yet be unable to use it. This is a testing trail made out for Mausoleum Hill, Syracuse, N. Y., but it can be adapted to any region. A woodsman should be able to follow the trail in either direction. A testing trail becomes a training trail after it has once been used. Anyone failing should take the test on a different trail. The notes in parentheses are hints to leaders laying out trails and were omitted in the original directions. The individual being examined should fill in the blank spaces.

   Commencing at the northwest corner of the area fenced in on Mausoleum Hill, follow the fence east (this gives the scout a chance to test his compass with the compass used in laying the trail) for __30__ paces (pace is not a stride); thence __E.10°N.__ for __18__ paces; thence __E.__ for __10__ paces; thence along fence line (by fence line is usually meant an abandoned fence or the place where it used to be) due __N.__ for __20__ paces to a corner tree. The trunk growth of a tree is upward, outward (cross out one of these words). Proof__________? Set course S.5°W., and proceed 30 paces (this gives an opportunity to check up on the average pace of the one who laid the trail) to a woodpecker hotel. The woodpecker got room and board for his services. This structure is also a squirrel storehouse and feeding station.

   From here, continue in same course so as to pass a shagbark hickory in 9 paces, a hop hornbeam in 3 paces, a red oak in 5 paces, a large-toothed aspen in 6 paces, and an American elm in 21 paces. Observe the American elm closely and continue pacing in the same direction until coming to an elm that is somewhat different from the American elm. This is the slippery elm, which is______paces from the American elm. If you have the correct tree, you will find that the inner bark is fragrant and mucilaginous. Cut off a twig and test it.

   Examine the large rock under the tree. Is this rock a resident or a transient? How do you know__________? What artificial fragments do you find at the western end of this rock__________? (Bits of broken glass. This is a means of checking up that the scouts find the right rock.)

Shift your course 20° more to the north and go 31 paces to an apple tree. It differs from the surrounding hawthorn in not having__________and in having__________. Near the tree is a stake. Sight from the apple tree past stake to some natural object.

Take bearing and walk in a beeline until reaching a cairn. (Rocks piled up. Not rocks arranged for a fireplace.) Keep on in the same direction to a second cairn. Check up directions now and then with the compass.

2. Setting up a scenic locator. Now proceed to summit of the hill. Orient your topographic map and locate by compass the following hills. (Number refers to elevation given on map.) Fill in compass readings to right of numbers.) 681______; 686______; 670______; 761______; 845______; 647______; Onondaga County Home______; University Farm______; Crouse College______; Water Tower______.

   A diagram of a compass might be made on a board and varnished to prevent wearing by the weather. This could be fixed in a permanent position on a hill or at camp, and then the various points of interest, visible from the site, might be printed on the compass lines. The compass is then known as a *scenic locator*.

3. Permanent nature locator. Set a board compass in a forest. Make out a tree table for 10 trees as follows: *Name of tree: compass direction; number of paces from compass.* Or make a birds'-nest table as follows: *Name of nest; compass direction; kind of tree; height from ground.* Another form of nature locator is to have a foot of 1-in. pipe on a swivel joint so that it can be rotated and raised or lowered. Have a list of nature objects and direction, such as: N.N.E. elevated 32° is an oriole's nest. A person looking through the pipe when it is in this position will see the oriole's nest.

F. Mimeographed material for observation-training trips in the city. Keen observation is the key to successful and enjoyable trips and trail following. Like other sense skills, it can be trained and grows sharper through practice. If nature leaders or recreational headquarters could have some mimeographed lists like those that follow, the papers could be given to hikers or nature clubs. This is a training game that might be followed by a new and more difficult testing trail. The answers can be penciled on the margin or in the blank spaces, and the paper can be quickly scored when it is returned. As a third step in progress, one group can make similar trails for others. The questions at the end of the article are for discussion by leaders after the various suggestions have been tried out. If this effort stimulates more interesting observation activities, it will be time well spent.

Name of Hiker__________Club__________Date__________Score_____.

You are about to go nature trailing. It will be a test of your powers of observation rather than of your knowledge. In nearly every case, the answer may be seen if you will leave smoked glasses at home. If you would like to know your score, you may bring this paper back when you have finished.

1. Gifts from Mother Earth. On a short walk, such as from the hallway or lobby to the curb, one may see most of the items named below. In the blank spaces, tell in one word such as window, floor, steps, and so on, where the following are seen. In scoring, allow one point for each material correctly located.

a. Asphalt______	*f.* Iron______	*k.* Brick______	*p.* Tungsten______
b. Rubber______	*g.* Cellulose______	*l.* Granilitic material______	*q.* Granite______
c. Copper______	*h.* Enamel______	*m.* Cement______	*r.* Plaster______
d. Lead______	*i.* Marble______	*n.* Sandstone______	*s.* Zinc______
e. Chromium______	*j.* Tile______	*o.* Brass______	*t.* Plate glass______

2. The parts of a plant. In the table headings given below, you will note the parts of a plant. In the window of a grocery store, you will note cans of asparagus tips, peas, succotash, and so on. In front of a market, you may see white potatoes, yams, spinach, and so on. These are from different parts of plants. Place the names of these plant products in the proper columns of the table. For example: Parsnips are roots, and celery is the stem.

	Leaf	Stem	Root	Bud	Flower	Fruit	Seed
a							
b							
c							
d							
e							
Score							

3. Nature shopping in downtown store windows. While mother is shopping, the children can try this game. One often sees imitations of flowers and artificial evergreens used for decorations. In the haberdasher's and dress shop and department-store windows, there will be goods made possible by minerals, herbs, trees, insects, furbearing animals, and so on. Anyone who can comprehend our dependence on nature will have no difficulty in filling out the following table.

ORIGIN OF OBJECTS

	Imitations of nature, as artificial flowers, leaves, fruit, and so on	Mineral kingdom	Vegetable kingdom		Animal kingdom	
			From herbs	From trees	From insects	From fur bearers
a						
b						
c						
d						
e						
Score						

4. Art from nature. If one glances into art shops, galleries, craft marts, or a Peter Pan gift shop, one will be able to "spy" many creations with ducks, frogs, shells, and so on, as motifs. One need not be very observant to list 10 such articles.

	Nature motif	Article on which used		Nature motif	Article on which used
a			*f*		
b			*g*		
c			*h*		
d			*i*		
e			*j*		
Score					

5. Nature in educational exhibits. Store windows, museums, and libraries often have seasonal, educational exhibits. The Enoch Pratt Free Library of Baltimore has window exhibits that are very popular. The following titles and questions were made for an observation trip held in early March. In the windows were books, pictures, charts, and other visual material attractively

arranged. The "answers" could be found in the exhibits. The procedure may be suggestive for other communities. Two points per window are allowed for correct observations.

a. The Emerald Isle.

Why did St. Patrick use the shamrock as an insignia?

What is used to cover the house roof in Ireland? (See painting by Paul Henry. Also, observe picture of "Cottage by the Rose Gate, County Dougal.")

b. The Gardener Plans Utopia. According to the exhibit.

What are the "ideal harbingers of spring"?

How many kinds of real flower (flowers that grow) can you find in the window?

c. Girl Scout International Month.

Who was the "progenitor" of the American movement?

What is meant by "hands across the sea"?

Fig. 46.—Rustic fountain made from the burl of an Engelmann's spruce.

d. The Story of Stone.

Examine the rock under the letter S in Story. Which face of the rock has weathered most?

Examine the "ancient table top." How much of the design would be left if nature motifs were omitted?

e. It's Maple-sugar Time in Maryland.

What sanitary improvements have been made?

What two pamphlets can you obtain about this industry from the University of Maryland?

What is a spile? A tank sled?

Would a maple-sugar party be recreational or educational?

f. A Foretaste of the National Flower and Garden Show.

Who wrote *Natural Rock Gardening?*

What did Ernest H. Wilson write?

g. Y means You, if You're in Your Teens.
How many of these books would be left if "nature" were omitted?
What two organizations make "Baltimore reading lists"?

h. Man's Climb to Civilization.
Study the chart and discover how many centuries existed between silk culture in China and Copernicus.

i. Cellulose in Everyday Life.
How many of the following can be made from "spruce chips": Pianos, handkerchiefs, shoes, salt shakers, towels, cement steps, upholstery, artificial silks, lacquers, buttons, iron kettles?

6. Some Challenges from a Patent-medicine Shelf (10 points).

a. New Discovery Indian Natural Herb Store's Tonic.
How many of these words are planned to attract a prospective customer?
Why have so many names?

b. Shure-Grow-Fast Double Hair Grower.
How long have these articles been on the shelf? (Give three evidences for your answer.)
What does this suggest as to their value?

c. Old Indian-style Herb-combination Liniment.
Can one medicine be a cure for bunions, headache, liver complaint, and cuts?

d. Golden Bells Life Horoscopes.
Why should this book be on the same shelf?
Was it given the name Golden Bells because the bells were printed on the cover, or were the Golden Bells printed on the cover because of the title?

e. Shaker Health Soap.
How many soaps will remove body odors?
Which do you consider more important for this purpose—a warm bath or the kind of soap?

f. Help-o-tone Female Vegetable Compound.
What percentage of alcohol does this compound contain?
What percentage of alcohol is there in legal beer?

g. Change Your Luck (four rabbit feet fastened to a cardboard)—The Sure Way.
Why should the owner of the store place four rabbit's feet in the center of the exhibit?

7. A Tree Walk (the numbers in parentheses indicate the score). This trip was planned for downtown Indianapolis. It may be adopted for any metropolis.

a. Go west on the south sidewalk of McMechen Street. The first tree is an elm and the second a linden. What are the third and fourth trees? (1)

b. The large tree opposite No. 539 McMechen is an ailanthus or tree of heaven. How many children does it have in the second yard? (1)

c. How many young sycamores have been planted on this street? Find three ways in which they have been cared for. (3)

d. The three trees near the corner are silver maples. Which are in blossom? (1)

e. The tree at the southeast corner of the church is a basswood or linden. Stand "unter den Linden" and discover what made the rows of holes in the bark. What color is a clean bud? (2)

f. The large tree near the linden is white ash. (3)
How did the tree dentist care for it?

Are most of the twigs opposite or alternate?

What proof can you find that it is a "female" ash?

g. At the corner of W. Mulberry and N. Charles Streets, there is a large elm. (3)
Observe the large buds printed against the sky. These are blossom buds.

How have tree surgeons cared for the wounds when they sawed off the large limbs? (Note two ways.)

What famous general camped near this site?

What organization put up the marker?

h. Go up the hill until you can see the two kinds of trees back of the brick apartment. They are Carolina and Lombardy poplars. The Carolina poplar spreads out more.
How many Lombardy poplars are there? (1)

i. At the next lamp post, look at the end of the 2 by 4 on the board fence. This is pine wood. The sapwood has secreted a pitch or resin. Is the sapwood on the top, on the bottom, on the right, or on the left of the 2 by 4? In what direction was the center of the tree from the piece that was cut out? (2)

j. Why does the cottonwood at No. 1740 lean streetward? (1)

k. Observe the cocoons of the bagworms hanging on the sycamores in front of Nos. 1677 and 1681. What did the worms place on the outside of the cocoon? Does this strengthen the cocoon or does it act as a camouflage? (1)

l. How has the tree in front of No. 1663 been mistreated? (2)

m. The nearest tree to the next sycamore is a ginkgo. Ginkgo trees are native to Japan. Where may another ginkgo tree be seen from this point?

You will see the largest ginkgo tree in the city on this trip. Locate it. (5)

n. The "witch's brooms" growing on the large tree in front of 1509 are on a hackberry tree. Where is the nearest hackberry to this one? (1)

o. Arborvitae has flat sprays. Juniper has three needles in a whorl. Which grow in urns at No. 1505? (1)

p. Why do the next trees have flypaper tied around the trunks? (1)

8. Nature Quests on Treeless Streets.

a. On this trip, locate an advertisement

(1) That shows a Christmas tree______
(2) That shows a mouse______
(3) That shows snow______
(4) That shows a star______
(5) That shows a white horse___
(6) That depends on tropical fruit______
(7) That shows that great oaks from little acorns grow______
(8) That teaches safety______
(9) That shows the value of sunshine______
(10) That uses natural scenery___

b. What made the stones of the "Alberta" round? (1)

c. What material is used for paving Capitol Street? (1)

d. At No. 315, it says "Dogs Vaccinated for Rabies." Who discovered how to prevent rabies? (1)

e. At the bridge over the canal, discover the following: (2)
Which way does the canal flow? Proof?______
Who owns the canal? Proof?______

f. At the Shoe Store. (2)
Name three animals that made these shoes possible?
The base stone is verdantique marble. What color is it?

g. Visit the Fountain. Go up the granite steps. (10)
How do you know that the pebbles came from a river?______
What kind of rock was used to make the benches or seats?___
A catfish has feelers, or antennae. How many catfish are there on the fountain?
How many fins does the scaly carp have?
Are the shell catch basins molds, casts, or models?
Where are the gargoyles? Do they represent real or mythical animals?
What instrument is the maiden playing?
What was the profession of Richard J. Depew?

h. Feed the Pigeons.
It is estimated that 300 pigeons are fed here every noon. On Sunday mornings, families feed the pigeons on the way to church. (5)

Can you recognize a young pigeon? How?

Do pigeons walk or hop, toe in or out, carry their feet out back or out front when flying? Do they use their tails? When?

i. Find six evidences at No. 910 that they care for plants. (3)

j. What causes the cement wall in front of No. 906 to be streaked with brown? (1)

FIG. 47.—Enos A. Mills, the "father of nature guiding." (*Courtesy of Mrs. Enos A. Mills, Longs Peak, Colo.*)

k. How many window boxes are there at No. 904? (1)

l. What bird, leaf, and tree decorate the new book sign on the south side of the library? (3)

m. Go to corner of South 4th Street. Observe the famous statue on a granite block. Where did this man get his education? (1) Where did he get his physical and moral strength? (1)

n. Cross the street. What animal is used for a trade mark on the side of the mail box? Why? (1)

o. Why are there spikes on the chimney at No. 716? (1)

p. Step just inside the gate made of limestone. Where can you see a robin's nest? (1)
Where is there an implement for removing mud? (1)

q. At the church, go up the sandstone step. (10)
Observe the bulletin board. Which parables mentioned were based on nature?

Was the silver grain shown in the door made by nature or by man?

Are the shingles slate, asbestos, or wood?

The foundation of the church is granite. It has three minerals—pink feldspar, black hornblende, and white or milky quartz. Number them in order of abundance. Which shines?

r. The "ground cover" vines in the churchyard are myrtle, ivy, pachysandra. Which are evergreen? (1)

s. What colors have the crocuses at No. 458? (2)

t. Cross the street to the window of the Purnell Galleries.
Find how and where the duck, frog, and shell are used as motifs.

u. Look in the gift shop. What can one make from a gray birch log? (1)

v. Observe the birds in the window at No. 461. Are they insect or seed eaters? What three foods are necessary for them? (3)

w. How many stones are necessary for the success of the goldfish at No. 453? How is the ivy grown in the same window? (2)

x. Observe two tropical products in this block.

References

CAVE. *The Boy Scouts Hike Book,* Doubleday, Doran & Company, Inc., 1913, 243 pp.
FORDYCE. *Trail Craft,* D. Appleton-Century Company, Inc., 1918, 202 pp.
TORREY and others. *New York Walk Book,* Dodd, Mead & Company, Inc., 1934, 332 pp.
WALLACE. *Packing and Portaging,* The Macmillan Company, 1912, 133 pp.

CHAPTER VIII

LEADERSHIP RESPONSIBILITIES ON THE HIKE AND OVERNIGHT TRIP

Before venturing on a hike, it is absolutely essential that the leader realize his responsibilities for group welfare. Equipment for this means a thorough knowledge of certain "rules of the road" and an ability, acquired through firsthand experience, to be at home in the woods for short or long periods of time.

Traveling comfort and physical protection for the group should be a leader's first concern. The following catechism is drawn up to call attention to and make definite suggestions for this obligation. Similar quizzes on other aspects of the hike follow. The answers appear separately so that the leader may use the questions as preparatory drill.

A NATURE-GUIDE CATECHISM

I. The Hiker

Preliminary Arrangements.

1. What announcements should be made in arranging for a hike?
2. What permission should a hiker have?
3. Should a hiker who has a cold be allowed to go?
4. What should be in the first-aid kit?
5. Who is responsible for the first-aid kit?
6. The time set for assembly for a hike is 9 A.M. What time should the hikers start?
7. The hikers' "shack" is just outside the city limits. Where should the hikers start to hike for the "shack"?

What to Wear and What to Carry.

1. What should a hiker put on his feet?
2. What care should be taken with the socks?
3. What care should be taken with the shoes?

4. What care should be taken with the shoelaces?
5. Who checks up the equipment?
6. When should the equipment be inspected?
7. What is a pedometer?

Safety.

1. It is a duty of hikers to prevent accidents. To whom is this a duty?
2. Name a sensible "dare" that might be accepted.
3. Give an example of a foolish "dare" that should be refused.
4. Which is better for hiking: cross country or the state road?
5. On which side of the road—when necessary to hike in the road—should hikers march?
6. What "command" should be given when an auto approaches?
7. What should the leader do about a hiker who does not obey?
8. What is a good hiking pace?
9. What four snakes are injurious?
10. How would you recognize poison ivy?
11. How would you recognize poison sumac?
12. How far should a hiker straggle from the party?

Health.

1. What speed record should be tried for on a hike?
2. What distance should be tried for on a hike?
3. What is the best manner to rest?
4. A good hiker will stop at how many houses for water?
5. Where else may one drink water?
6. How often should a hiker drink water?
7. How soon after lunch should a hike be continued?
8. What activities are good on a hike?
9. What should a hiker do if his feet ache?
10. How would you treat a blister?
11. How would you prevent a blister?
12. Where should dismissal take place?
13. Where should a hiker go after dismissal?

Etiquette.

1. How does the scout law apply to hikers?
2. What animals should hikers kill?
3. What snakes are harmless?
4. What flowers should you pick for a bouquet?
5. What flowers should not be picked for a bouquet?
6. What land areas should not be "crossed"?
7. What care should be taken of fences?
8. What attitude should be taken in regard to fruit?
9. Where may one throw stones?

10. What relation is there between hikers and farm animals?
11. What should be done with waste from a lunch box?

II. The Overnight Hiker

Equipment.

1. What equipment is necessary for an overnight hike?
2. When should the blankets be rolled?

Safety.

1. When should the hikers use a camp guard?
2. What precautions would you take in regard to insects?
3. How would you arrange a camp light?
4. How would you make a camp stove?

Health.

1. How would you keep from getting wet?
2. How would you make a camp bed?
3. How would you build a camp latrine?
4. What should be done with wet clothing?
5. In bedmaking, what should be placed beneath the camper?

Other Rules.

1. What should the hiker do first upon arrival at destination?
2. How near or far apart should the beds be grouped?
3. How many hikers should have "duties"?
4. What "night rules" would it be best to observe?

III. The Firebuilder

The large amount of damage caused by campfires makes firebuilding a serious responsibility, and the time is near at hand when every guide will be required to have a license to build fires outside certain designated spots.

Law.

1. What is the law in regard to forest fires?
2. What is the fine or term of imprisonment, if a fire results from carelessness?

Fuel.

1. Which of the following are the best tinders? Twigs flat on the ground. Sticks under leaves. Upper twigs of fallen oak branches. Weed tops above the snow.
2. Which of the following woods make lasting embers? Oak, pine, birch, hickory, apple.

3. Which green woods make good fuel?
4. When is a fire permit necessary in this state?
5. Who should gather the wood?
6. What kind of wood should be gathered?
7. What should be gathered for tinder?
8. How would you get dry wood when there is a drizzling rain or deep snowdrifts?

Firemaking.

1. How should you lay material for building a fire?
2. How would you break large pieces?
3. What kind of fire should you use in time of drought?
4. Why do campers make fire by friction when matches are so cheap?
5. How does a bonfire differ from a campfire?
6. Why should a hiker never build a bonfire?

Safety and Health.

1. How should a hiker carry matches?
2. Where should a hiker build a fire in relation to: rocks, lakes, brooks, pine trees, logs, leaves?
3. What would you do about a campfire on a windy day?
4. How would you prepare an area for a campfire?
5. How is an underground fire started?
6. What dangers are there in using a coal or oil stove or lighted lantern in a closed room?
7. How would you improvise a spark catcher for a stovepipe?
8. What can a camper use as a substitute for a hot-water bottle or electric heating pad?

Etiquette.

1. Which of the following tinder might lead to breaking a law of wood etiquette? Cedar bark, birch bark, dead twigs on a tree.
2. What is the courteous thing to do before building a fire upon any property?
3. What is the courteous thing to do before collecting wood upon any property?
4. How many living trees should be cut down? Hacked? Barked?
5. How many trees should be blazed?
6. What evidence should there be of your having camped anywhere?
7. How would you extinguish the fire? When?

IV. The Camp Cook

Cooking is one of the most interesting and available of outdoor activities. Most enthusiasts do not realize, however, the obligations that go with it. When it comes to staying overnight and cooking several meals, the health and life of the campers require all this knowledge plus the other safeguards.

Equipment.

1. What is essential for a cooking kit?
2. How can you clean dishes in the field?
3. What should you do to prevent soot from sticking to the utensils?
4. What is meant by "pegging down the crane"?
5. The lug pole should be green, dry, or wet? Thick as a pencil, broomstick, or wrist?
6. The pothooks should be the same length or different lengths? Explain.

Food.

1. How much food is necessary for eight people? For three meals?
2. Why is canned food not so good for hiking?
3. What organ gives the final test to outdoor cooking (brain, stomach, tongue, eye, nose)?
4. What is meant by food that "sticks to the ribs"?
5. What should one do with the leftover food?
6. How do frozen and frozen-thawed potatoes differ for cooking and eating purposes?
7. How should a person "packing food into the brush" regard dehydrated vegetables and canned goods?
8. In what form would you transport eggs and milk if you wished to reduce bulk?
9. How are bouillon cubes rated for nourishment?
10. When packing, how should you prevent food from getting the grease from the bacon?
11. Does snow water quench thirst?

Fire.

1. Which is the best cooking fire: big bonfire, small-sized bonfire, bed of coals the size of a chair bottom, a baby fire the size of a plug hat?
2. Do you put the large pieces of fuel on before or after you start to cook? Why?
3. Should you cook over a roaring fire, a dancing flame, smoking embers, or glowing coals?
4. Which is better for the bottom of a fireplace (stone, earth, logs, duff)? Why?

Cooking.

1. For roasting, should one have a good blaze, a bed of coals, or smoking embers? How do you prevent or remove the undesirable types of fire?

2. Which of the following should be cooked rapidly: stew, cereal, chicken, beans, pot roast?
3. How would you roast a fowl or leg of lamb turnspit style if you had a fireplace?
4. How many utensils should be placed directly on the coals?

Etiquette and Safety.

1. What should you do with paper, peelings, string, and so on?
2. What should you do with tin cans and bottles?
3. How does freezing purify water?
4. How do you make drinking water safe?
5. Should a scout with a knapsack thumb a ride or "bum his way"?
6. How does a greenhorn differ from an old-timer in camp cooking?

ANSWERS

I. The Hiker

Preliminary Arrangements.

1. Time and place of meeting; carfare, if necessary; material needed, such as knife, compass, map, cup, spoon, or ax; food arrangements; distance to walk; time and route planned for return. Place and time of dismissal.
2. A young hiker should have the permission of his parents. Fire and trespass permits may be necessary.
3. Leader will have to use judgment. If cold is in an infectious stage and the group has the habit of passing about a canteen and drinking from a common cup, I would send such a "liability" home.
4. Adhesive, a clean bandage, absorbent cotton, iodine. First aid is first aid. Nothing more.
5. The leader.
6. 9 A.M. If you start at 9:15, they will always come 15 or more minutes late.
7. Energy should not be used hiking through the city. Get to the shack as soon as possible and start to hike from there.

What to Wear and What to Carry.

1. Low-heeled tramping shoes that will keep out moisture.
2. Woolen socks are best. Do not have wrinkles. Carry extra pair for long hike. During rest period, bathe feet, dry thoroughly, powder toes, and change right to left. If any part of the foot is chafed, cover with adhesive.
3. Shoes should fit, be waterproofed, and somewhat flexible. (New shoes should not be broken in on a hike.)
4. Shoelaces should be strong, snug, but not too tight.
5. The leader or someone assigned by the leader.

6. Before starting.
7. An instrument to measure distances walked by person who carries it.

Safety.

1. It is a duty to self, to the group, to the leader. If a scout, it is a duty to scouting.
2. To pick up a garter snake.
3. To slide across unsafe ice until it breaks.
4. In hiking, avoid the highway as much as possible.
5. Hikers should walk on the left-hand side of the road. They will then see automobiles coming and can step aside.
6. "All left."
7. He should not be sent home in the middle of a hike, but the leader should refuse to take him next time.
8. Three miles an hour with rest periods. Do not have a foot race or an endurance test.
9. The four injurious (United States) snakes are the rattlesnake, the coral snake, the copperhead, and the water mocassin.
10. White berries and three leaflets. Woodbine has blue berries and five leaflets.
11. Poison sumac has white berries and grows in swamps.
12. No one should straggle from the party. It always causes alarm and inconvenience.

Health.

1. Leaders should not try for speed records on a hike except in case of an emergency.
2. Fifteen miles should be the day's limit.
3. Lie down and relax. Feet up in air relieves blood pressure.
4. Greenhorns are forever stopping to get a drink. This may become a nuisance to house dwellers, and there is also the danger of exposure to disease. Seasoned hikers prefer not to stop to get a drink of water.
5. One may carry a canteen or drink from a spring. Sumac berries or barberries will help quench the thirst.
6. Hikers tend to drink too often and too much water. They should train themselves to go without water. Those who stay in the house do not drink enough. We should drink about 12 glasses a day.
7. Hikers should rest for half or three-quarters of an hour after eating.
8. Observation games, collecting, stories during rest period, getting acquainted with inhabitants.
9. If tempòrary, bathe, change socks, and rest. If chronic, have feet examined for fallen arches.
10. Insert sterilized needle under skin near base and drain. Wash with antiseptic. Dry with powder. Build up around with adhesive or use a corn cushion. Remove cause.

11. Use adhesive on threatened part.
12. At some place agreed upon, as starting place or headquarters.
13. In the case of young hikers, they should go home.

Etiquette.

1. The scout law applies to hiking. Illustrate by concrete examples.
2. None needlessly. Some think that they should kill a snake on sight.
3. Most snakes are harmless.
4. Those in the open fields, as daisies, buttercups, Queen Anne's lace, goldenrod, everlasting, dandelions, asters, milkweed, and cattails.
5. Laurel, flowering dogwood, arbutus, Indian mocassin, adder's tongue, columbine, anemones, maidenhair ferns, hepaticas.
6. We should not cross lawns, gardens, hayfields, orchards, or areas containing domestic animals.
7. Leave them the way you find them. If you knock down a stone wall, replace it. Do not leave bars down or gates open.
8. Fruit belongs to the owner. Often he is willing to give it to hikers. It should never be disturbed without permission, even if it appears to be going to waste.
9. Do not throw stones into hayfields, at domestic animals, into private ponds, or toward buildings.
10. Hikers should respect farm animals. Do not frighten them. Do not make it possible for them to get out of enclosures.
11. Papers, string, and refuse should be buried. Do not throw away sandwiches. Waste food may be left for birds.

II. The Overnight Hiker

Equipment.

1. Food, blankets, poncho, matches, flashlight, latrine.
2. Sun and air upon getting up. Roll up after breakfast.

Safety.

1. When playing a game for the experience.
2. Go when or where insects are not pests. Carry mosquito netting. Camp near a shelter.
3. Each group should have a flashlight. If possible, have a lantern to show way to latrine. Campers often get bewildered and lost at night.
4. Make a stone or clay stove.

Health.

1. One poncho under and another over. Make trench each side of bed. Camp near a shelter.
2. Dig a hip hole. Fill with leaves or spruce boughs. Put poncho on top. Try it for comfort. Fold blankets and pin with horse-blanket pins.

3. Dig a trench and use a small log for seat. An old nail keg is handy.
4. Wet clothing should be removed and dried.
5. One poncho under and as many blankets under as over.

Other Rules.

1. Choose site for bed and make it.
2. This depends on group discipline and how many greenhorns are present. Beds should be far enough apart so that one group will not disturb their neighbors. There should not be more than two in a group.
3. Every hiker should have a "duty."
4. Agreed time on retiring and arising. No disturbance.

III. The Firebuilder

Law.

1. In many states, there is a law that the person who sets a forest fire is financially responsible for the amount of damage done.
2. The leader should look this up for the community in which he is leading.

Fuel.

1. Twigs flat on the ground or under leaves are wet and soggy. Weed tops, bark from a dead birch, and frayed cedar bark are the best tinder. Dead twigs can usually be found on the lower shaded branches of evergreens.
2. The hardwoods, like oak and apple, make live coals.
3. Birch has an oil, sumac and ash burn readily, and the coniferous trees have a resin that favors burning. Beginners are sometimes unable to tell green wood from deadwood. Nick the bark with thumbnail or pocket knife. If inner bark is green, it is called green wood.
4. Know dates for your particular community.
5. Everyone except those assigned other duties, as preparing the food or getting water.
6. Dry lower limbs, rather than damp wood from ground.
7. Birch bark, cones, dry leaves, cedar bark, chestnut frays, standing stalks.
8. Select standing dead timber without bark. Split the wood, and the inside will be found dry. The fire may be nursed with these splinters until the wet wood catches.

Firemaking.

1. The "tepee" or "log cabin" is a good way to lay material to start a fire. These methods give a draft.
2. Break large pieces by hitting over a sharp corner of a boulder, or better, by prying between two trees growing from same stump.

3. A trench fire dug well below duff line. If it is an open trench, it should be covered with piece of sheet iron or flat rocks. Amateurs cannot always recognize duff. It is dark soil with vegetable matter and will burn. It is a dangerous source of forest fires.
4. There is a satisfaction in accomplishing pioneer skills.
5. A bonfire is larger than a campfire.
6. Bonfires are wasteful and not adapted to cooking.

Safety and Health.

1. In a waterproof container.
2. He should clean away duff. If there is danger from sparks, he should make a stone fireplace or trench the fire. A beach with the wind blowing toward the water is best.
3. Build a fire in a gravel or sand pit. I have gone without a fire rather than take a chance of having the campfire spread.
4. Rake away all forest litter and build a fireplace. Be sure that there is a fire extinguisher such as loose soil or water handy.
5. By fire catching in the humus. Such a fire may smolder for days before the blaze appears. It is better not to build a fire where there is thick humus.
6. A fire hazard; they exhaust the air of oxygen; they present the problems of transportation; they are easily knocked over; and they give off carbon-monoxide gas, which is colorless, odorless, and deadly.
7. An 8-in. galvanized wire cloth spark catcher over the top of a stovepipe will prevent sparks setting a fire. The soot should be removed occasionally.
8. My parents wrapped hot soapstone in flannel or newspaper to put at our feet or to carry in our hands on a long winter drive. A brick or rock will do as well. It's an old custom with merit.

Etiquette.

1. Bark should not be removed from any living trees. This rule has been broken most often in the case of the white birch. It is better to cut a birch if there is no dead birch available.
2. Get permission of owner.
3. Get permission of owner.
4. Living trees should not be cut. Bark should not be cut from live birches.
5. Trees should not be blazed with an ax. Other means such as paint may be used for laying a trail.
6. There should be no evidence that anyone has been there.
7. Extinguish the fire when through with it and some time before leaving. Use considerable water. Keep stirring ashes and using water until there is no smoke or sizzling. Then cover with soil and weight material down with stones from fireplace.

IV. The Camp Cook

Equipment.

1. Cooking can be done without utensils. A mess kit usually consists of plate, cup, knife, fork, and spoon. A frying pan or metal kettle is handy.
2. Wood ashes and wet sand are excellent for scouring. If you cook over coals, there is less soot. Insisting on clean kettles at the end of each meal is a good custom.
3. Rub a film of soap over the outside of the kettle.
4. A crane holding a kettle over the fire must have a greater weight on the opposite end to prevent a catastrophe. This may be a rock but is safer if held down by a peg. Cut a forked stick. One of the forks is cut short to act as a notch, and the other is sharpened for driving into the ground.
5. The lug pole should be green and about the size of a broom handle.
6. Pothooks should be different lengths so that kettle may be lowered as fire dies down.

Food.

1. See outdoor cooking recipes.
2. Water is an added weight for hiker.
3. The stomach.
4. Something that is substantial. Thus provisioned, you can go on a long hike without continuous munching.
5. Leave "scraps" on flat rock for wild life. Pack sandwiches for the "near future." Most vegetables and meats can be combined for a "mulligan" or a "loaf."
6. Frozen potatoes are sweet. Many people like the flavor. It is not the freezing but the freezing and thawing that spoils them.
7. Dehydrated vegetables are just as nourishing and much lighter in weight.
8. Egg powder and milk powder mean food from which the water has been removed (dehydrated).
9. They have high reputation and low value.
10. Use wax paper and a separate container.
11. Snow increases thirst.

Fire.

1. A bed of coals the size of a chair bottom. The size of the fire depends on what you plan to cook. Greenhorns usually build bonfires.
2. Long before so as to get a bed of coals. Green logs or flat rocks are handy for supporting kettles and frying pans.

3. Glowing coals. Move smoking embers to one side. Prepare vegetables, and so on, while fire is burning to coals.
4. Stones as they hold the heat.

Cooking.

1. A bed of coals. Remove blazing sticks and smoking embers with green sticks.
2. They should all be cooked slowly. Green campers are always in too much of a hurry.
3. Hang it by a chain or wire with a rope top so that it can twist. Then let it unwind slowly. This rotates the meat in front of the coals. A fireplace is a good reflector fire. A drip pan is usually placed underneath and used for basting.
4. None.

In Camp Cooking.

Greenhorns usually do these things	instead of these
1. Stand around and watch the wood gatherers.	1. Join in on getting wood.
2. When they realize their duty, get green and wet wood from the ground.	2. Break lower dead branches from evergreen trees.
3. Leave the duff.	3. Clean away leaves and vegetable matter.
4. Have a small wood pile, just enough to start the fire.	4. Reserve a supply to maintain fire.
5. Put large pieces on bottom or put them on too soon.	5. Have a goodly supply of twigs for kindling.
6. Pile wood horizontally and airtight.	6. Build loosely in a tepee formation.
7. Light fire on top and to leeward.	7. Light fire on bottom and to windward.
8. Cook over a flame.	8. Cook over live coals.
9. Leave papers, cans, banana skins, and string.	9. Leave no trace.
10. Leave smoldering coals.	10. Make absolutely sure that fire is out.

Etiquette and Safety.

1. Burn before putting out fire.
2. Bury or place in rubbish container. It is a good camp rule to require tin cans to be flattened so that wild animals will not get their heads caught and die a gruesome death.

3. Freezing does *not* purify water.
4. By boiling or by chlorinating.
5. Thumbing rides is dangerous and undesirable. In some places, you are liable to arrest for vagrancy.
6. See table on p. 200.

Camp Cooking Contraptions

1. **Automatic Stew Fire.** Dig pit 2 ft. deep and 2 ft. in diameter. Line with rocks. Place green lug pole on Y sticks so as to be over fire pit.

Fig. 48.—"Pine-tree Jim" (James Wilder) supervises the building of a clay oven. Note the chimney outlined by stones.

Start fire and stand 3-ft. firewood on end in pit. As fire burns, the sticks will automatically drop to feed the fire. Have pothooks of different lengths to lower kettle as fire dies down.

2. **Backlog Fire.** Use large log—not a live tree. Use stones or short logs for "fire dogs." If you use a log with a punk center, there is always danger of leaving the fire to fan into a blaze several days afterward. Often used as a reflector fire.

3. **Hunters' or Trappers' Fire.** Two logs arranged in a V so that wind will enter the wide part of the V. If top of logs is hewn, they will be more convenient for kettles and frying pan. V arrangement is suitable for utensils of all sizes.
4. **Log-cabin Fire.** Arrange dry 2-ft. sticks like a log cabin with tepee in center. This assures a good draft. Useful for campfire where light is needed. A quick fire for a bed of coals.
5. **Outdoor Ice Chest.** Metal barrel or can that can be closed. Stand in shade in brook or lake, with two-thirds of barrel out of water. Old shirt or bag—wick around outside. Evaporation from wick cools the barrel. On the farm, we lowered milk and butter into the well.
6. **Outdoor Oven.** Dig into a clay bank or make form with rocks, bent green sticks, old nail keg, or what have you. Cover with clay. Make chimney. Make fire to bake the clay. Rake fire out. Satisfactory stoves or ovens may be made of metal barrels or drums.
7. **Reflector Fire.** Use large log, rock, or bank for reflector. If none is handy, pile logs on top of each other. Brace and chink with sod or clay. Use two logs or stones for andirons. The logs or rocks reflect heat for baking or for warming a lean-to.
8. **Rustic Toaster.** Green hickory is pliable. Obtain forked stick and braid ends for frame. With a dozen or more green sticks the size of a pencil (or a little larger), weave a toaster resembling a coarse tennis racket.
9. **Tepee Fire.** Make fuzz sticks by whittling 10 dry pine sticks so that shavings remain attached. Arrange in tepee with shavings hanging down. Place tinder in center. Light on windward side. Add sticks to tepee as fire gathers headway.
10. **Trench Fire.** Dig trench 3 ft. long, 2 ft. wide, 2 ft. deep. Line with stones Be sure to remove humus near top to prevent underground fire.

Recipes

The object of publishing this little collection of recipes is to put them into convenient and accessible form for outdoor planning. Most of the recipes have been used by campers in varied forms, in the preparation of outdoor meals. They have been planned for a group of eight or a patrol of scouts. The quantities given should vary according to whether fruit and candy are added.

A. The Staff of Life

1. **Baking in a "Spider."** Grease pan. Mix up prepared flour and flatten in pan. Hold over coals to get a bottom crust. Prop pan up before the fire to brown the top or turn bread to brown other side.
2. **Banana Shortcake.** Roast banana in skin on coals. Split, season with salt and lemon juice. Spread on buttered toast.

3. **Beanhole Corn Bread.** 1 cup corn meal; 2 cups hominy; 3 eggs; 1 tsp. butter; 2 tsp. sugar; salt. Mix with milk in Dutch oven. Fit cover tightly. Bury in hot ashes 1 hr.
4. **Berry Flapjacks.** 1 small package prepared flour, 1 egg, salt, and can evaporated milk. Add milk to make above consistency of batter. Add blueberries, wild strawberries, or cut pieces of fruit, as apple. Melted cheese, thinned with milk, makes a good sauce for pancakes.
5. **Big Boy Bannock.** ¼ lb. crisp bacon and crumble, 1 pt. corn meal, ½ pt. flour, 2 tbs. bacon fat, 1 tsp. salt, 2 heaping tsp. baking powder. Mix ingredients and add milk to make thick batter. Grease pan and fry.
6. **Biscuits in "Ten-cent Store Oven."** Get two tins with straight sides and about 1 in. deep. Grease pans. Mix flour and put in one pan, using other for a cover. Can invert and bake on both sides or may cover completely with embers.
7. **Bran Bread.** 2 cups bran, 1 cup flour, 1 tbs. melted butter or bacon fat, 1 tsp. salt, 3 tsp. baking powder, 3 eggs, 1 cup raisins, ½ cup nut meats. Mix dry and then add milk to make a thick batter. Make into patties and bake in reflector.
8. **Corn Batter.** Mix dry, ½ level tsp. salt. Make thick batter with cold milk or water and pour enough to cover a sizzling fry pan. When top is bubbled like a sponge cake, turn.
9. **Corn Bread.** 2 cups corn meal, 2 cups flour, 4 eggs well beaten, 2 tbs. melted butter, 1 tsp. salt, 4 tsp. baking powder. Add enough evaporated milk to make paste and bake brown.
10. **Indian Corn Bread.** 2 cups flour, 3 cups Indian corn meal, 4 heaping tsp. baking powder, 1 tsp. salt, 1 tbs. sugar, 2 eggs well beaten. Mix batter with milk and bake in large shallow pan. A slightly larger tin pan inverted over the first makes a tin-pan oven.
11. **Corn Flapjacks.** Make batter and add half as much canned corn. A dustin' of salt and a bit of sugar. Fry in sizzling pan of bacon drippings. Fold strip of crisp bacon into pancake.
12. **Corn-meal Griddlers.** 2 cups corn meal stirred into 2 cups boiling water; add 2 tbs. shortening, 1 cup milk, 2 tbs. molasses, 2 tsp. salt, 1 cup flour, 4 tsp. baking powder. Fry on hot greased griddle.
13. **Corn-meal Mush.** ¾ cup corn meal. Stir into quart of boiling salted water or milk. Double-boiler arrangement best. Be generous, if you wish leftovers for fried mush. When mush is partly done, pour a 1-in. layer in shallow pan, brown well, and you have "Johnny-cake" original. Before the mush cools, try stirring in ½ cup grated cheese. When cold, slice and brown on hot greased griddle. Not only a surprise, but a balanced meal.
14. **Fried Mush.** Slice corn-meal mush, fry in sputtering pan of fat, and serve with sirup.
15. **Virginy Hoe Cake.** Beat 2 eggs. Add 2 cups water. Stir in 3 cups white corn meal, 8 tsp. baking powder, 1 tsp. salt, 2 tsp. sugar. Cover griddle

with coating of meal. Place spoonfuls of dough on griddle so they will not touch bare griddle. Cook slowly 15 min. Turn for 15 more minutes. Serve hot with butter.

16. **Hominy Hoe Cake.** 1 cup cooked hominy, 1 cup milk, 1 tbs. bacon fat (of course), 1 cup white corn meal, 2 eggs (heap the cups when possible), 1½ tsp. salt. Mix and bake in shallow pan (8 by 4 in.).
17. **Johnny Cake.** 2 cups corn meal, 2 cups white flour, 1 level tsp. salt, 8 tsp. baking powder, 1 egg. Mix well, stir into milk to make thick batter, and bake immediately in hot drying pan. Stand pan vertically in front of fire. Turn in pan to brown both sides.
18. **Reflector Oven Biscuits.** Reflector oven may be made from galvanized iron. Use prepared flour. Pour evaporated milk into package and make small patties with fingers. Have pan well greased. Build a hot fire in front of a rock. Stand oven in front of fire, moving it nearer or away according to the amount of heat. In season, make strawberry shortcake, *i.e.*, split biscuit and add berries crushed with sugar.
19. **Rice Griddlers.** To 2 beaten eggs and 2 cups milk, add 2 cups boiled rice, 2 tbs. shortening, and good tsp. salt. Stir in gradually 2 cups of flour to which has been added 3 good tsp. baking powder. Fry on hot greased griddle. Called rice spoon bread when baked in individual cups.
20. **Snow Biscuits.** Light fluffy snow is best. Use instead of water or milk. Mix ingredients while cold. Bake right after mixing. Have hot fire.
21. **Twisters.** Get sassafras or black birch club about 3 ft. long and 1 in. in diameter. Heat stick and then wind ribbon of dough around it spirally. Place over hot coals. Turn slowly. Bread tubes filled with jelly are "dee-licious." To make dough: 3 fingers of salt, 4 fingers baking powder, 2 hands of flour, and 2 hands of water. Mix in paper bag.

B. Drinks for Campers

1. **Birch Tonic.** Black birch is stronger than the yellow. Steep twigs and bark. Checkerberry leaves give similar wintergreen flavor. Some woodsmen crave it.
2. **Bouillon Tea.** Has more of a reputation than it deserves. A hot drink but not high in nourishment. Easily packed.
3. **Camp Cocoa.** 1½ cups powdered milk. 10 tsp. cocoa. 10 tsp. sugar. Pinch of salt. Mix and carry in a covered can. Add 2 qt. water and boil 5 to 10 min.
4. **Cereal Coffee.** Lacks caffein. Better for younger groups. Can parch and grind almost any grain.
5. **Cocoa Sirup.** Mix ½ cup cocoa with ½ cup sugar and 1 cup of warm water, making a thin paste. Add 1 cup of water. Boil 5 min., being careful not to burn. This sirup, added to 4 cans of evaporated milk and 4 cans of water, will make 1 gal. of cocoa.

6. **Coffee.** 1 heaping tbs. to a pint of cold water for each person and one for the cook. When water comes to boil, stand pot near fire. Settle with cold water or a stick firebrand from fire.
7. **Dandelion Coffee.** Made from lactic root of dandelion. Very bitter. Has characteristics of "bitters" used for medicine. Said to be good for the appetite.
8. **Hemlock Tea.** Use needles of the evergreen. The hemlock that Socrates drank was made from an herb. Lumbermen often use hemlock tea. Labrador tea, sage tea, thoroughwort tea, camomile tea, and so on, ad infinitum, but hemlock tea outranks 'em.
9. **Hike Chocolate.** Sweet milk chocolate makes a good drink as well as hike ration. It is a light-weight energy food, convenient for the pocket on long hike.
10. **Indian Lemonade.** Use red berries of sumac. Too many stems make it tannic in taste. Sweeten with sugar. Acid from sumac berries alleviates thirst if held in mouth on a hike.
11. **Powdered Coffee.** Comes in crystals. Easily handled, satisfying, quickly made.
12. **Sassafras Tea.** Wash root of sassafras. Shave bark of root into cold water. Boil. Add sugar.
13. **Tea.** Do not boil the tea. Pour 1 pt. boiling water onto 1 heaping tsp. tea. Lemon juice makes it more satisfying on the hike.

C. Frills for Campers

1. **Apple Fritters.** Make a batter out of 1 cup of prepared flour, pinch of salt, 1 egg, and enough milk to make thin. Pare and cut tart apples into batter. Stir and drop by spoonfuls into hot fat. Fry brown and coat with powdered sugar.
2. **Chili Con Carne.** Chopped beef, peppers, onions, and tomatoes. Salt and pepper. Simmer for several hours. Add puff balls or coral mushrooms in season (if you know them). Serve with beanhole beans.
3. **Cottage Cheese.** Heat skim milk and buttermilk at 90°F. until firmly coagulated. Pour onto clean white cotton cloth. The "whey" drains off and leaves a "curd." Salt the "curd."
4. **Flag Root Candy.** Dice the root of sweet flag. Boil in slightly salted water to get out strong taste. Drain and drop into a sirup (equal parts of water and sugar). Allow to simmer.
5. **Frogs' Legs.** First get the frogs. Night torching is a good charm. Soak in cold salt water. Drain, dry, roll in flour, fry slowly. Good as chicken. Really a tidbit.
6. **Fruit Jumble.** Cover dried apricots and prunes with water and soak overnight. In morning, simmer over coals or bury kettle in beanhole. Acid desserts are always more satisfying to campers.
7. **Glazed Apples.** Make a sirup of Karo and water. ½ pt.-can dark Karo plus 2 lb. sugar well cooked will glaze 20 apples. Keep sirup warm

over fire. Spike a tart red apple on a stick and dip apple into the sirup.

8. **Hike Ration.** If you are going on a long hike or mountain climbing, you can carry a hike ration. Put dried fruit—prunes, apricots, raisins, nut meats—in pocket and a cake of chocolate with a few crackers.
9. **Indian Pudding.** 1 qt. milk, 2/3 cup cornmeal, 2 tsp. ginger, 1 cup molasses, 2 tsp. salt. Cook milk and meal in double boiler 20 min. Add other ingredients. Pour into buttered pudding dish and bake slowly 2 hr. If any cream is around, use it. Oh, boy! Add butter and 2 eggs for "delicates."
10. **Mint Sauce.** To 2 cups of water add juice of half a lemon and 5 tbs. sugar. Add 2 cups of mint leaves. Bring mixture to a boil.
11. **Snow Pudding.** Dry, mealy snow best. Mix with 2 cans condensed milk. Flavor with 1 tsp. lemon extract or vanilla. Add grated pineapple. Shake or stir 10 min. in covered container. Pack in large container with snow and salt.
12. **"Some Mores."** Two graham crackers for outsiders. Square of chocolate to fit. Toasted marshmallow. Repeat order until satisfied.
13. **Sweet Chocolate Sandwich.** Put between two slices of buttered bread and toast.

D. Substantials for Campers

1. **Baked Stuffed Peppers.** Cut out the core of 10 peppers and cook in boiling water about 10 min. Fry 1 lb. hamburger steak flavored with onion. When done, mix with cracker crumbs or cold potato or leftover vegetables or can of corn. Season and moisten with milk. Stuff peppers and bake in reflector oven or clay oven.
2. **Barbecue.** Dig a pit 3 ft. wide and 3 ft. deep, and as long as necessary. Put in small rocks to a depth of about 20 in. Fill with dry wood and burn until getting coals. Place iron bars over pit of coals to hold meat. Make a sauce using water, butter, vinegar, salt, pepper, tomato sauce, celery sauce, and cayenne to taste. Tie rag on stick and use as a swab. Baste meat, turning often. The slower the meat cooks the better. Time depends upon size of meat. 6 lb. of boned lamb should suffice or two 3 lb. prepared chickens.
3. **Buffalo Steak.** Bed of hard-wood coals. Rub salt and pepper into both sides of slabs of tender beef (4 lbs.). Fan ash lint off bed of coals. Throw steak on coals. In a minute, or more, turn steak over on fresh coals. Brush off charcoal, cut in small servings, and drop into pan of melted butter. Serve between split bun with sliced tomato and onion. (There's no way to make tough beef tender unless you club it, and club steak won't do for this.)
4. **Camp Corn Chowder (The 3-C's).** Dice 1/2 lb. salt pork and fry. Dice 3 medium-sized onions and sauté in pork. Dice 4 potatoes and boil in as little water as possible. When nearly done, add 2 cans of corn and 1 qt. milk, stir and heat (not boil).

5. **Cap'n's Toast.** Chop a small onion and cook slowly in butter. Add flour mixed with salt and cayenne, and stir until smooth. Add small can of tomato soup, 1 tbs. mustard, ½ lb. sliced cheese. Cook in double boiler until smooth. Add well-beaten egg, stirring until thickened. Serve on toasted bread.
6. **Clam Bake.** Line a hole in the ground (2.5 ft. deep and in diameter) with stones as large as the two fists. Keep a big fire in it for a couple of hours until the stones are very hot. Remove unburned chunks of wood. Quickly cover embers with layers as follows: moist rockweed (or seaweed); potatoes (small); corn in husks; thin layer of seaweed; clams; thick layer of seaweed. Let steam about 45 min. or until the clams gape open. Outside husk of corn should be removed, leaving just one layer of husks. Tie loose ends with a piece of husk.
7. **Club Sandwich.** Toasted bread, lettuce, tomato sliced, bacon or ham, salt, pepper, mustard, or mayonnaise.
8. **Cottage Cheese Sandwich.** Spread cheese on two slices of bread. Moisten with chili sauce. Put two slices of crisp bacon between and press bread together. Toast over coals. Tasty and filling.
9. **Dogs in a Blanket.** Skewer thin slices of bacon wrapped spirally around frankfurters. Roast over hot coals. Turn frequently to save drippings. Then baste and sear it on all sides.
10. **Dog on the Rind.** Slit a frankfurter lengthwise and press a string of pork into it, using a skewer to hold it in place. Roast over a fire, turning frequently.
11. **Emu à la "Pine Tree Jim."** Line a hole 5 ft. long by 3 ft. deep by 3 ft. wide with rocks. Have a good supply of oak or apple wood. Lay fire and start early (2 hr. before cooking) to get hot coals. With shovel, move most coals to end of pit. Cover coals at lower end with leaves. Place lamb, turkey, chicken, or small pig on poultry wire and lower onto leaves at lower end of pit. Place vegetables (covered with clay)—potatoes, corn, carrots, onions, apples—alongside. Cover with rhubarb leaves or lawn mowings and then burlap. Rake back coals. Seal with foot of earth. Leave for 5 to 6 hr. Remove coverings. Lift out with wire. If meat is large, wrap hot stones inside. I first saw this done by James A. Wilder, the first Chief of Sea Scouts.
12. **Fish Cakes.** Remove bones from boiled salt codfish. Mix with equal parts of mashed potato. Season with salt and pepper. Mix in thoroughly a well-beaten egg to hold cakes together. Fry in deep fat or pan fry.
13. **Fried Eggs on a Rock.** Place a dry flat rock in coals. Be sure rock is dry so that moisture will not explode it in your face. Igneous rocks are safer than sandstone. In ½ hour, rake rock out of ashes, level rock, brush off, and make triangle fence with bacon. If rock is right temperature, the bacon fat will creep inside "fence." Break egg inside triangle. Can be turned or served sunny side up in a sandwich. A slice of toast with center out for a fence and placed on top of slice of bacon is a variation.

14. **Goulash.** 1 qt. tomatoes, 1 qt. (2 cans) corn, 4 good-sized boiled potatoes, 6 slices of bacon, 2 medium-sized onions, salt and pepper to taste. Serve on pilot biscuit or in tin cup. May put in any leftovers in vegetables or meat. Quickly prepared, filling, and good on a cold day. It is well to cut up onions and fry with bacon before adding other materials.
15. **Gypsy Bake.** Clean fish, leaving outside skin and scales. Cover with thin layer of clay. Place in a bed of coals from ¾ to 1 hr. Clay oven may be made. Make form out of rocks or green sticks. Plaster with clay. Dry with fire, filling in cracks. Bake on a flat rock closing door and chimney.
16. **Hunter's Stew.** Use an enamel pail. Cut up 6 slices of bacon on bottom of pail. Put pail over thin layer of coals (not flaming fire or deep coals). Cut up and brown 6 onions. Braise 1 lb. top round steak cut into 1-in. squares. Stir or "jiggle" often. Put in carrots sliced very thin. Pour in boiling water. Cut up 4 large potatoes and 2 parsnips. Six green peppers may be added. Wild carrot root, horseradish, or wild onion may be used for seasoning instead of cultivated material. Add salt and pepper. Let simmer for 1 or 2 hr. Thicken with flour or oatmeal. Serve in tin cup. Excellent on cold day.
17. **Hunter's Stew.** Cut 2 lb. meat into small squares. Sear meat in frying pan. Add 1 lb. dried vegetables. Cover mixture with water and allow to simmer for a long time. Add salt and pepper.
18. **Kabob.** Get green stick as large as small finger. Rub salt and pepper into steak. Impale 1½-in. slice of steak, 1½-in. square of bacon, slice of apple, and ½ an onion layer obtained by cutting the onion vertically and making a hole in the center with the curved blade of the scout knife. Repeat these in order as many times as needed for a meal. Roast over coals.
19. **Lumber-boss Stew.** 1 can tomato soup, 1 can pea soup, ¼ lb. bacon diced and fried, 4 onions diced and fried. Mix and serve with pilot crackers.
20. **Planked Fish.** Split fish and clean. Do not scale. Peg to flat board. Stand in front of bed of coals. Strips of bacon draped over adds to flavor.
21. **Rarebit—"Rabbit."** Melt 1 tbs. butter. Add 1 heaping tbs. flour. Level 1 tsp. mustard. ½ tsp. salt. Cut up ½ lb. mild cheese and add 1 can tomato soup. Melt all together and thin with milk. Serve on crackers or toast.
22. **Rock Fry.** Heat a flat rock in hot ashes and fry steak or ham on it. Eggs may be held on by a triangle, bacon fence. Pancakes from a package of prepared flour may be browned and turned when the cake has distinctly bubbled. Grease rock before pouring on batter and when turning it. The fire may be built under thin rocks. A steak between two hot rocks is quicker.
23. **Rum Tum Tiddy.** 1½ lb. cheese (Young America), 1 good-sized pepper (green), spoonful butter, 1 small can tomato soup, 1 small can evaporated

milk, 1 tsp. flour to thicken, pinch of salt. Melt butter in pan. Cut up cheese and melt in pan. Stir *constantly* to prevent sticking. Pour in can of soup. Mix flour with milk gradually. Pour into mixture. Add salt and red pepper. Stir until smooth. Serve hot on toasted bread.

24. **Sandwich Meal.** Fry 3 slices of bacon. Drop 2 eggs directly from shell into fat. Put bacon, lettuce leaf, and 2 eggs between 2 slices of bread.
25. **Slum Gully.** More expensive than goulash. 2 cans tuna fish (1-lb. tins), 2 cans peas, 1 pt. cream sauce seasoned, 1 can pimento, 4 hard-boiled eggs.

FIG. 49.—Rock tripe (*Umbilicaria dillenii*). This picturesque lichen saved the lives of the explorers on the Franklin Arctic expedition. The plant is more filling than nourishing, however. (*Photograph by Robert Coffin.*)

Serve on pilot crackers. To make cream sauce, use 2 tbs. of butter (or bacon fat), 2 tbs. of flour, and 2 cups of milk.

26. **Tuna Omelet.** 2 cans of fish, 1 lb. cracker crumbs, salt, pepper, and butter to taste. Mix well. Add 1 egg and enough milk to moisten. Try out 3 slices of bacon. Turn mixture into hot fat and cook as an omelet.

E. Vegetables

1. **Baked Potatoes.** Does not mean spuds smoked and eaten raw. Cover medium-sized potatoes with clay. Cover with 3 in. of glowing embers. Rake one out and crack open in 40 min. Test with sliver.

2. **Beanhole Beans.** Soak 1 qt. dried beans in cold water for 8 hr. Boil in kettle until soft or until skins crack. Put beans in pot or Dutch oven. Level tsp. of salt and ½ tsp. of soda and 1 cup molasses. Cover with boiling water. Lay 3 slices of bacon or ½ lb. salt pork on top; then add layer of sliced onions. Fasten cover tightly. Bury in deep bed of coals overnight.
3. **Puff Ballette.** Dice a puffball while it's white (before it's brown and ripe). Cook in butter in frying pan. Add 2 eggs and stir slowly. Serve on buttered toast. Season with pepper and salt and a little onion.

FIG. 50.—Puffballs (*Scleroderma aurantium*). Fry in butter and serve with steak. (*Photograph by Robert Coffin.*)

4. **Rice.** Beginners always use too much. Remember ⅓ cup of rice will absorb 1 whole cup of water. Add salt to 1 qt. boiling milk or water. Start with ½ cup of rice and add slowly to boiling water so it will not stop boiling. After 20 min., drain water. Mix with seedless raisins. Add butter and sugar to taste.
5. **Roast Corn.** Remove outer green husks and silk; break nub off end. Tie yellow husks over broken end. Dip in water and cover with glowing ashes for 1 hr. Or roll on a ¼-in. mesh galvanized wire near coals.
6. **Scalloped Parsnips.** Mash 1 lb. boiled parsnips. Mix in 2 tbs. of butter, 1 tsp. grated cheese, salt, and dash cayenne. Add milk to make creamy consistency. Pour into greased scallop shells, sprinkle tops with more grated cheese, and bake 10 min. Blends of pure carrots, turnips, potatoes, and so on, for variety.
7. **Stuffed Onions.** Half boil 8 large onions. Drain and remove centers. Mash centers with 4 tbs. cold hamburger, 4 tbs. grated cheese, 2 tbs. bacon fat or butter, 1 tsp. salt, and fill onions with mixture. Place in pan. Keep basting tops with fat.

EIGHT TYPE MENUS FOR OUTDOOR COOKERY*
(See recipes for amounts and procedure)

Considerations	1	2	3	4	5	6	7	8
Process	Boiling and stewing	Roasting	Frying	Stewing	Baking	Braising and stewing	Roasting	Roasting
Main stand-by or substantials	Goulash	Kabob	Bacon and eggs (breakfast)	Slum gully	Beanhole beans	Hunter's stew	Barbecue	Buffalo steak
Staff of life	Twisters	Reflector oven biscuits	Toast	"Spider" bread	Big boy bannock	Johnny cake	Berry biscuit	Snow biscuits in tin-pan oven
Camp drinks	Camp cocoa	Tea	Coffee	Hike chocolate	Bouillon tea	Powdered coffee	Cereal coffee	Coffee
Dessert	Snow pudding	Glazed apples	Rice and raisins	Lemon wiggle	Fruit jumble	Banana short cake	Arrowroot	"Some mores"
Fire	Automatic stew	Reflector and open trench	On a rock, in a paper bag	Backlog and crane	Clay oven	Trapper's tin-can cookery	Trench	Community
Forage (in season)	Pothooks, lug pole, black birch	Sassafras tea	Milkweed greens	Clams. Gathering nuts	Frogs' legs or roast apples	Blueberry duff	Planked fish or turtle soup	Skunk cabbage
One-sider	Baked potato	Dehydrated corn	Desiccated codfish	Hominy	Chili con carne	Hardtack	Popcorn	Sugaring off
Budget for eight	$2	$4	$2	$3	$3	$2	$4	$5
Kamp kink device	Camp pail and pot hangers	Tin-can reflector	Rustic toaster	Tin-can craft	Paul Revere lantern	Camp coffee pot	Improvised popper	Homemade percolator
Entertainment	Tracking	Homemade weather bureau	Winter photography	Packing	Handcraft	Scout's own	Skyscraping	Old scout a guest
Procedure	Group	Individual	Individual	Group	Mass	Individual	Group	Mass
Special kit	Nest outfit	Individual mess kit	Without utensils	Individual cup and spoon	Bake oven	Dutch oven	Grill	Steak tosser
Frill	Chili sauce	Olives	Marmalade	Pimento	Catsup	Pickles	Piccalilli	Tomato

* The suggestive table has been arranged to give variety of experience as to budget, foods, cooking, and frills. The knack of outdoor menus once obtained, there are hundreds of pleasing combinations. Like a railroad timetable, they often have to be changed without notice. Sassafras root cannot be easily mined when the ground is frozen, and snow biscuits cannot be made without snow. Camping means adaptable but pleasant outdoor living.

8. **Sweet Potato Pone (Dixie Style).** Grind up raw sweet potato in meat chopper to the amount of 2 qt. Add tablespoonful of lard and teaspoonful of allspice. Mix with molasses to thick dough. Bake in cake tin.
9. **Turnip Purée.** Dice 4 medium-sized turnips. Boil 20 min. in 1 pt. water to which has been added ½ tbs. butter, 1 tsp. brown sugar, salt and pepper to taste. Mix ½ cup rice, pea, potato, or barley flour with 1½ pt. milk, and add to turnip mixture. Bring to boil, stirring all the time. Simmer gently for 5 min.
10. **Vegetable Chowder.** ½ lb. dried lima beans, 1 lb. dried vegetables, 1 onion, 1 tbs. fat, 1 tbs. flour, 1 cup milk, pepper, and salt. Soak beans overnight (or use 2 cans of lima beans and 2 cans diced carrots) and cook slowly until tender. Brown onion in fat and add to beans and carrots and cook for ½ hour. Add blended flour and milk, pepper, and salt.
11. **Tasty Spring Greens.** ½ peck fresh dandelion leaves washed clean. 6 strips of bacon fried crisp. Pour hot fat and crumbled bacon over the greens and mix well.

Rotation of Camp Duties for a Group of Eight

At each meeting, each person moves up one number, number 1 going to 2, number 8 to 1, and so on. This system gives opportunity

Name	Preduties	Cooking assignment	Post duties
1	"Chief": purchasing agent; delivers food and assists commissary	Gives necessary instruction. Supervises activities. Takes notes for the future	Inventory, accounting, criticism, and summation
2	Quartermaster or commissary: gives out grub-stake rations and assists purchase	Forages and prepares dish	Assists sanitary police
3	Equipment sergeant: provides kit and checks it out	Assists cook	Checks in kit with cook packing
4	Stoker: provides fuel	Firekeeper	Inspection of fire out and campground
5	"Cookie": comes prepared to cook	Chief cook: cooks main dish	Packs kit as sergeant checks
6	Water boy: provides safe supply	Prepares drink	Sanitary police: cleans up. Places leftovers for birds
7	Old scout: prepares new camping device	Prepares bread	Demonstrates device
8	Ranger: lays log cabin tepee fire for council	Prepares dessert	Responsible for campfire, program, and story

to share in work and in experience. Camping is cooperative living. This is why some people say, if you want to know a person, go camping with him. The real test of outdoor cooking is the food. Also—a chain is no stronger than its weakest link. A good cook, for example, is no better than his fire. If the commissary has no salt, the whole group suffers.

Check List of Regular Equipment for Party of Eight Cooking Out

8 mess kits—each consisting of

☐ 1 cup	☐ 1 spoon	☐ 3 vials—sugar, salt, pepper
☐ 1 plate	☐ 1 knife	☐ Soap and wet cloth
☐ 1 fork	☐ 1 small frying pan	☐ Matches

Community kit (nest equipment—2 sets of 4-party size best)

☐ 1 large frying pan	☐ 3 paring knives	☐ 3 kettles
☐ 1 coffee pot	☐ 1 large knife	☐ 4 serving plates
☐ 1 can opener	☐ 3 tablespoons	☐ 1 Dutch oven
☐ 1 pack basket		

Staples on hand—labeled screw-top containers when possible. Refill for each trip

☐ Pepper shaker	☐ Bacon	☐ First-aid kit
☐ Salt shaker	☐ Pork	
☐ Corn meal	☐ Butter	
☐ Prepared flour	☐ Sirup	
☐ Sugar	☐ Vinegar	
☐ Cocoa	☐ Milk powder or evaporated milk	
☐ Coffee	☐ Potatoes	
☐ Tea	☐ Onions	
☐ Raisins	☐ Eggs	

Overnight for each individual

☐ 3 blankets	☐ 2 candles
☐ 2 ponchos	☐ 1 flashlight or lantern
☐ 2 towels	☐ Toilet paper
☐ 1 ax (not necessary if packing on back)	☐ 6 horse-blanket pins
	☐ 1 tent (not necessary)
	☐ 1 shovel (a luxury if hiking)

Sign name here________________Date checked out______Date checked in______

Tin-can Camping

In August, 1931, Mrs. Vinal and I camped on St. Mary's Lake in Glacier National Park. Our tent was about 50 miles from the nearest chain store. We had to "tote" our food. When one is one's own pack horse, one travels light. That is the reason that I had to resort to tin-can camping.

It has been said that, if city people should lose their can openers, they would starve to death in a week. If I had lost mine, I would not only have run short on food but would have lost good storage tins, cooking utensils, lights, shower baths, and all.

Many of the sketches showing the various uses of tin cans (see page 93) explain themselves. During rainy days or "time off," try tin-can handcraft. Here's hoping that you enjoy it as much as we did.

Shower Baths. A gallon can will be ample. Make holes in the bottom with a nail. Hang on a limb, fill with warm water, and you will be surprised to see how far a gallon of water will go. You can siphon from a can higher up if you want reserve. Make the second can cold water, if you want to do it right.

Windy-night Lantern. Make a hole through the side of a tin can. The candle is pushed up as it burns.

Reflector Oven. This is best made from a square-sided tin. One side is propped up for the biscuit pan. The sides of the tin are bent to an angle of 45 deg. The upper one reflects the heat onto the top of the biscuits, and the lower one tends to brown them on the bottom. Prepared flour is very satisfactory. If the fire is made in front of a rock, the heat will be reflected into the baker, and the biscuits will be ready in 10 min.

Ice Chest. The cover that snugly inserts is nearer bearproof. Of course the bear can use his toenails for a can opener if he really wants to. Stones were placed against the can to discourage any raids that bears might have in mind. The old shirt served as a wick. The evaporating water kept the ice chest several degrees cooler.

Birdhouse. One should not make a birdhouse out of tin and just leave it at that. Tin absorbs the heat and would almost "roast" the birds. It should be heavily thatched. Don't forget to make drainage holes. A funnel roof gives the proper slant for drainage.

Designs on the candleshade may be made with a small nail. The light coming through the small nail holes gives a pleasing effect. Make the sketch before you start punching.

Mrs. Vinal thought my mousetrap was "worse than the mice." I will tell you about it, and you can judge for yourself. A piece of haywire was run through a tin-can cover. This was placed over a pail of water. A long rock was just balanced over the tin. An inclined board was placed against the pail to serve as a ladder for the mouse. He was invited up the ladder with bits of bait. A large tempting morsel was placed at the far end of the tin.

The trap was so finely balanced that, when the mouse got out on the end of the tin, his weight was just enough to make the tin turn over. As a result the stone, bait, and mouse went plunging into the watery depths below. The commotion was startling, especially if one was in deep slumber, but it was quiet for the rest of the night.

CHAPTER IX

SUPPLEMENTARY SUGGESTIONS FOR EXPERIENCES IN THE SEVERAL FIELDS OF NATURE LORE

BIRDS

Birds are feathered animals. Frogs invented fingers and toes, but birds invented feathers and have monopoly on the output. Fish

Fig. 51.—Three young great horned owls. Naturalists should not jump at conclusions. It is most unusual for owls to lay three eggs. These owls never took anything from near-by farms. The food was entirely rats, mice, skunk, weasel, and many rabbits. (*Courtesy of C. M. Shipman, Willoughby, Ohio, who made a 4-year study of the great horned owl.*)

invented scales, but birds have them on their legs. There are "flying" fish and "flying" reptiles. Although flying is characteristic of birds, some of the larger ones have lost the art. Being a toothless race, they pick up pebbles and have a grist mill in the form of a gizzard. A nest is a nursery but not a home. Because birds are insect and weed-seed eaters, they are very useful. This includes 95 per cent of the hawks, which are our best rattraps. Protecting the birds is an economic necessity. Their songs are thrown in for good measure. The hundreds of bird enthusiasts in every city make the study one of our most important nature activities. It is a wholesome, instructive enjoyment.

Launching bird study[1] (September to March).

Set a hen on a dozen eggs, or, better yet, obtain an electric incubator. Open an egg each day to show the development of the chick.
Discuss the feeding of birds. Survey the neighborhood for trees, shrubs, and herbs that attract birds. (See section on Trees.)
Have a sunflower contest. Prizes for tallest, largest, heaviest. Feed seeds to birds.
Make a habitat group—as red-wing blackbirds with proper background of cattails, and so on.
Make a Who's Who in Bird Study in your community.
Start a Junior Audubon Club. Write National Audubon Society, 1130 Fifth Avenue, New York City, for set of literature.
Make a diary about a nesting pair of birds, experiences at a birdbath, from egg to chick, an orphan bird, or spring migration.

Write to:

Superintendent of Documents, Washington, D.C., for price list 21 on *Fish and Wildlife*.
National Audubon Society, 1130 Fifth Avenue, New York City, for list of publications.
Director, U.S. Fish and Wildlife Service, Washington, D.C., for bulletins on birds.

Obtain:

Recordings of bird calls from your record dealer.
Field glasses.
Bird charts, Massachusetts Audubon Society, 174A Newbury Street, Boston, or South Great Road, South Lincoln, Mass.
Bird Pictures—*Birds of New York*, by Howard Eaton. New York State Museum, Albany. Excellent plates, unbound.

[1] For further suggestions, see pp. 156 and 172.

Library for Bird Study

Reference Shelf:

Chapman. *What Bird Is That?* (colored illustrations), D. Appleton-Century Company, Inc., 144 pp.

Matthews. *Wild Birds and Their Music*, G. P. Putnam's Sons, 1921, 325 pp.

Stories to Tell:

Burgess. *The Bird Book for Children*, Little, Brown & Company, 1919, 351 pp.

Mathews. *The Book of Birds for Young People*, G. P. Putnam's Sons, 1921, 323 pp.

Patch. *Bird Stories*, Little, Brown & Company, 1921, 211 pp.

Handcraft. *A Bird Furniture Exhibit.* Bird furniture is desirable for the city home grounds, the playground or park, the camp or farm.

The bird furniture contest should be announced near the first of the year and a date set for an indoor exhibit (about Mar. 1st).

Dimensions for Bird Boxes*

Species	Floor of cavity, in.	Depth of cavity, in.	Entrance above floor, in.	Diameter of entrance, in.	Height above ground, ft.
Bluebird	5 by 5	8	6	1½	5 to 10
Robin	6 by 8	8	(†)	(†)	6 to 15
Chickadee	4 by 4	8 to 10	8	1⅛	6 to 15
Tufted titmouse	4 by 4	8 to 10	8	1¼	6 to 15
White-breasted nuthatch	4 by 4	8 to 10	8	1¼	12 to 20
House wren	4 by 4	6 to 8	1 to 6	⅞	6 to 10
Tree swallow	5 by 5	6	1 to 6	1½	10 to 15
Barn swallow	6 by 6	6	(†)	(†)	8 to 12
Martin	6 by 6	6	1	2½	15 to 20
Song sparrow	6 by 6	6	(‡)	(‡)	1 to 3
Phoebe	6 by 6	6	(†)	(†)	8 to 12
Crested flycatcher	6 by 6	8 to 10	8	2	8 to 20
Flicker	7 by 7	16 to 18	16	2½	6 to 20
Redheaded woodpecker	6 by 6	12 to 15	12	2	12 to 20
Hairy woodpecker	6 by 6	12 to 15	12	1½	12 to 20
Downy woodpecker	4 by 4	8 to 10	8	1¼	6 to 20
Screech owl	8 by 8	12 to 15	12	3	10 to 20
Sparrow hawk	8 by 8	12 to 15	12	3	10 to 30
Saw-whet owl	6 by 6	10 to 12	10	2½	12 to 20
Barn owl	10 by 18	15 to 18	4	6	12 to 18
Wood duck	10 by 18	10 to 15	3	6	4 to 20

* *Farmers' Bulletin* 609.
† One or more sides open. ‡ All sides open.

In the case of bird boxes, specifications as to size of floor area, height of box, and height and size of opening should be available.

The judging team might include a carpenter, a birdman, an artist, and a teacher. Each judge should fill out the score card independently.

The contest could be limited to such items as houses for the wren, bluebird, tree swallow, and woodpeckers. Robin shelters might be added.

The contest could be extended to include the renting of the house and a diary of the occupants.

References on Birdhouses

Fish and Wildlife Service Leaflets:

269, How to Control Vagrant Cats.
CB 1, Attracting Birds.
CB 14, Homes for Birds.

Other Sources:

BAXTER. *Bird House Architecture,* Bruce Publishing Company.
Good Bungalows for Good Birds. Southern Cypress Manufacturers Association, Jacksonville, Fla.
SIEPERT. *Bird Houses Boys Can Build.* Manual Arts Press.
SOLAR. *Handcraft Bird Houses,* 1923, Bruce Publishing Company.

SCORECARD FOR JUDGING BIRDHOUSES

Each item may be given a score of 1 or 2 points according to whether the builder meets the requirements completely or not. If they are not met at all, they should receive no credit.

Name of bird for which the house was definitely built______.
Correct size of opening (Perches are unnecessary)______.
Opening centrally placed and correct height above floor______.
Correct floor area______.
Good ventilation, higher than entrance____Good provision for drainage____.
Convenient arrangement for cleaning out______.
Device for attaching to a tree or to a building______.
Soft color to harmonize with environment______.
Originality (simple, not extreme)______.

Skill and Workmanship.

Careful measurements______No splitting or splinters at bored holes______.
Tightly fitting joints______Nails do not split wood______.

House draughtproof across nest________House rainproof________________.
Cleanout door fits tightly________Interior free from nails and splinters____.
House made of good material (Wood, and not metal, which conducts heat)__.
Wood smoothed and sandpapered before painting____________________.

Card.

With builder's name, grade, bird built for, and showing where house is to be placed (Tree, building, post)________________________.
How high from the ground________How will it be protected from cats______.
In what direction will it face to avoid storms?____________________.
What will be around the house (Opening, shrubs, trees)_______________.
TOTAL SCORE__________________.

GARDENING

Gardening is an educational enterprise of a high order. Home gardens are the best. Landless children may have window boxes.

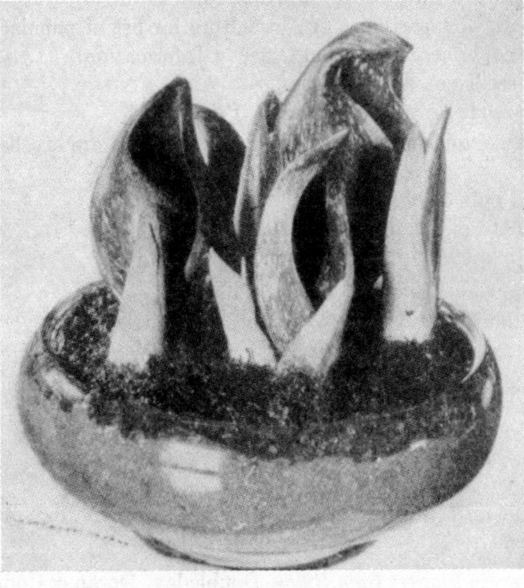

Fig. 52.—Is gardening a lesson in health, cooperation with the home, citizenship, vocational stimulation, dissemination of knowledge, a worthy use of leisure, character building, or an experience in all seven? Worthy activities can stand the seven-point test. (*Photograph by Robert Coffin.*)

Tin-can gardens are the last resort. Gardening has too often failed in the past because it has just been a combination of arithmetic and hard work. There is plenty of evidence that gardening can be recreation.

Plan a goodly mixture of discovery, experimentation, service, pride, and beauty.

Detroit is an example of a city in which gardening has been carried on by the Department of Recreation.

Launching.

Issue an invitation to a garden club, to make and plant a window box, to landscape the playground, to make a pool or rockery, to visit a greenhouse, to take a garden tour.

Materials for Gardening.

Write to U.S. Department of Agriculture for list of popular publications (single copies available from Office of Information).
Write to seedsmen and nurseries.
Purchase seeds by pound rather than package.
Beans, peas, squash, and corn seeds and seedlings are excellent for indoor study.
Bulbs and pots or bulb bowls.
Grow tomato plants for transplanting.
Bulletins available from Department of Agriculture:

G 7, Growing Vegetables in Town and City.
G 9, Suburban and Farm Vegetable Gardens.

Write state agricultural college and county agent for lists of publications.

Library for Gardeners

Reference Shelf:

NORTON. *Spring Flowers from Bulbs*, Doubleday, Doran & Company, Inc.
MEIER. *School and Home Gardens*, Ginn and Company.
WAUGH. *The Natural Style in Landscape Gardening*, Richard G. Badger.
WEED and EMERSON. *Garden Book*, Charles Scribner's Sons, 1909, 334 pp.

Stories to Tell:

Any history of the Mormons. How the Franklin Gulls saved the Crops of the Mormons.

Biographical Dictionary. Millardet and Bordeaux Mixture.
DEFOE. *Robinson Crusoe*, Robinson Crusoe's Garden.
EDGAR. *The Story of a Grain of Wheat*, D. Appleton-Century Company, Inc.
History of Ireland. The Irish Famine.
LONGFELLOW. *Poems*, The Birds of Killingworth.

TRIPS

To the right of each, note where there is a local example. To the left, write proposed date of trip.

Calendar		*Where to Go*
________	Formal and informal landscaping	________
________	Flower show	________
________	Greenhouse	________
________	Community garden with plots	________
________	Rock garden	________
________	Nurseries	________
________	Rose garden	________
________	Seed store	________
________	Sunken garden	________
________	Water garden	________
________	Wild-flower garden	________
________	Collecting rocks and minerals	________
________	Collecting seeds	________

Outstanding Garden Projects. 1. *Garden Center.* The garden clubs of Cleveland took over an abandoned boathouse in the Fine Arts Garden and arranged it as an attractive garden center. A continuous program of lectures and exhibits adapted to the season attract a large number of people. The clubs have furnished a garden library. The center serves as a plant clinic and is a continuous source of inspiration to the home gardener. School children frequently visit the garden center. Pittsburgh and other cities are adopting the idea.

2. *The Garden Tour.* This has been in vogue for several years. Many communities have such a pilgrimage. The gardens of Old Virginia are visited annually. Homeowners who have attractive gardens are included in the itinerary. Conspicuous numbers are placed near the street, and a ticket of admission with corresponding numbers is punched as the visitor enters the grounds. The proceeds are used for some worthy cause.

3. *Cultural Gardens of the Nations.* Perhaps Cleveland is outstanding in this respect. The Shakespeare Garden has plants mentioned in

the writings of Shakespeare. Nationality groups have planted and dedicated a Hebrew Garden, Germanic Garden, Italian Garden.

4. *Best Garden Contest.* Usually run by a newspaper. Must enter contest in spring. City divided into districts. Home gardens winning first prize in the district 2 years in succession not allowed to compete in

FIG. 53.—A spider's web consists of cables, roadways, and sticky threads to catch insects. Identify the kinds of thread. (*Photograph by Robert Coffin.*)

district contest but may enter city-wide contest. Gas stations, schools, playgrounds may contest in classes.

INSECTS AND SPIDERS

Launching an Insect Club.

Have a honey party.
Plan an insect circus.
Raise some silkworms (will eat dandelion leaves if they have never tasted lettuce or mulberry).
Show film on housefly, honeybee, or silkworm.
Observation beehives are sold by the A. I. Root Co., Medina, Ohio.

Insect Study Material.

Write to the Department of Agriculture for the following bulletins that you need:

L 390, The House Fly.
G 24, Clothes Moths and Carpet Beetles.
G 28, Ants in the Home and Garden.

Write Perry Picture Company, Malden, Mass., for list of colored pictures (send 35 cents for complete catalogue).

Write to U.S. Bureau of Entomology for list of bulletins.

FIG. 54.—Truth is stranger than fiction. What is the truth, and what is fiction in the case of dragonflies? What distinguishes this species (*Plathemis lydia*) from all other dragonflies? (*Photograph by Robert Coffin.*)

Library for Insect Study

References:

COMSTOCK. *Ways of the Six-footed,* Comstock Publishing Company, 1903, 152 pp.
LUTZ. *Field Book of Insects,* G. P. Putnam's Sons, 1921, 562 pp.
WEED. *Insect Ways,* D. Appleton-Century Company, Inc., 1930, 325 pp.

Stories:

Robert Bruce and the Spider.
DUPUY. *Our Insect Friends and Foes,* John C. Winston Company, 1925.

HAWKSWORTH. *Clever People with Six Legs.* Charles Scribner's Sons, 1924, 294 pp.

Life of Henri Fabre, *The Insects' Homer.*

FIG. 55.—*Thalessa lunator.* The only correct name is the scientific name. Consult a good insect book, and be able to tell why this insect is useful. (*Photograph by Robert Coffin.*)

National Geographical Magazine, Vol. 28, 1915 and *Asia Magazine* for February, 1931. "Jerusalem Locust Plague."

PATCH. *Hexapod Stories*, Atlantic Monthly Press Publications, 1920, 178 pp.

PETS

A pet club or "activities with animals" is one of the best means of teaching cleanliness, correct food habits, parental care, dependability, life history, and conservation. One learns to be kind by practicing kindness. For this reason, the care of animals is a laboratory experience in humane education. This experience also offers an unusual opportunity in sex-character education. Leaders interested in this basic study may obtain help and advice from the American Social Health Association, 1790 Broadway, New York City.

Launching a Pet Club.[1]

Make a neighborhood pet survey.
Have a pet show or parade.

[1] For further suggestions, see pp. 77–81.

Animal Study Material. Check items you will need. Have children write the letters.

Perry Picture Company, Malden, Mass. 7 by 9 in., sepia or natural colors. Send 35 cents for complete catalogue.
Plaster of Paris or babbitt metal for casting animal tracks.
Linoleum for block printing.

Fig. 56.—The playground pet show has many concomitant values. Sanitation, humaneness, health, cooperation, balanced meals, and the story of life itself are fully as valuable as knowledge that was once considered the only royal road to power. (*Photograph courtesy of V. K. Brown, Director of Recreation, Chicago Park District.*)

Old boxes or wood for constructing cages.
¼-in. mesh galvanized wire screen for animal cages.
Beaverboard for jigsaw animals.
Oilcloth or window curtains for charts.
A catalogue listing materials concerned with dairying and the dairy industry is available free on request from National Dairy Council, 111 North Canal Street, Chicago 6, Illinois.
U.S. Department of Agriculture for list of publications.
County Agent. Pamphlets on animal clubs.

Library for Animal Work

Reference Shelf:

BEARD. *American Boys' Book of Wild Animals*, J. B. Lippincott Company, 1921, 309 pp.
BRUNNER. *Tracks and Tracking*, The Macmillan Company., 1909, 217 pp.
COMSTOCK. *The Pet Book*, Comstock Publishing Company, Inc., 460 pp.
FUERTES. *The Book of Dogs*. National Geographical Society, 1927, 109 pp.

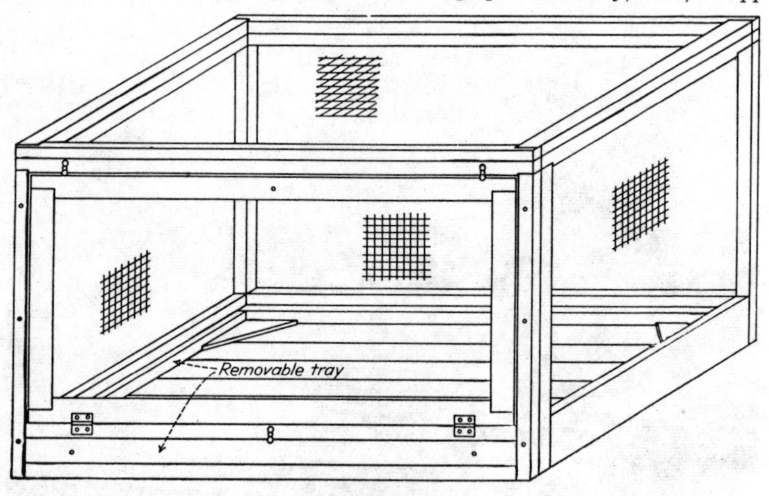

School Room Pet Cage

FIG. 57.

Stories:

BAYNES. *Animal Heroes of the Great War*, The Macmillan Company, 1927, 307 pp.
BAYNES. *Sprite, the Story of a Red Fox*, The Macmillan Company, 1924, 134 pp.
BURGESS. *Animal Book for Children*, Little, Brown & Company, 1920, 363 pp.
CARR. *The Stir of Nature*, Oxford Book Company, Inc., 208 pp.
CARTER. *Stories of Brave Dogs*, D. Appleton-Century Company, Inc., 1904, 197 pp.
LOPP. *White Sox*, World Book Company, 1924.
SEWELL. *Black Beauty*, John C. Winston Company, 1934.
SETON. *The Biography of a Grizzly*, D. Appleton-Century Company, Inc., 1918, 167 pp.

Handcraft Suggestions.[1]

Charts. To show kinds of cows, poultry, dogs, pigeons, and so on. Story of a bottle of milk, life history of a kitten, the zoo, the parts of a horse.

[1] For further suggestions, see p. 276.

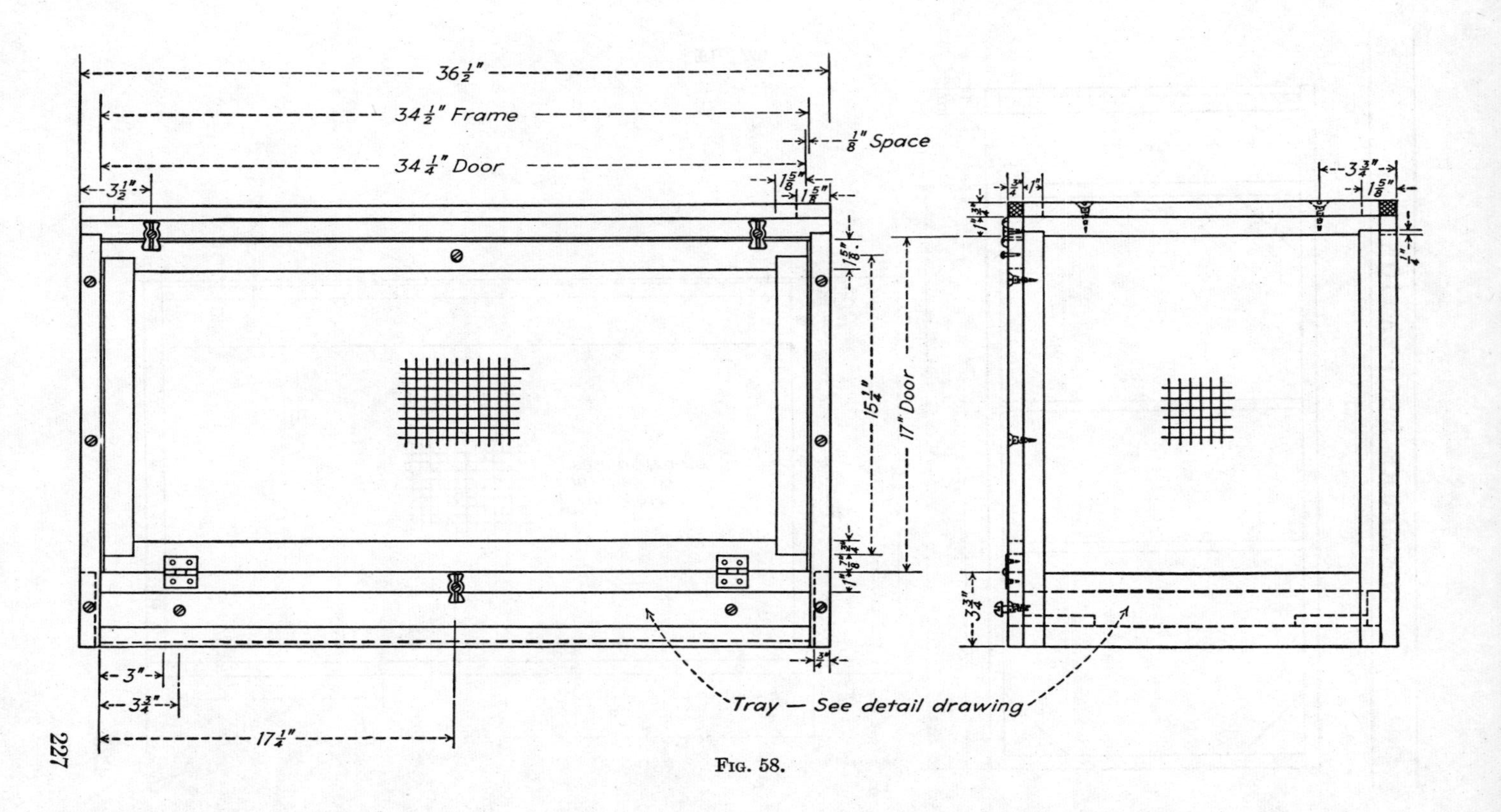

36 1/2"
34 1/2" Frame
1/8" Space
34 1/4" Door
3 1/2"
1 5/8"
15 1/4"
17" Door
3"
3 3/4"
17 1/4"
Tray — See detail drawing

FIG. 58.

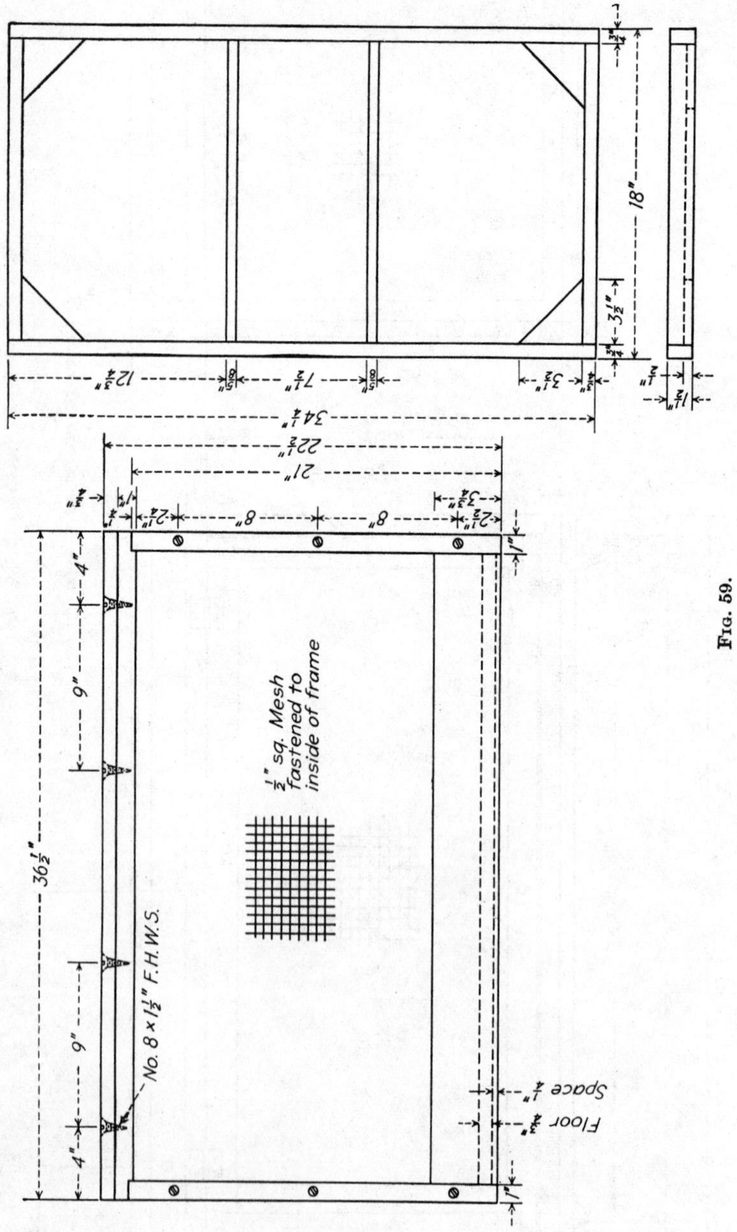
18"
34 1/4"
22 1/2"
21"
36 1/2"
1/2" sq. Mesh fastened to inside of frame
No. 8 × 1 1/2" F.H.W.S.
Space 1/4"
Floor 3/4"

FIG. 59.

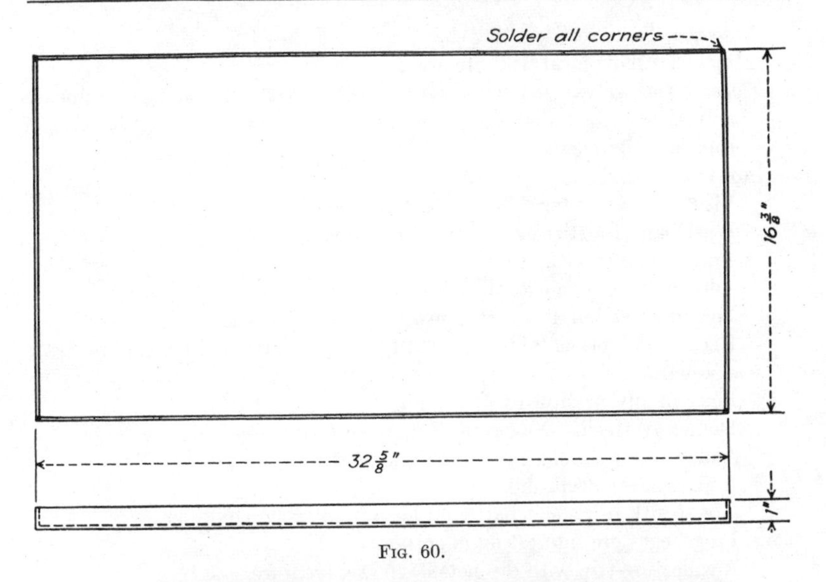

FIG. 60.

FIG. 61.—Baby red squirrels, Harrison, Me. (*Photograph by Clyde Fisher.*)

Posters. To advertise a dog show, livestock show.

Map. To show local wild-life areas.

Cages. Use galvanized wire, ¼-in. mesh. Nail on inside of frame so animal will not gnaw cage. Removable galvanized tray at bottom of cage is easily cleaned.

Aquarium Care.

Visit a pet shop for a demonstration.

Wash sand by stirring and pouring off water.

Anchor plants with stones.

Add water so as not to dislodge plants.

For every gallon of water: 1 fish, 2 snails, 2 tadpoles.

Keep carnivorous animals—perch, frogs, water insects—in separate aquaria.

Place in any window except the south.

Do *not* overfeed. Never allow uneaten food to remain.

Added water should have room temperature.

A glass cover keeps out dust.

Give a sick fish a salt bath and keep in separate container.

Frogs' eggs are interesting in spring.

A collecting trip with dip nets is great adventure.

A Dog Show.

DOG SHOW ENTRY CARD

Name of Exhibition____________________Address______________
School______________________Grade________________
Kind of dog____________________Name of dog______________
Age of dog______________

To the best of my knowledge, the dog mentioned above is gentle and can be controlled by the exhibitor. I am willing that he enter the dog in the Dog Show to be held________________at____________________o'clock.

Sign here____________________
Parent

DOG SHOW SCORE CARD

Exhibitor__________________Dog______________Date______________

__________Attitude of owner
__________Knowledge of owner
__________Cleanliness
__________Health
__________Friendliness
__________Intelligence
__________(Tricks)
__________Total points

Score 1 to 5 points for each item on left For example: if dog is too fat, too thin, diseased, poor teeth, watery eyes, sore eyes, bruised feet, and so on, take off 1 point for each on health. If owner nags, does not give a drink when needed, jerks rope, slaps dog, deduct from score on attitude.

Awards: Ribbons to pin on contestants.

30 points—red ribbon—first prize.

28 to 30 points—blue ribbon—second prize.
26 to 27 points—brown ribbon—third prize.
24 to 25 points—green ribbon—fourth prize.
20 to 23 points—orange ribbon—fifth prize.
Less than 20 points—yellow ribbon.

Other Suggestions

Animal

1. Dog should be on a leash and under control.
2. Reserve right to send dog home if disturbing or diseased.
3. Whether or not a dog is a purebred is unimportant in this show.

Exhibitor

1. Exhibitor should be 10 years or over.
2. Exhibitor and dog should come from same home.
3. Chairs about 10 ft. apart should be provided for exhibitor, who should keep the dog in place.
4. Instruct children to go directly home after show.
5. Pin entry card on exhibitors upon arrival and assign a chair.
6. Exhibitors should know ahead of time the points on which the dog will be judged.

Exhibit

1. Hold exhibition inside in a gymnasium if it is likely to rain.
2. Insist that entry cards be signed by parents.
3. A dog show is excellent publicity material.
4. Advertise the event by posters.

Judging

1. Judging should be done and ribbons awarded before the show is opened to the public.
2. Judges should work together and not take over 1 hr.
3. The number of entries may be limited, or there may be more than one team of judges.

Visitors

1. "Dogless children" can act as hosts and traffic officers, and run errands.
2. Have one-way traffic for viewing dogs.
3. You may expect parents as well as children.

A Zoo Trip for Animal Clubs.[1]

Most zoos are nothing but amusement parlors. They can be made more meaningful. The object of this trip is to show 50 ways in which

[1] Written for recreation leaders' trip to Swope Park Zoo, Kansas City, but can be adapted to any zoo.

the zoo may be "more than amusing." You are about to go on a "voyage of discovery." You will visit several continents in a short walk. After entering the main door, turn to the right and observe each animal according to the suggestions. The numbers on the right indicate the score if you observe correctly.

Name________________
Score________________

How Is Your Eyesight?

(Possible score = 75)

The Red Kangaroo (*Macropus rufus*). Australia.

1. What three things does he use for a tripod?__________(3)
2. How many fingers does he have on one hand?__________(1)
3. How many toes are there on one foot?__________(1)
4. Which is the big toe? (Sketch)__________(2)
5. Do kangaroos ever move on all fours?__________(1)
6. Where is a kangaroo's knee? (Sketch)__________(2)
7. Where is a kangaroo's ankle? (Sketch)__________(2)

The Lion (*Felis leo*). Africa.

8. How many pads are there on the back foot?__________(2)
9. What kind of footprint would a lion make in the mud? (Sketch) __________(2)
10. Does a lion have a "hare lip"?__________(1)
11. Does a lion have whiskers like a cat?__________(1)
12. Can a lion climb a tree?__________(1)
13. Where is there black on a lion?__________(3)
14. What is the name of a female lion?__________(1)
15. Where is the hair long on a lion?__________(1)
16. Are the lion's claws visible?__________(1)
17. When is a lion more active, day or night?__________(1)
18. Which is the lion most like: a dog, cat, or mouse?__________(2)

The Tiger (*Felis tigris*). Sumatra.

19. How does the tiger differ from a lion?__________(1)
20. Are both tigers marked the same?__________(1)
21. Does one tiger have the same markings on both sides?__________(2)
22. Which of the three felines is a panther?__________(1)

The Leopard (*Felis pardus*). Africa.

23. How can you recognize a leopard by his markings?__________(1)
24. What proof can you find that he preys?__________(2)
25. Does the black leopard have spots?__________(1)

26. Are the pupils slits or round?______________(1)
27. Are the spots solid or rosette?______________(1)

The Chimpanzee "Sally" (*Anthropopithecus troglodytes*). Africa.

28. Draw a line through the parts named that are missing in a chimpanzee: big toe, thumb, nostrils, tail, eyebrows, fingernails, brain, skin, whiskers______________(5)
29. How far do the hands reach in relation to knees?______________(1)
30. What evidence can you discover of intelligence?______________(2)
31. Discover three resemblances to man______________(3)
32. Name three physical differences from *all* humans______________(3)

Elephants (*Elephas indicus*). India. Presented by Ararat Temple (Shriners) to the children of Kansas City (Oct. 10, 1920).

33. How many fingernails on one front foot?______________(1)
34. How often do elephants lie down?______________(2)
35. Do elephants have eyelashes?______________(1)
36. Do elephants have hair?______________(1)
37. Do these elephants have tusks?______________(1)
38. What organ would an elephant use to drink milk?______________(1)
39. How do they drink water?______________(1)

Sea Lions (*Zalophus californianus*) California.

40. Is a sea lion a seal?______________(1)
41. Do sea lions prefer to travel in pairs, alone, or in herds?______________(1)
42. Could a hunter get a fur coat from a sea lion?______________(1)
43. Do sea lions have bones of the legs similar to ours?______________(2)
44. What is the name of a sea lion's arm?______________(1)

The Hippopotamus "River Horse" (*Hippopotamus amphibius*). Africa.

45. If any of these items are missing in a hippopotamus, cross them out: hair, lungs, toes, ears, lips, blubber______________(3)
46. Does the hippopotamus breathe air or water?______________(1)
47. Write the plural of hippopotamus______________(1)
48. Is the "hippo" herbivorous or carnivorous?______________(1)

The Canary (*Serinus canaria*). Canary Islands.

49. Why give the canary sand?______________(1)
50. Why give the canary lettuce? Cuttlefish bone?______________(2)

PHYSICAL NATURE INTERESTS

Children often learn about physical science in spite of parents and leaders. Action and learning go hand in hand. Physical nature recreation is not departmental but a part of the whole picture. Space in a handbook does not allow a complete treatment of the subject, but the sample topics selected and the references added point the way to a rich mine of child play.

Fields of Interest. 1. *Brooks.* To explore a brook, to build dams and water wheels, and to fish upstream are childhood ambitions that should be gratified. To keep in step with such ambitions will be an achievement. A leader who has enthusiasm will romp with the child adventurers. The brook is a whole world of life enrichment.

References

FULLER. *Along the Brook,* The John Day Company, 1931, 81 pp.
MILLER. *The Brook Book,* Doubleday, Doran & Company, Inc., 1929, 237 pp.

2. *Clouds.* Obtain U.S. Weather Bureau *Manual of Cloud Forms and Codes for States of the Sky* (Circular S) from Superintendent of Documents, Government Printing Office, Washington 25, D.C. (30 cents).

References

HUMPHREYS. *Fogs and Clouds,* The Williams & Wilkins Company, 1926, 104 pp.

3. *Ponds.*

Under-water glass. Fit clear glass on bottom of a wooden box 6 in. square and 4 to 6 ft. long. Peak through open end.

With galvanized ¼-in. wire mesh fence off a section of a pond as an aquarium.

With a dip net, go "submarining" for insects and water life of all kinds. Leeches, minnows, tadpoles, caddis houses—in fact everything is game that comes to the net.

Map the local pond. Take soundings across the pond in several directions. Locate inlets, outlets, pollution, beaches, and so on. Indicate water plants. List kinds of fishes.

References

MORGAN. *Field Book of Ponds and Streams,* G. P. Putnam's Sons, 1930, 449 pp.
NEEDHAM. *Life of Inland Waters,* Comstock Publishing Company, 1930, 438 pp.
PATCH. *Holiday Pond,* The Macmillan Company, 1929, 147 pp.

4. *Rocks and Minerals.*

Trip with a geological hammer.
Carving and polishing beach pebbles.
Collecting "gems" for metal craft.

References

FAIRBANKS. *Rocks and Minerals,* Educational Publications Co., 1903, 236 pp.
HAWKSWORTH. *The Strange Adventures of a Pebble,* Charles Scribner's Sons, 1921, 296 pp.

HOTCHKISS. *The Story of a Billion Years*, The Williams & Wilkins Company, 1932, 137 pp.

ZODAC. *How to Collect Minerals*, Rocks and Minerals, Peekskill, N.Y., 1934, 80 pp.

5. *Shore Line.*

Mount red seaweeds by bringing up cards under floating plants.
Sand machines.

FIG. 62.—Pirates are not the only ones who have gathered gold from the ocean. These July Jaunters from the pavements of the metropolis are gaining both health and wealth. (*Photograph courtesy of the Children's Museum, Jamaica Plain, Boston.*)

Sand-modeling contest.
Campfire on the beach.
Search for magnetic sands with a magnet.
Search for garnets with a hand lens.

References

ARNOLD. *Sea Beach at Ebb Tide*, D. Appleton-Century Company, Inc., 1901, 490 pp.

BROWN. *The Green Gate to the Sea*, Silver, Burdett & Company, 1924, 176 pp.

BURGESS. *Burgess Seashore Book for Children*, Little, Brown & Company, 1929, 336 pp.
DUNCAN. *Wonders of the Sea*, Oxford, 1928, 6 vols. pp. 72–86.
PATCH and FENTON. *Holiday Shore*, The Macmillan Company, 1935, 150 pp.

6. *Snow.* Snow crystals on a coat sleeve are worth looking at. They are examples of mathematical law. Samuel Colinan's *Nature's Harmonic Unity* gives a basic concept.

Snow modeling. Minneapolis has a snow-modeling contest and the Bureau of Recreation, Chicago, is a pioneer in this activity. Write National Recreation Association, 8 West Eighth Street, N.Y.C., for their booklet *88 Successful Play Activities*, which includes a section on snow sculpture.

7. *Stars.*

Use binoculars for sky study.

Occasion may be a comet or an eclipse.

Make constellations by fastening stars to under side of umbrella or to ceiling of room.

Make an electric board, wired to show constellations.

Use flashlights on a cliff to represent constellations.

References

BURNS. 1001 *Celestial Wonders as Observed with Home-built Instruments*, Pacific Science Press, Morgan Hill, Calif., 1929, 273 pp.
JEANS. *Through Space and Time.* The Macmillan Company, 1934, 224 pp.
JOHNSON. *The Stars for Children*, The Macmillan Company, 1934, 224 pp.
PROCTOR. *Young Folks' Book of the Heavens*, Little, Brown & Company, 1925, 256 pp.
REED. *The Stars for Sam*, Harcourt, Brace & Company, Inc., 1935, 140 pp.
SWEZEY and GABLE. *Boys' Book of Astronomy*, E. P. Dutton & Company, Inc., 291 pp.

8. *Weather Bureau.* Run a playground weather bureau.

Sundial. The shadow is cast by a vertical gnomon that points north, and the angle of the gnomon toward the center of the hour path must equal the degrees of latitude of the place. Mark position of shadow at 1 o'clock, 2 o'clock, and so on.

References

Boy Scouts of America. *Weather*, 1929.
BROOKS. *Why the Weather?* Harcourt, Brace & Company, Inc., 1924, 310 pp.
HEILE. *The World's Moods*, Follett Publishing Company, 1930, 111 pp.
TALMAN. *The Realm of the Air*, Bobbs-Merrill Company, 1931, 318 pp.

Handcraft. For further suggestions, see page 94.

Dry cells, bulbs, and sockets can be obtained at ten-cent store.

1. *Airplanes*

References

CLAUDY. *Model Airplanes*, Beginner's Book, Bobbs-Merrill Company, 1930, 184 pp.
National Recreation Association. *For Model Aircraft Beginners.*
National Recreation Association. *How to Start a Model Aircraft Tournament.*

2. *Magnet.* Electromagnets can be made by beginners.
3. *Cartesian Diver.* Illustrates principle of specific gravity.
4. *Boat Building.* Consult booklet published by Boy Scouts of America.
5. *Kites.* Kite Tournaments. National Recreation Association.

References

GARBER. *Kites and Kite Flying*, Boy Scouts of America, 1931.
ROY. *Kites*, Recreation Department, Chicago, 1935.

6. *Indian Drum.* Chopping tray with wet woodchuck skin stretched tightly and held by pegs. Use as war drum to send messages by Morse code. Can be decorated with Indian design.

References

BARUCH. *Big Fellow at Work* (Shovel), Harper & Brothers, 1930, 103 pp.
BOND. *Scientific American Boy*, Munn and Co., New York, 1916, 419 pp.
BORNANN. *Bridges*, The Macmillan Company, 1934, 78 pp.
COLLINS and ROWE. *Radio Amateur's Handbook*, The Thomas Y. Crowell Company, 1933.
COOLIDGE and DI BONA. *Story of Steam*, John C. Winston Company, 1935, 48 pp.
EDELSTAT. *Steam Shovel for Me*, Frederick A. Stokes Company, 1933, 56 pp.
JONES. *How the Derrick Works*, The Macmillan Company, 1930, 45 pp.
KELLER. *Working with Electricity*, The Macmillan Company, 1929, 119 pp.
LAMBERT and MITCHELL. *Skyscraper*, The John Day Company, 1933, 80 pp.
PETERSON. *Educational Toys*, Manual Arts Press, Peoria, Ill., 1920.

TREES AND FORESTS

Recently, tremendous man power and funds have been turned to the development of public properties. Anyone who has not followed this work in forest management which includes fire protection, forest planting, erosion control, and cultural activities will be astonished at the changes. Closely following the physical improvement will come a substantial increase in the social uses of the forest. This increased opportunity for the recreational use of the forests has come overnight,

Projects with Trees

Ornamental Planting for Bird Life

Fruit-bearing Trees and Shrubs That Attract Birds

(Check those that already grow in your back yard and number the others in the order in which you might acquire them. What do you have to exchange?)

Common name	Scientific name	Remarks
Trees: Use for background.		
Buckthorn	*Rhamnus cathartica*	Introduced. Makes a hedge not easily penetrated by cats. Fruit on in winter
Dogwood	*Cornus florida*	Has few red berries eaten by many species. Worth having for large white flowers. Grows in open hardwoods. Ornamental
Hackberry	*Celtis occidentalis*	Once common around homesteads
Holly	*Ilex opaca*	Few berries. Ornamental evergreen. Grows in shade
Juniper or red cedar	*Juniperus virginiana*	Few blue berries. Grows in open. Liked by waxwings and thrushes. Evergreen
Mountain ash	*Pyrus americana*	Clusters of red berries. Ornamental
Mulberry	*Morus rubra* *Morus alba*	Red is native and white is introduced. Great favorite with birds. A summer fruit
Sassafras	*Sassafras variifolium*	Few berries. Usually small tree
Sour gum	*Nyssa biflora*	Few berries. Grows in moist places. Berries in fall. Distinct autumn colors
Wild cherry	*Prunus serotina* *Prunus pennsylvanica*	Black cherry may become a pest. Most birds are fond of cherries. Some introduced species as *P. tomentosa* is worth adding
Shrubs: Plant in front of trees.		
Bayberry	*Myrica carolinensis*	A popular fruit for birds. An interesting shrub. Fragrant. Low growing. Will grow in sand region and coast
Blueberry	*Vaccinium*	All species are good. Can grow back of bayberry
Chokeberry	*Pyrus melanocarpa*	Rather ornamental
Elderberry	*Sambucus canadensis*	Both common and red are popular with birds. Common one is edible
Greenbrier	*Smilax rotundifolia*	Not desirable on farm as spreads. Few berries. Thorns make a good bird retreat
Spicebush	*Benzoin aestivale*	Will grow in shade. Fragrant. Not many berries
Sumac	*Rhus glabra* and *R. aromatica*	Smooth and fragrant sumacs are the most desirable species. Very popular shrub with birds. Ornamental. Spreads
Viburnum	*Viburnum acerifolium*	Will grow in hardwoods. *V. dentatum* is also valuable
Virginia creeper	*Psedera quinquefolia*	A climbing vine. Blue berries liked by many birds. Ornamental
Wild grape	*Vitis vulpina*	Frost grape perhaps best favorite of birds
Perennial herbs: May be planted in margin of shrubbery.		
Bunchberry	*Cornus canadensis*	Low-growing native plant. Thrives in shade. Red berries in fall
Pokeweed	*Phytolacca decandra*	Many berries. Fleshy root is poisonous unless cooked
Sarsaparilla	*Aralia nudicaulis*	Holds berries during winter. Grows in shade

as it were. Leaders will need to give this phase of nature recreation priority consideration in their plans for the immediate future.

A Sugar-bush Party

FIFTY QUESTIONS ON THE MAPLE-SUGAR INDUSTRY

This is a pretest for those planning to attend the sugar-bush party. If you are pedagogically meticulous, I daresay that you can find biology, chemistry, physics, mathematics, history, literature, or "what-need-you" within the test. In the meantime, the fun is all yours.

1. Who wrote the following:

   "I wonder if the sap is stirring yet,
   If frozen snowdrops feel as yet the sun.
   I am still sore in doubt concerning spring."

2. Anyone going to the "sugar bush" ought to be versed in "sugar-bush" parlance. What do the following terms mean: "treacle," "first run," "season," "stone boat," "caldron kettles," "sugar off"?
3. When was maple sugar a necessity, and when did it become a luxury?
4. What is the real sugar tree?
5. What part of the tree is the sugar factory?
6. Name a state in which the maple is the state tree?
7. How much maple sugar is made in Europe?
8. For what purpose do they use the ax in the maple-sugar camp?
9. What is ideal maple-sugar weather?
10. What are two distinguishing characteristics of maple-sugar buds?
11. What is the purpose of maple sugar?
12. Of what material was the sap spout of the Indian days? Of the present day?
13. Does the tapping of the tree leave a wound that will usually be infected by fungi?
14. What was the Indian method of concentrating the sugar?
15. What is the longest tapping season?
16. From what direction does the sap come?
17. On what side of the tree does the sap flow first?
18. What causes the sap to flow?
19. Name four animals (other than man) that have discovered that maple sap is good.
20. What were the earliest vessels for collecting maple sap?
21. About how much sap is required to make 1 qt. of sirup?
22. What should be the size and position of the hole for sap flow?

23. Through what part or parts of the tree does sap flow?
24. What is the purpose of a "neck yoke?"
25. What is the advantage of locating a sugar house on a slope?
26. Why is skimming necessary?
27. How is the "evaporator" prevented from boiling over?
28. How many pounds should maple sirup weigh to the standard United States gallon?
29. If a utensil has a full gallon when the liquid is hot, will it be a full gallon when cold? Why?
30. Why did "sugaring off" always occur at night in colonial times?
31. From what maples can sugar be made?
32. How is "maple wax" made?
33. What is the most important New England state in the production of maple sugar?
34. What is often used to adulterate maple sugar?
35. How is the sugar separated from the water in sugar making?
36. What were the three commonest articles of barter of our early forefathers?
37. How much sugar will a sugar-maple tree yield in one season?
38. What causes maple sirup to crystallize?
39. How much maple sugar is produced in the United States annually?
40. How can the concentration of the sirup be told by a thermometer?
41. What other instrument is often used to determine the density of the liquid?
42. Why is the "evaporator" made of metal?
43. Why did the cane and beet sugar take the place of maple sugar?
44. Why will the maple-sugar industry probably not pass into the hands of a corporation?
45. Which come first in the sugar maple—the flowers or leaves?
46. What causes the sap to ferment?
47. Why does fruiting cause the sugar maple and not the red maple to fork at the twigs?
48. What causes "birds'-eye" maple?
49. Is maple sugar a confection or a food?
50. What is the maple-tree borer?

ANSWERS TO QUESTIONS ON THE MAPLE-SUGAR INDUSTRY

1. Christina C. Rossetti in "The First Spring Day."
2. "Treacle" is the sirup drained from sugar in refining. "First run" is the first few weeks that the sap is flowing. "Stone boat" is the sled that is drawn by horses or oxen to bring in the sap to the sugar house. "Caldron kettles" are the large iron kettles in which the sap was formerly boiled down. "Sugar off" is the changing of the thick sirup to sugar.

3. In colonial times, maple sugar was considered a necessity. It is now a luxury.
4. The honey locust bean has 20 per cent sugar, and the sap of the sugar maple is from 3 to 6 per cent sugar.
5. The leaves are the factories where starch and sugar are manufactured.
6. Rhode Island.
7. Maple sugar is an American product. It is not made in Europe.
8. The ax is used to cut firewood and not to scarf the trees.
9. Thawing days and freezing nights.
10. Compared with other maples they have sharp-pointed buds with many bud scales.
11. To make new leaves and wood.
12. The Indians made the sap spout from sumac or elder stems. They are now made of galvanized metal.
13. The wounds made by the augur usually heal in one season and are not infected.
14. The Indian dropped hot stones into the sap. When it froze, he threw the ice away.
15. Three to four weeks.
16. The sap comes from all parts of the tree. If you break a twig it will "bleed." Sap comes from above and from below. During the first part of the season, more comes from above than from below.
17. South.
18. When the tree is warmed, the air in the cell spaces expands.
19. Sapsucker, porcupine, red squirrel, insects (flies and bees).
20. Bark vessels and hollowed logs.
21. 32 qt.
22. ½-in. hole, 2 in. deep; breast high, slanting up.
23. Up the sapwood and down the inner bark.
24. For individuals to carry pails of sap to the kettle to be "boiled down." It is a piece of wood that goes across the shoulders to hold a pail on each end.
25. So that one can use a siphon and run the sap by gravity.
26. To remove impurities such as bits of ashes, bark, and so on.
27. By putting in cream, lard, or salt pork to break the surface tension of the foam.
28. Eleven.
29. Hot liquids contract when cooled.
30. They had to attend to sap buckets in the day.
31. Although the sugar maple makes the best sugar, it is also made from the red and silver maples.
32. By pouring driblets of thick sirup on clean snow.
33. Vermont produces the most sugar and New York the most sirup.
34. Brown sugar, because it is cheaper. Sometimes glucose.
35. By evaporation.

36. Furs, corn, and maple sugar.
37. 1 to 6 lb.
38. It concentrates to the point where it is no longer soluble in the water present.
39. In 1860, 40,120,205 lb. In 1910, 14,000,000 lb. In 1920, 9,691,854 lb. These are estimates from the U.S. Census Bureau.
40. The boiling point of a liquid varies with the altitude and also concentration.
41. A hydrometer, usually the Baumé.
42. Conductor of heat that is necessary for evaporation.
43. Lower priced, steady supply, and modern machinery for refining.
44. Trees are scattered and mostly hand labor.
45. The flowers and leaves appear at the same time in the sugar maple.
46. Bacteria.
47. The fruit comes from end buds in the sugar maple and from side buds in the red maple.
48. The cause of birds'-eye and curly maple is unknown. It is not due to woodpeckers.
49. Although once thought of as food, it is now considered a confection.
50. The maple-tree borer is the grub of a beetle.

Stump Scouting

Recognizing trees and reading their past history from their stumps make a study in keen observation, one that opens a new page of nature.

The following questionnaire proved an exciting project at a nature-lore-school session at Camp Andree. Each patrol was given opportunity to observe and make out its own report.

THE QUESTIONS

1. What kind of tree was this?
2. What did it come from?
3. When was it cut?
4. Why was it cut?
5. What tools were used?
6. Order in which tools were used?
7. Number of workmen?
8. Where did he (or they) stand? (Compass directions.)
9. In what direction did it fall?
10. During what season was it cut?
11. Was it cut during a strong wind, a gentle breeze, or a calm?
12. During the forenoon or afternoon?
13. On a cold or warm day?
14. By an amateur(s) or a woodsman (or men)?
15. At what time of year did it grow most?

16. At what time of year did it grow most rapidly?
17. How old was it when cut?
18. In what year did it grow most rapidly?
19. How much was it increased in diameter per year in its youth?
20. Was it cut before or after it died?
21. Why did it die?
22. About how long has it been dead?
23. Which appeared first—the tree or the stone wall?
24. With what instruments has the stump been struck since the tree fell?
25. How many times has it been burned?
26. When was it burned?
27. In what direction was the wind blowing when it was burned?
28. It was burned just before what event?
29. What animals besides man have visited it?
30. What flowering plants are building themselves out of the stump dust?
31. How many kinds of nonflowering plants (lichens and mosses) can you find growing on the stump?

THE EVIDENCES AND CONCLUSIONS

Question 1. Two patrols decided that it was oak because of the bark, and another patrol decided that it was "sweet chestnut" because of the thickness of the bark. This was strange, since there was no bark present. Possibly the decaying wood or "punk" fooled them. Crude logic, instead of evidence, often appeared. For example, a patrol decided that the stump was oak, because the surrounding oaks may have been "seed children" or that it was chestnut because that was the wood used in building Camp Macy. Then there was the indefinite statement that it was chestnut because of its color and texture. The stump was chestnut and should have been distinguished from oak by the absence of silver grain (medullary rays). Three out of eight patrols got the correct answer, but the evidence given indicated guessing. In other words, they "guessed right."

Question 2. One patrol said that it came from an acorn, since that is the "only method." The three others who said "acorn" may also have been unaware that hardwoods may originate by sprouting from stumps, which is known as coppice reproduction. The tree was one of our primeval chestnuts and came from a chestnut, as evidenced by the one stump rather than a circle of stumps.

Question 3. Two patrols judged by the "appearance" of the stump that it was cut 5 years ago, but neglected to designate the particular appearance that suggested 5 instead of 4 or 6. One patrol judged by the "state of decay" that it was cut 7 to 10 years ago, whereas, in distinct contrast, another patrol told by the "freshness of the stump" that it had been cut within a year. Apparently no one observed that small dogwood trees had been cut at the same time or that the top of a wild cherry had been broken by the fall of the chestnut. These trees had grown sprouts 1 year old. It would be rather a simple step to reason out the age of sprouts that had been growing for one or two seasons.

Fig. 63.—Trees, like animals, have characteristic coverings. This is not an alligator but the trunk of a Western white pine. When Enos Mills went snow-blind on a mountain summit, the feeling of the barks of trees became all-important. Why?

Question 4. In every direction, there were contradictions to the reasons offered for the tree's having been cut. There were many trees in sight with "bark all off" that were "dead" and many were "decaying." There were other large trees with "lots of small trees around" that had not been cut. If it was cut for "firewood," the fuel had not been used. The tree died because it had the "blight" years before. The disease does not exist on a dead tree. The tree died because it had the "blight," and young chestnut sprouts that had the blight were still growing. Since there were new buildings in sight with large beams of chestnut and since the trunk was the only part removed, it would appear that this particular tree was cut to help in constructing the camp.

Questions 5 *and* 6. Saw marks and ax marks are still recognized by most people. A nail had been straightened on the stump, and some patrols mistook it for evidence of a wedge. The ax was used first to direct the fall of the tree. The short cut made by the ax indicated that the wood was dead and not alive when the tree was cut down.

Question 7. The crosscut saw would suggest that two men, at least, had a hand in felling the tree. No patrol made any mistake as to questions 7, 8, and 9.

Question 8. The direction of the saw marks indicated the location in which the men stood, *i.e.*, east and west of the stump. They started to saw on the north side.

Question 9. Every patrol was able to gather evidence enough to infer that the tree fell toward the south. The ax cut on the stump, the broken limbs on the near-by trees, the splintered break on the stump, and the cleared space in the forest all pointed in the same direction.

Question 10. The time of year when the tree was cut was a puzzle indeed. Each of the four seasons was credited, by the various patrols, with the cutting. One thought that it was cut in summer, because the spring wood was on the outside, and others thought fall, because the summer wood grew last. The state of decay made it impossible to observe the last layer which grew—which might be different from the existing outside ring. One patrol speculated by surmising that it was cut in winter which is the "usual time." No one discovered the charred remains of a small cooking fire (not bonfire) where the wood choppers had evidently warmed up or made hot coffee. Woodsmen are not apt to stop to make a hot drink in any season but winter.

Question 11. All the patrols recognized that it was nearly sawed off before it broke. This indicates that the weather was nearly calm with practically no wind.

Question 12. If the men had a hot drink, it suggests that they cut the tree in the forenoon. Some thought it "too big to cut in the morning," but cutting through a trunk measuring less than 3 ft. in diameter would not take half a day.

Question 13. The logic used as to whether the day was hot or cold seemed to be tainted with book geography. Several patrols said that, since winter is cold, it was "cut on a cold day" or, since late spring is warm, "it must have been warm." The weather, of course, refuses to behave that way. Another group said, "There would have been more saw strips if it had been warm; therefore, it was "cold." But the next patrol, observing the same marks, said that "they stopped sawing now and then; therefore it was warm." The variation in pauses might be due to old age.

Question 14. Six out of eight patrols recognized that the tree was cut by woodsmen.

Questions 15 *and* 16. The tree grew more in the summer, as shown by wider ring, but more rapidly in the spring, as evidenced by the porous ring. Five patrols made correct observations and conclusions.

Question 17. The answers ranged from 55 to 61 years. The difficulty was caused by a hollow center and outside decay. The rate of growth could be used as a measuring stick but would give only approximate age.

Questions 18 *and* 19. All patrols observed that the greatest growth was made in early youth, but two patrols did not realize that the diameter would be increased by the width of two annual rings. In some years, the tree had increased its diameter ¾ in.

Question 20. Opinions also varied as to whether the tree was dead or alive at the time of cutting. Speculation was rampant on this question. One patrol thought that "it would not have been cut unless dead, as it was too valuable and fine." Another that "good timber is cut before it dies." A third, that, "due to our ideas of conservation, it must have been cut before." Two patrols decided that, since the tree had no bark, it must have been dead when cut. This last conclusion was the only one based on evidence.

Question 21. Two patrols thought it died because it was cut; one, because of fire; one, because of insects; one, because of fire and fungus; and three thought that death was due to blight. The chestnut blight was the real cause, and the other things were merely secondary.

Question 22. The estimates as to how long it had been dead ranged from 1 to 15 years. One patrol said 5 years and based their decision on the amount of decay. They could not tell how it would differ in appearance if it had been 4 or 6 years. The 15-year estimate was deducted from the knowledge that the blight struck this section of the country about 18 years ago. A more exact conclusion could have been reached by inspecting the sucker growth on near-by chestnut trees.

Question 23. All patrols decided correctly that the stone wall was there first because "the tree grows out of it." One patrol, however, based its answer on the observation that the stone wall looks old and broken.

Question 24. The ax, hammer, nail, and knife marks were easily recognized by all the patrols.

Question 25. Several patrols thought that the stump had been burned three times because it had been burned in three places, but a tree might be burned in more than one place because of debris or exposure. One fire scar had partly healed and the growth again burned. The evidence did not indicate that it had been burned more than twice.

Questions 26, 27, *and* 28. The chances are that a tree will be burned on the side from which the fire approaches. If on a steep hillside, debris often is caught by the tree, and, in that case, the trunk is charred on the uphill side. In each burning of the trunk, the charring took place before the cutting.

Question 29. Squirrels (partly eaten nuts); ants (present); beetle grubs (borings); and birds (castings) had visited the trunk. The evidence was easily gathered.

Question 30. A baby black birch and a maple leaf viburnum were growing out of the decaying cavities.

Question 31. A green alga and a gray lichen were also discovered.

References

ALEXANDER. "Recreation on the Nature Trail," *Recreation*, December, 1932, pp. 438–442.

BLAKESLEE and JARVIS. *Trees in Winter*, The Macmillan Company, 1931, 292 pp.

Boy Scouts of America. *Merit Badge Booklet.*

Files of *Journal of Forestry.*

Forest Recreation Handbook (Region 9) U.S. Forest Service.

Guidebooks such as those published for the Allegany State Park by the New York State Museum and Science Service at Albany.

KEELER. *Our Native Trees*, Charles Scribner's Sons, 1900, 533 pp.

MILLS. *The Story of a Thousand Year Pine*, Houghton Mifflin Company, 1914, 119 pp.

National Forest Manual.

ROZMAN. "Recreational and Forestry Uses of Land in Massachusetts," *Experiment Station Bulletin* 294, January, 1933. Massachusetts State College.

WILD-LIFE MANAGEMENT

Some Junior Activities and Projects in Wild-life Management.[1]

Quail census previous to hunting season and just after.

Bringing aspen logs to lake margin for beaver.

[1] For further suggestions, see p. 81.

Coon hunting—Bring 'em back alive. They mate in early fall.
Leave hollow trees for dens.
Woodchuck census. Make good pets when started on a nursing bottle.
Bluebird "lane" to towns—houses built according to specifications.
Mousetrap line, the kind that catches them alive, to start a small rodent menagerie, meadowmice, shrews, moles, and so on.

References

These popular bulletins related to wild-life management may be obtained from the U.S. Department of Agriculture, Washington, D.C.

M 759, Windbreaks in Conservation Farming.
Lt 9, Publications on Fur Farming, Rabbits, and Laboratory Animals.
F 2131, Raising Rabbits.

The following may be obtained from the U.S. Fish and Wildlife Service:

CB 36, Control of Destructive Mice.
CB 11, Rabbits in Relation to Crops.
WL 409, Bird Control Devices.

CHAPTER X

NATURE GAMES

Nature games are an integral part of the nature-recreation program. Nature play is instinctive and has the power of developing the play habit. Childhood is the time for fixing this play habit in the out-of-doors. If neglected, the individual will usually be deficient in that particular training. Man is the only animal that ever neglects or trains away from the games of nature.

Many of these games have been adapted from old games that have been handed down from generation to generation. It will take but a little ingenuity to modify them for new games. All the rainy-day games may be played outdoors. They are classified this way as a matter of convenience in using them.

Suggestions: Know your game. Play with spirit. Have everyone take part. When possible, play outdoors. Play old games by request. Always teach a new game. Adapt games to fit conditions.

Test of a game: Is it used spontaneously afterward? What does it teach? What physical, mental, or moral traits does it develop? What social traits does it involve?

RAINY-DAY GAMES

Birds

Bird Identification. Give each one a stuffed specimen or bird skin, card or ticket, and a good bird key. When the student gets the right name from the key, the ticket is punched, and a new bird is presented for identification. The one who identifies the greatest number of birds in a given time wins. The cards are gathered at the end of the time limit, and a curve is placed on the board to show the number identifying 1, 2, 3, and so on, birds. Each one then knows how he ranks with the average in ability to identify birds.

Bird Description. Have cards on which is written the description of birds. Read slowly. The one guessing the name first is given the card. Anyone making a wrong guess has to give back a card.

"Swat" the Blindman. Have Audubon charts hung on the wall. Have a player stand with back to the chart. Name a bird, such as the flicker. Ask if he remembers the black cap? The red breast? The yellow on the tail? This always furnishes a great deal of amusement to the audience.

Hawkeye. Cover a bird quickly and ask questions. What color is the robin's breast? His head? His bill? How many white spots are there? Where is the black? What color is his throat? How many noticed white around the eye? This is fine training for observation.

Gyp. The group thinks of some bird. They are given several books in order to become well informed about the bird. "It" then comes in and asks questions which may be answered by "yes" or "no." How many questions does "it" require to name the bird?

Bird Silhouettes. Either the outline of the bird is cut out of black paper or the form of the bird is thrown on a cloth by a light. The one identifying the greatest number wins.

Bird Picture Contest. The colored pictures of birds are cut into four parts—head, body, tail, and legs. The pictures of the legs and, in the case of the seed-eating birds, the beaks, are scattered on the following tables: ducks and other swimming birds, wading birds, climbers, insect feeders of the air, birds of prey, and seed eaters. When the whistle blows, the players select a picture of some bird's leg and from the characteristics of the legs try to find the other parts of that bird. As soon as one picture is completed, another leg is taken, and so the game progresses until the supply is exhausted.

Bird Logomachy. Use cardboard letters printed on one side. Place face down on the table. Players take turns drawing letters and placing face up on the table. When a player can make a bird name from these letters, he takes the letters and spells the word in front of him. The person getting 10 birds first wins.

Bird Rogues' Gallery. Slips of papers are passed out to players, and they are given 2 min. to draw a picture of a bird for the Rogues' Gallery. The exhibit is then set up, and the judges walk by the exhibit. Recognizable birds are given honorable mention (1 point). Birds represented in action may be given red ribbons or red-pencil marks (2 points). The best sketches may be given blue ribbons or blue marks (3 points). The judging may be made very funny. The team getting the greatest score wins.

Bird Spotting. The object of this game is to spot birds when accurately described. The most general things are said first, and, as the description goes on, it focuses toward one bird, until the name is finally given. Whoever first names the bird correctly receives a point. If someone gives the wrong name, he is fined a point. Whoever has the most points at the end of the game wins.

The following are given as samples:

I am thinking of a bird that is 7 in. long. He returns on a warm, sunny day in March, and gladdens the hearts of ramblers as he "carries the sky on his back and the earth on his breast." His song is of clear notes which poets have described as "pur-i-ty, pur-i-ty." He sets up housekeeping in a cavity of an old apple tree or in a well-built birdhouse. This thrush could hardly be mistaken for the bluejay, and it is much larger than the indigo bunting. This bird is called the *bluebird.*

I am thinking of a bird 7 in. long. He is a friendly fellow and seeks the society of man. He is not noted for his color, as it is a dull gray above the white below. His tail is constantly "pumping." His nest is made of moss and lined with mud and hair. It is usually built under a bridge or in a shed. This flycatcher is often mistaken for the pewee, but it has a black bill and black feet. If you have not recognized it already, you will when I tell you that it has a plaintive note that sounds like "phoebe."

The bird that I have in mind is about 13 in. long. He looks quite grand with his crest and blue coat. His white collar and dark belt make his uniform look quite trim. He has a harsh voice. He has a sharp eye and a sharp beak. (Up to this point, it might be either the bluejay or the kingfisher.) To provide alertness, the describer may fine whoever ventures a guess and proceed to set forth the other bird.

He usually perches on a limb that overhangs a stream or pond. Suddenly he makes a dart to the water and comes back with a fish. Two of his toes are grown together, which makes it easier to scoop a hole into the sand bank to make a nest for the young. This fisherman is the *kingfisher.*

This bird is the length of a foot rule. He is brownish-gray, and, when you get him in the right light, he is iridescent. The pointed tail is tipped with white. His wings "whistle" when he flies. His nest is made of twigs and the eggs are limited to two white ones. Some of you may recognize its Latin name, *columba.* It is related to the extinct passenger pigeon and because of its mournful song is called the *mourning dove.*

One of our most graceful aviators is about 7 in. long and comes here from the tropics to spend the summer. The coming of the garage has made it difficult for him. His nest is made of pellets of mud and lined with feathers and is placed high on the rafters of the barn. He prefers to skim over the surface of water to gather insects. This bird wears the original swallowtail coat. It is steel blue in color. His chestnut shirt is not so fashionable as the shiny one of his smaller relative the tree swallow. You now know that I refer to the *barn swallow.*

This game may be played with the Audubon bird cards. There are three sets: spring, summer, winter birds of eastern North America from color drawings by Allan Brooks. The sets are published by the National Audubon Society, 1130 Fifth Avenue, New York City. The price per set, 50 in a box, is $1 postpaid. In order to facilitate the game, the statements in the description on the back of each

FIG. 64.—A scout is observing. It takes three seasons for a pitch-pine cone to mature and open. Can you find the three stages or sizes of cones? The youngest is purple, the second-season cone is green, and the third-season or mature cone is brown. Staminate or male blossoms may also be seen by the very observing. They resemble a miniature bunch of bananas. The new bundles of leaves have not reached full growth. Bundle scars are in evidence along the older bark.

card may be numbered for the order of presentation. Camps may also place these cards on the bulletin board to show the close-ups of local inhabitants.

TREES

Twig Matching. Obtain several kinds of twig 8 to 12 in. long. Cut into two parts. Mount the lower half on a board. Scatter the other halves on a table. At a given signal, the players observe closely one of the twigs and then run to the unmounted group to get the other half. If the wrong half is brought back, he tries again. This game requires close observation. Leaves may be used in the same way, or flowers with short stems may be fitted to longer stems, or leaves to leaf scars.

Jack-in-the-box. A branch or flower is held up quickly from the back of a box. The players write down the names. See which team gets the highest average.

Getting the Clue. Have a sheet of paper or cloth with a hole in the middle. Show the edge of a leaf, a little more at a time. Whoever gives the name correctly first is given the leaf. The one who gets the largest collection wins. Pictures of birds may be shown in the same way, the beak being the first to appear.

Indoor Twig Relay. Have a group of winter twigs scattered at one end of the room. Have as many of each kind as there are players. Show a twig such as the white ash. The players may look as long as they wish. Samples are then passed back, and the players are given 30 sec. to get a white-ash twig. Everyone back in his seat with a white-ash twig at the end of 30 sec. gets 1 point.

Spot the Tree. Give each player a sample twig of a tree that may be seen from the window. The players go to the window and mark on a local map the tree from which they think the twig was taken. Maple twigs, horse chestnut, pine, spruce, and so on, are well suited to this game. This is a very interesting game for training long-distance observation.

Tree Silhouettes. Cut from black paper the silhouette of trees. The trees particularly well adapted to this game are spruce, pine, elm, red cedar, weeping willow, palm, sugar maple, Lombardy poplar, and white oak. Hold up the silhouette for naming.

General

Nature Alphabet. This is played with "sides." The leader names a letter of the alphabet. Each player on each side in order names a bird, flower, or tree (decided upon before starting) which begins with that letter. Anyone who cannot do so in less than 5 sec. is out. No one is to name an object which has already been named. The patrol having the greatest number of players left at the end of a certain time is the winner, or the last group to name an object commencing with that letter wins 1 point for his team.

Authors. A homemade set of bird or tree authors may be made that is similar to the well-known game of authors. In authors, there are 20 books of 5 cards each. The cards are dealt evenly to the players. Each in turn asks for cards until a player does not have the card asked for. When a book is obtained, the cards are put down as a book. The person having the greatest number of books wins.

Games of Touch. The players are blindfolded, and a natural object is placed in their hands. They have 30 sec. to feel it. The name is then written down. Some objects particularly suited to this game are: various seeds, leaves, fruits, evergreens, flowers, barks of trees, nuts, feathers, shells, vegetables, and soils.

Game of Smell. As a variation, a team may elect its "best smeller." The players are blindfolded and allowed to smell of common objects. The name is then written down. Objects with a distinct odor are: mints, black birch, wintergreen or checkerberry, balsam, pennyroyal, skunk cabbage, onion, parsnip, tomato, tansy, rose, sassafras, sarsaparilla, spice bush, turnip, cedar, kelp, apple, orange, mold, strawberry, and cucumber. Strong odors such as skunk cabbage or onion should not be given first.

Game of Taste. Many of the objects suitable for smell are adapted to the game of taste. Others are rhubarb, sorrel, licorice, sugar, salt, clove, cinnamon, radish, catnip, peach, and cabbage.

Color in Flower Outlines. This contest may extend over a long period of time, as a week. Divide into teams. No outline is to be colored in unless the flower is found and brought in by someone in the team. All coloring to be done from specimens.

Acornicle. A game for four or less. Each player names his kind of acorn and gathers 50. The ground or a piece of paper is marked off into 200 or more squares. The object of the game is to get five acorns of one kind in a row (in five successive squares). One player puts an acorn in any square. Each player takes a turn placing one at a time in an empty square. Opponents may be blocked by placing an acorn at the end of his row. The first one to get five in a row wins. A good game for learning the differences between oak acorns. May be played with twigs or leaves.

Getting Partners. If in the beginning of a meeting or group entertainment it is desirable to get partners, this may be done as follows: (1) Cut leaves in two, crosswise or lengthwise. (2) Give leaves to boys and fruit of same kind of trees to girls. (3) Give tree questions to boys and answers to girls. (4) Use bird characters, Mr. and Mrs. Robin, Mr. and Mrs. Downy Woodpecker, and so on. (5) Give duplicate slips to boys and girls, having names of birds. Each boy imitates the bird by voice, walk, or flight. If the girl recognizes it as the one named on her slip, she claims him as her partner.

Flower Favor Game. Use reeds for stems; colored plasticine for receptacles; pine-cone scales, feathers, shaving, or shells for petals; insert petals into plasticine. Sealing wax, dyes, paint, and enamel will be useful. Have a real flower as a guide and give a definite time limit. Judges choose the best.

Shadowgraph. Attach a white sheet as a curtain with a bright light behind it. Pass several objects behind the sheet so that a shadow is cast. Use such objects as a pine tree, horseshoe crab, cabbage, dog, turnip, rhubarb leaf, pear, hen, goat, stuffed birds, pine cone, wooly bear, cattail, lily, lemon. Let audience have a sheet of paper and write names.

Stunts. (1) Leaf throw. Throw a leaf as far as possible without folding or breaking. (2) Imitate the call of a cow or duck. Nearest wins. May decide by pointing to competitors and the one that the audience claps loudest for wins. (3) Who can make the best poem using the words rabbit, habit, white, fight. (4) Hop like grasshopper. (5) Make a speech on fishing.

OUTDOOR GAMES

Birds

Birds'-nest Jackstraw. The catbird's nest may be taken to illustrate this game. It should only be played with an abandoned nest. Before dissecting it, each player lays claim to the kind of material he thinks most abundant in the nest. It may be a hemlock twig. He has first claim on hemlock twigs but on no other. Take out a stick for example. The same is true for all the sticks, leaves, weeds, grasses, fine roots, and strips of bark. Remove the parts one by one. If someone recognizes a part as grass and no one else knows the kind, he is entitled to the specimens of that kind. Ten seconds or a count to 10 is allowed for each to claim his kind of twig. If it is not claimed by the one entitled to it, the object is given to the next one recognizing it. Have the players count the number of each kind of material. Add 5 points for the naming of any one kind. The second part of this game consists of finding the source of material. The director of the game holds up a strip of bark that probably is that of the grapevine. After everyone has examined it carefully, the leader blows a whistle, and the first one discovering the grapevine gets a point. This is repeated for each kind of material.

Birds' Nest Tag Day. This contest lasts all day, and the best results are obtained when a good library is available. The camp is divided into teams. A tree having a nest may be tagged with a conspicuous card that must *not* be so placed as to frighten the bird. The tag must have the name of the bird-proprietor of the nest observed. If the member of any other team discovers that the nest is wrongly named, it may be retagged, and the first tag cannot be counted in the final score. Otherwise, the nest is only to have one tag. A team discover-

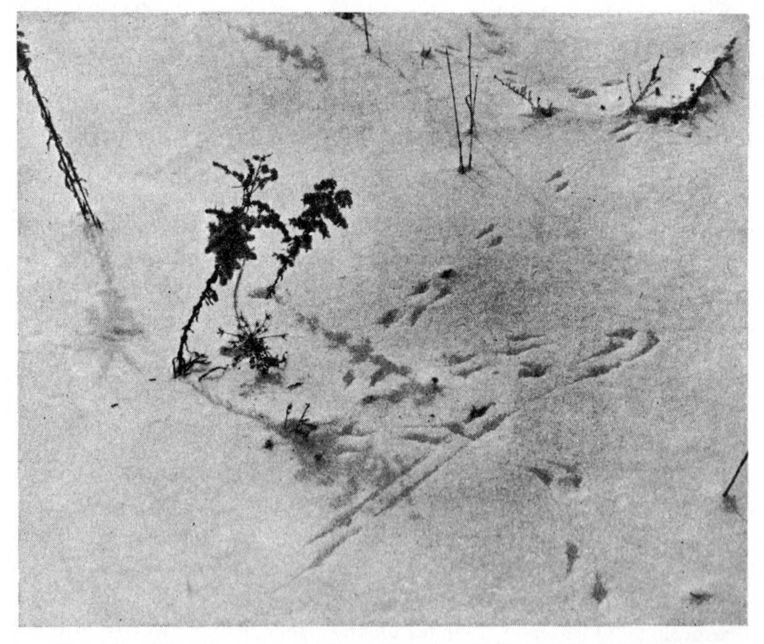

Fig. 65.—What story can you detect here? (*Photograph by Robert Coffin.*)

ing a nest and not knowing what kind it is may watch for the builder or investigate in the library. Other ingenious methods will develop.

Spot Spy. This game is great fun when resting on a hike or when loitering along the way. The leader says: "I can see five white oaks." The group is given 1 or 2 min. to spot the white oaks. All those who see them may indicate it by sitting down, taking off their hats, or by some other agreed signal. All those who see the object get 1 point.

Sign Language. This game is similar to pantomime. A player does the whole thing by the sign language. He may come out and point to himself. This means "I." He then flutters his hands like a bird. This means "I will fly like a bird." He may then imitate the flight of a swallow. It may be a hawk. He shows that it is not a swallow by measuring. He holds his hands apart the length of a swallow and shakes his head. He then holds his hands apart the length of a hawk and points into the air and with a sweeping motion of the hand indicates the spiral soaring of the hawk and, by signals, shows that the hawk is looking for the frog and when he sees the victim pounces upon it and eats it. The hand held over the eyes means "look." Patting the abdomen and smiling means "that tasted good." Or the food might have given a stomach-ache. This game gives an unusual opportunity for ingenuity. The one guessing the name of the bird gives the next pantomime.

Trees

Tree Tag Day. Give each player 10 tags with the names of 10 trees common to the tag area. Give them 20 min. to pin the tags 5 ft. from the ground on the north side of the trees named. No tree is to have more than one tag. A great number of tags may be given for an all-day tagging. The one tagging the greatest number correctly wins. A second game of "Calling in the Tags" may then be played. A player may bring in any tag except his own. If he finds a tree incorrectly tagged, he leaves it and on a later tour of inspection obtains 2 points if he can correct the mistake.

Tree Spying. Stop at a tree, such as the wild black cherry. Each one identifying the tree by use of the leaf chart within 3 min. is given 1 point. For each mistake, a point is subtracted. At the end of the trip, add the scores and announce the winners.

Tree Scouting. Appoint leaders to choose teams. Tell them to study the oak leaves on the chart and then, at a given signal, give 2 min. to obtain a white-oak leaf. The tree given should be known to be near by. At the end of 2 min., blow a whistle. Those back in their places with a white-oak leaf (no more, no less) score 1 point. Next send them scouting for a red-oak acorn, a balm-of-Gilead bud, and so on. The team scoring the greatest average represents the group of best tree scouts.

Forest Good Turn. The scout law, "Do a good turn daily," is well illustrated by this game. Give each group a few minutes to discuss the meaning of a "forest good turn." When the whistle is blown, they are given 5 min. to do a good turn. Each good turn is worth 1 point. If no one else did that particular good turn, it is worth 2 points. This encourages originality. The team performing the greatest score wins.

The reports are not the least important in this game. Some good turns are: Labeling poison ivy, destroying a tent caterpillar's nest, neatly cutting a broken branch, removing a tree fungus, hiding a rare flower, cleaning away fire bait, picking up rubbish, burying broken glass, hanging out a piece of suet for birds, and planting the seed for a desirable plant. If each scout troop played this game once a year, the amount of good accumulated would be inestimable.

A Forest Census. This game is well adapted to a permanent or temporary camping site. Mark off a forest area as the "outdoor museum." Have a large number of sale tags such as used in a department store. Divide into groups called foresters, miners, florists, birders, and so on. If there are a large variety of trees and a small display of minerals, give each tree the value of one and each mineral the value of three. The naturalists are then given 15 min. to label and list the natural history objects under their department. In the case of birds, it would be the nest of the bird rather than the bird itself. The reports around the council ring are instructive and often amusing.

Tree Trailing. Hide messages "en route" and send out companies 30 min. apart. The messages may read as follows: Take the valley trail to the east until you see a large yellow willow. In an abandoned flicker's home, there is a note. Read it carefully. This note may read: Within sight of this spot is a silver poplar. As far from that tree as it is high in the direction of the noonday shadow is buried a message on birch bark. Please leave this scroll as you find it. Before sending out the trailers, it should be announced that skill and not speed is the essential thing. The group following the farthest wins. The trail, therefore, should become more difficult as it goes on. Such a trail may be made more interesting and exciting if it follows a story. Possibly some pirates landed and hid some booty the night before.

Hare and Hound. Instead of paper, use leaves such as the chestnut leaf. This does not litter the country and is much more instructive.

Tree Cribbage. This may be played for a time on a hike. One group may take one side of the road and the other the opposite, or the the points may go to the side recognizing the tree first. It should be limited to trees on the road side of the fences. Counting the number legs on the right and left is fun and usually ends up when coming to a poultry yard or a cemetery. Sometimes it is stated beforehand, as a joker, that a blue rabbit or a white horse seen first will count as 5 points.

Tree Pantomime. *Epoch* 1. Equip a person with smoked glasses, cotton batting in ears, gloves on hands, adhesive over lips, and clothes-pin on nose. Nothing in the environment makes any impression. *Epoch* 2. Meets a scout or woodsman. The woodsman teaches the greenhorn. He gets his eyes open, the cotton batting out of his ears, and so on. He is now able to recognize trees by feeling, taste, and smell. Being in the woods becomes a delight.

Pitch-pine Tag. Something like puss in the corner except that player cannot be tagged while touching a pitch pine, or some other tree agreed upon.

Leaf Passing. Choose a broad leaf. Players stand in rows. At a given signal, the one in front passes the leaf overhead to the one behind, who passes it between his legs to the next, and so on, alternating over and under. The one at the back of the line runs to the front, and the leaf is passed back again. This is repeated until the one who started in front is back again. If the leaf is torn or injured in any way, the game is lost.

Prove It. Players sit in a circle. The one starting the game says, "From where I am I can see a gray birch." The next one says, "From where I stand I can see a gray birch and a black cherry." The next player repeats all that the previous players have said, in exactly the same order, and adds another tree or bird. It may be limited to what is seen on one gray birch tree. If anyone doubts the statement, he may challenge the speaker. Anyone caught unable to defend his statement drops out of the game.

Opposite and Alternate. The players are divided into two lines, one called "opposites" (refers to buds and leaves) and the other "alternates." They face each other. When the leader calls "opposite," all the players in that line run and tag a tree that has opposite buds or leaves, and the "alternates" try to tag them. Anyone tagged before he finds a tree of his own becomes an "alternate." The side having the greatest number of players at the end of a given time wins. The same may be played with annuals and perennials.

Twig Diaries. Suited to late fall. A tree is named, such as tulip. The players must run and get a tulip twig that grew in the preceding summer. He counts the number of leaf scars and searches for a corresponding number of leaves that grew on the tulip tree.

Tree Jerusalem. On a hike through the forest, call out the name of a tree such as "black birch" and give 30 sec. for hikers to find one. All those claiming a tree in an allotted time get a grain of corn. The one getting the greatest number wins.

Leaf Relay. Line up in groups. Give each one at the head of the line a list of trees. At a starting signal, the first player hands the list to the second player and runs and gets a leaf of the first tree on the list. When he returns with the correct leaf, the second player passes the list to the third in line and runs for the leaf of the tree second on the list. The group getting the greatest number of leaves in a given time or finishing the list first wins.

Grand Change. Players are divided into four groups, as black oaks, red oaks, chestnuts, and elms. Players stand by their trees—no two at any one tree. "It" stands at the center and calls the name of a group—elms, for instance. At each signal, the designated group must change place. "It" tries to claim a tree in the interchange. If the center player calls forest, everyone is required to change but must keep to his particular kind of tree.

General

Curiously Shaped Animals. This game is well liked by children on nature guide trips. Give them 5 min. to get a curiously shaped animal. The scaling bark of the yellow pine is particularly well adapted to this use of the imagination. Driftwood and washed roots are suggested. Pine cones as the bodies of "filli-loo" birds, knots as curious hands, and berries to be used as eyes on invented figures add to the fun. In camp, it may be announced that there will be an exhibition that evening. This furnishes a good ending for the day.

Blind as a Bat. It is well known that a bat is not blind. Some people who are blind can see more than some people who are supposedly not blind. Blind the player with a neckerchief. Each player has a keeper who may have a string attached to the player to guide him. He is not allowed to carry on conversation. The keeper writes a list of natural objects identified by the "blinded player." As he walks through the woods, the one naming the most things correctly in 10 min. is the winner. The keepers may then take their turns.

Trailing. Let a person walk through an untraveled region. He should walk rather recklessly without taking care about footprints, snapping twigs, or breaking branches. At the end of 10 min., have him sit down in an inconspicuous place. At this moment, start off the group and see who can first find the trailmaker.

One Old Cat. Have a home base, umpire, and any number of fielders. The game is played with a volley ball or an indoor baseball. The batter hits the ball with his hand. He is out if a fly is caught or when hit with the ball. When the ball is hit, the umpire calls the name of a plant, such as primrose. The runner has to get on one of these plants to be safe. A fielder getting on one of these plants first makes it unsafe. The same plant cannot be named in succession. A runner on a plant must change to the new plant when the batter hits a fair ball. Fielders cannot hold the ball but must keep passing it. The umpire acts as pitcher and tosses up the ball for the batter to hit.

Camouflage. The group hide their eyes while one person or a stuffed animal is hidden in some conspicuous place, but not entirely

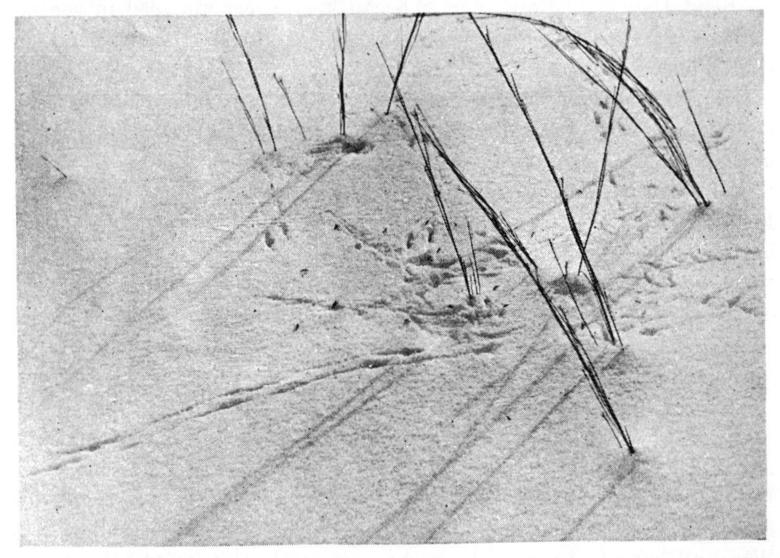

Fig. 66.—Reading signs in the snow. Was this grass visited by two-legged or four-footed animals? Did the animal walk or hop or jump? What was its covering? What was it after? (*Photograph by Robert Coffin.*)

out of sight. A confederate may assist in the camouflage by using green boughs, grasses, etc. He may make misleading sounds such as breaking of limbs to suggest climbing a tree, and so on. When all have seen through the camouflage, the first discoverer is entitled to be the next person for camouflage.

Aggressive Resemblance. This game is similar to the one given above but is more exciting. Post a lookout. Players render themselves indistinguishable and try to creep up on the lookout. If the lookout names and points to a person, that person is out of the game. The one who gets nearest to the lookout in a given time is the winner.

Outdoor Smelling. This is a variation of the indoor smelling game. To count, the object must be scented before being seen. It may be new-plowed ground, a pine wood, new-mown hay, a salt marsh, a dinner cooking, a forest fire, a stove coal fire, an underground fire, peat burning, a tar barrel, and so on.

Nature Sounds. The group are given 5 min. to see who can make the longest list of things heard in the woods during that time. It may be a raindrop, crow, rooster in distance, rustling leaves of oak or the swish of the pine, tapping of the woodpecker, or song of the brook.

Seed Dance. The player who can keep a certain seed in the air longest, without using the hands, wins. Milkweed seed is good for this amusement.

Sand Tracking. Make puzzles on the beach, such as: Someone has a pickaback ride, someone falls down and is helped up, someone crawls on hands and knees to view a bird, and so on.

Observation Game. This is a game commonly given in scouting. For city children, it may take place in front of a store window. It is better to use common objects of the out-of-doors or even rare birds that should be known about. Allow the group time to observe the coloring of the wood duck, for example. Have accounts made of what each player saw. Read one description at a time and have the players check off each point mentioned.

All-round Scouting. This game is a real test of scouting. The group is divided into patrols. Tell them that this game is to see which patrol is best adapted to go into the woods and shift for themselves. First of all, if they do not have matches, they need something to make a fire. Show them a piece of flint or quartz that is in the neighborhood. When all have had a good look at it, give them 1 min. to get a piece. Everyone having a piece and back in place at the end of 1 minute is given 1 point. Next say that they need good tinder. If they bring back good tinder, such as gray birch bark, shreds of red cedar, nest of a mouse, give them 1 point. Next they must have kindling wood. It should be fine, dry, and preferably resinous. Then they are sent for edible plants, such as have been found in the neighborhood. The specimens must be shown each time. Suggestions for "finds" are milkweed for greens, pine knot for a candle, sumac berries for lemonade, maple-sugar leaf to identify the sugar tree, pokeweed leaf for locating starch food, nuts for fat, and so on. Players are given a minute for each. The patrol having the best average is best suited to roughing it.

Compass-pacing-nature Trailing. This again is a game for real scouts. A meter is given that may read something like this:

Left-hand checks	Compass paces	Right-hand checks
	N.E.	
White pine	2	Granite boulder
Open field	16–30	White oaks
	N.20W.	
Brook	7	Alders
	N.15E.	
	10 Fence	
Fox den	13	White ash
Poison sumac	25	Ledge

The Plant Geography Game. There should be a library of good botany books, which tell whether certain plants were introduced from Europe, or Asia, and their points. The contestants are given a day or two to make their collection. All assemble for the final reckoning. The plants that come from Asia by the way of Europe will count 2 points if the side presenting the plant discovers that its original home was in Asia. Only 1 point is allowed for a European origin. Players will discover that the majority of plants introduced from Europe are weeds. Some interesting "whys" result from this game.

Foraging Expedition. This is a game of life that is played by all animals. Civilization has made it impossible for most people to play the game successfully. Have edible plants count 1 point, medicinal plants 1 point, and plants useful in crafts 1 point.

Spelling Bees. Divide players into groups. Play the game with fall flowers, insects, or trees. Hold up a fall flower. The first in line must name it and give an interesting fact about it. If he fails, he drops out of line. The side having the greatest number remaining wins. It is better to commence with the most common and well-known plants.

Intelligence Trail. This is one of the few trail games where time as well as intelligence may be the important factor. For example: trail starts at a granite boulder. If this granite has

Mostly pink feldspar............go S.S.W. 16 paces to a gray birch.
Considerable hornblende........go N.N.W. 10 paces to a gray birch.
No black mica.................go N. 20 paces to a red maple.
Over 50 per cent fine-grained
quartz.....................go S. 15 paces to a sassafras.

The next station is the red maple. If this tree has

Bark on upper limbs resembling
beech.......................go E. 12 paces to an elm.

Alternate leaves................	go E.	24 paces to an elm.
Leaves with same shade of green above and below.............	go W.	18 paces to a red maple.
Twigs with strong odor when crushed.....................	go W.	30 paces to a smooth sumac.

The next station is an elm. If this tree is

Over 125 ft. tall................	go N.N.E.	20 paces to a woodchuck hole.
Less than 50 ft. in crown spread..	go S.S.W.	30 paces to an anthill.
4 to 5 ft. in diameter..........	go S.E.	38 paces to a coral mushroom.
Has leaves averaging over 6 in. in length....................	go N.W.	17 paces to a limestone boulder

(To get the height of a tree, sight it with a pencil held vertically at arm's length. Turn the pencil to a horizontal position and locate a. corresponding distance on the ground from the trunk. Pace off this horizontal distance.)

Best Curio Collector. Played with a group walking through the forest. Name the curio and let the crowd scatter to find it. The one discovering it first gives a war whoop, and others gather around him. If he is successful, that is the starting point for the next. Send for such things as the following: A humpbacked tree, a tree struck by lightning, a tree with last year's catkin, a tree with scale insects on it, a tree infected with galls, a tree with branches on one side, last year's fruit stem, a tree with moss on the north side only, a tree with lichens on the south side, a tree that has a stone in the center of the fruit, a deciduous tree that has cones, an evergreen tree that does not have cones, a red maple that has had fruit, a red maple that has not had fruit, a twig that took 10 years to grow 1 in., a twig that grew 10 in. in 1 year, a twig that grew 36 in. or more in 1 year. See who can find the oldest twig 5 in. long, a sumac bush 5 years old, a rock with a quartz vein, a tree with a rock callous, where a woodpecker has been feeding, a woodpecker's home, the work of the sapsucker, a feldspar crystal, pine pitch enough to fill a thimble, fruit of the ash tree, a mud dauber's nest, a leaf miner's home, nuts gnawed by a squirrel, an owl's pellet, evidence of a rabbit, a robin's nest, an animal footprint.

Sentinel and Marauders. A game adapted for rest hour on a hike. Seat one patrol in a circle with individuals at least 10 ft. apart. Cut shrubs 3 ft. high and stick them in the ground 5 ft. in front of each member of patrol. Blindfold players with neckerchiefs. A judge stands in the middle of the circle. The second patrol is given 10 min.

to steal into the circle and get a shrub and walk away with it without being detected. The seated patrol, or sentinels, when hearing a footstep, twig snap, or unnatural rustling of leaves, points in that direction. Any marauder pointed at in this way is eliminated. The judge indicates this by a wave of the hand. The eliminated individual must go to a point some 60 ft. away, decided upon before the game starts. The score equals the number of shrubs taken out of the circle for at least a distance of 30 ft. in the 10 min. The sentinels and marauders exchange positions. The team securing the greatest number of shrubs in 10 min. wins. Dead twigs and dried leaves may be placed around the circle, or it may be played amongst a thick growth of shrubs. This game develops great skill in stealthiness.

Sound Locator. A good woodsman can locate a sound quickly both as to direction and distance. As a preliminary training, have "It" stand with back to 10 or 12 people. No person to be nearer another than 10 ft. A leader points to someone who whistles. "It" turns around quickly and names the one who whistled. If correct, the whistler takes his place or score the best average for 10 trials. Outdoors, this may be tried by rustling autumn leaves on the ground, by wading in water, by jumping in sand, by dropping a stone a few feet away and having the person identify the stone, by snapping a twig, by taking three steps, and so on.

Firefly Tag. Played when it is dark. A fast runner is provided with a flashlight. He must give occasional flashes. Pursuers must tag the runner. Whoever catches him becomes the firefly.

Shell Divers. The diver scores the number he brings up at one dive, or different values may be given to different kinds.

Pine-cone Baseball. Use pine cones instead of baseball. The pitcher throws a cone at the batter. If the cone hits the batter, a "strike" is made. If not, it is a "ball." Count strikes and balls as in baseball. The batter may hit the ball. If it is a fair hit, he becomes a base runner. Runners may be put out between bases by being hit with the cone in play. Players cannot run with cones. The batter may catch the cone and throw it into the field.

Gall Test. The players try to collect the greatest number of galls in a given time. One point for each kind obtained and one additional point for each one identified.

Trail Observation. A good scout can retrace a trail because he remembers certain objects along the trail. Walk for a certain distance over a trail and then ask 10 questions, or each one may write 10 questions and then exchange. Arguments will follow, and it will usually be necessary to go over the trail again. Various objects may be placed along a back-yard walk. They then return to the house and are given a pencil and paper to make a list of what they saw.

The Balance of Nature. The players impersonate a hunter and various animals. Each has a safety spot, his "home" on which he cannot be touched. The hunter traps the skunk, the skunk eats mice, the mice eat bumblebees, the bumblebees assist the clover (they may sting the cow), the cows eat clover, the hunter drinks milk. The skunk is safe in a hole in the ground. (In the game, this may range from an anthole to a hole of the groundhog.) The mouse is safe in a hollow tree or in an abandoned bird's nest. The bumblebee is safe under a stone (standing on stone is allowable). The cow is safe under a tree. The hunter is safe at home.

At a given signal, the struggle for existence begins. Anyone tagged by his particular enemy—when away from his safety, becomes that animal. The game may be ended by saying that, after a given signal, anyone tagged becomes *hors de combat* and is out of the game.

Sense of Direction. Greenhorns get lost going into the woods, and braggarts get lost when they try to get out. Zigzag a group through a forest and then have them try to go straight back to camp. This is not a running race. Everyone is expected to walk. The one getting back first may have gone on the most direct route. If a fire tower is at hand, the lender may check up or all scouts may point toward camp and one climb a tree and determine the winner.

Breaking through the Line. Outline the region in which the contest is to take place. It may be between the lake and a certain road. Half of party guards the line and other half tries to break through. Pine cones may be used for ammunition. To be killed, the scout must feel the bullet. Anyone killed is out of the game and must lie down until scalp (neckerchief) is taken or until he is rescued by his own army. A player cannot take active part in game after he has been "killed." This game may be scored on a point basis. Five points for a patrol leader, 2 for a scout, and 10 for the scoutmaster. Everyone getting through line gets 2 points for his side.

Spying. Have one group ¼ mile away from other groups do something. The other groups are on a hilltop and take notes on what they see. Each group on the lookout may have binoculars. The group having the most accurate description, according to the judgment of the party in action wins.

What's Wrong with These Plants and Animals? To give you a start, we shall tell you that there are three things that are wrong in the sketch of the hawk. Before reading any further, try to discover what the trouble is. If I say, "Is the hawk a good neighbor?" some of you will answer immediately, "No, because he steals chickens." I shall then say, "How do you know this?" You will probably have to say, "Someone told me." And, in turn, someone else told that person, for although the cooper's hawk has been known to feed on poultry, most hawks prefer mice and other animals that eat our grain and gnaw our fruit trees. It is unjust to blame all for the misdeeds of a few. The hawk in the sketch has brought an ear of corn to the stump. Hawks, however, do not eat corn. They eat the mouse that eats the corn, and that is a different story. It is very easy for people who do not observe to make ignorant statements.

The hawk is one of our most graceful fliers. When he wishes to go up, he faces the wind. When he decides to drop, he lifts his wings. When he soars in a spiral path, he steers with his tail. All hawks need a long tail for a rudder. Short-tailed birds, like the duck, fly straight ahead and would have a great deal of difficulty in turning a corner. The hawk in the picture, then, has the wrong tail for cutting corners. It would mean disaster on his first trip.

The main tools of the hawk are his sharp, curved claws. He keeps them sharp and well polished for immediate use or inspection. When seizing a mouse, he must have a strong grasp or perhaps miss his breakfast. All hawks have three toes in front and one in back for this purpose. His toes are just as important as our fingers. The loss of either may change the whole future.

There are at least three things wrong in the sketch of the bat. Before you find them, here are a few statements about the bat; check them "right" or "wrong," according to what you believe. (1) The bat is blind. (2) The bat has pointed ears. (3) The bat is a bird. (4) The bat eats insects. (5) The bat is a fur-bearing animal. (6) The bat has a voice. (7) Bats like to get in ladies' hair. (8) Bats have five fingers. (9) Bats take their young for joy rides during the evening. (10) Bats suck blood. (1), (3), (7), and (10) are wrong. Strange, is it not, how much we learn that is not so?

The large eyes, beak, and three toes on the hind foot are wrong in the picture.

Following the game, you may wish to have a discussion.

CHAPTER XI

ADMINISTRATIVE LEADERSHIP IN THE COMMUNITY PROGRAM FOR NATURE RECREATION

Any executive organizing a community program in nature recreation should consider several items.

The Formation of a Coordinating Council of Nature Activities. Every community has several organizations which are concerned with nature activities in its various aspects. There are clubs (Bird, Hiking, Izaak Walton League), museums, government agencies (county agent, foresters), schools, park departments, recreation departments, and private agencies such as the Scouts, Y.M.C.A., Y.M.H.A. Often one organization is jealous of the incorporation of new nature endeavors by another agency. This may cripple a desirable undertaking. A coordinating council of nature activities, which consists of a representative from each organization, is needed.

Delegates to this should be appointed for their genuine interest in nature recreation, training, experience, and civic influence so that the resulting council may be comprised of men and women who have recognized training and leadership in the philosophy and methods of nature recreation.

Meetings should be called at least twice a year (March and September); otherwise as emergencies arise.

Such a council may have the following *objectives:*

1. *To act* as a body before which any individual or organization may place problems which relate to nature education or nature recreation.

2. *To coordinate* efforts for new nature projects such as youth hostels, trailside museums, nature trails, nature guide service in parks, work in schools and on playgrounds, and training courses.

3. *To prevent duplication of effort.* To prevent a new movement from being monopolized by an organization that is not so well adapted to handle the project.

4. *To unite efforts.* Especially for nature legislation and conservation policies. To protect nature shrines that are suddenly endangered. To thaw out frozen ducks, to de-oil ducks, to feed pheasants that are being winter killed, to prevent pollution of a stream.

5. *To disseminate information* of opportunities in courses of study, lectures, trips, and calendar events. To coordinate programs so as not to have conflicts in dates.

FIG. 67.—A portable voting booth is easily set up as a day camp museum. This trailside museum shows Frank Elliott, park naturalist, bringing in a new specimen. (*Photograph courtesy of Tam Deering, Director Public Recreation Commission, Cincinnati, Ohio.*)

6. *To speak with force* as well as authority in emergency situations and as needed. When gardening is needed in the schools, when a county home has no nature recreation, when a misinformed official is having his men "skin the parks," when the last duck is about to be exterminated, when the last marsh is to be drained for agriculture, and when the last forest is to be subdivided for house lots.

7. *To be a bulwark against political pressure* that is unfavorable to the nature movement and that is based on patronage rather than facts.

8. *To take an active part in developing and enriching* local nature recreation and maintaining it on a high standard.

9. *To present a plan for intelligent conservation of our natural resources.*

Some Suggestions for Activity Procedure. (Renumber according to needs of community.)

1. One of the first steps is the provision for an outdoor *training institute.* It is needed for scouts, playground leaders, Y.M.C.A.

FIG. 68.—California day camp museum, Cincinnati, Ohio. The interior of the trailside museum set up in a salvaged election booth. In charge of the museum is Mr. Frank Elliott, who has set out to make a display of the materials to be found on the area, in the form of fossils, wood, and specimens of fauna and flora. Visitors are most interested in what they themselves contribute. (*Photograph courtesy of Tam Deering, Director of Public Recreation Commission, Cincinnati, Ohio.*)

leaders, teachers, 4-H leaders, garden-club leaders, volunteer leaders, camp leaders, and so on, to certify leaders on merit.

2. The *school curriculum* should provide an adequate program in nature education that includes conservation.

3. If a *new school* is to be constructed, there should be a provision for a nature room, and the property should be large enough to include landscaping, a garden area, and an ample playground.

4. Steps should be taken to encourage a more meaningful use of the *parks, conservatories,* and *zoos.*

5. The parks should include a *nature guide service, trailside museums, nature trails,* and *youth hostels.*

6. It is not financially practical—nor is it desirable—that any one organization monopolize the *youth-hostel* movement. That is a facility that should be developed for the benefit of the public as a whole.

7. Set up a *nature calendar* that announces courses of study, lectures, trips, and important nature events of various clubs. This acts as a clearing house to prevent conflict of important nature events and duplication of effort.

8. Crusades are needed to *protect wild-life areas,* such as the last marsh, the last beaver pond, the native wild flowers, and in good outdoor manners.

9. Use all publicity possible to develop an enlightened *public opinion* as to conservation, forest-fire prevention, and dust control.

10. *Create a nature leaders service bureau* to bring together leaders and organizations needing nature leaders.

11. Encourage nature activities such as a *children's science fair* and an historical pageant.

12. Be prepared to meet the situation when the Federal government cuts off unemployment relief.

The setting up of committees, such as the following: (Every member of the council should serve on at least one committee. Any committee not functioning is automatically disbanded.)

1. *Legislative.*
2. *Leadership.* Training. Service.
3. *Wild-life Propagating.* Planting, stocking, release of game.
4. *Calendar.* Integrating community calendar and publishing monthly.
5. *Public Relations.* Parks, schools, playgrounds. Newspapers.
6. *Children's Science Fair.*
7. *Field Committee.* Day camp, hostels, trails, and trailside museums.

Every Community Should Have a "Master Plan."

1. *Base Map.* Showing topography, existing and proposed parks, parkways, trails, playgrounds, waterways, lakes.

2. *Zoning Plan.* Agriculture, forestry, wilderness areas, recreation areas, historical points, residential development, commercial districts.

3. "*Ten-year Program.*" Annual goals, priorities, funds, personnel. The more nearly the plans of a community approach national-park policies the greater the service it renders.

This program will include:

Parkways. Landscaped lanes to the country or connecting park drives with trees, shrubbery, and lawns. No buildings fronting them.

National parkways—usually historic routes. Cook County Forest Way, Shaw Garden Way.

Playgrounds. Within ½ mile of every neighborhood. Apparatus, field house, swimming pool. Determined by centers of population. Trained leaders.

Neighborhood Parks. Within a mile of every neighborhood. "Squares," "commons," public gardens, village "greens." Boston

Fig. 69.—Playground leaders need imagination. A tennis court is more than a place to bounce a rubber ball. A wire fence around a playground is more than a safety device. The grounds keeper should not deprive children of an opportunity for recreation through service. (*Photograph courtesy of V. K. Brown, Chicago Park District.*)

and Philadelphia. Jewel Box of St. Louis; conservatories of Chicago and Pittsburgh.

City Parks. Within 2 miles of every neighborhood. City forest, city water supply, land reservations; Central Park, New York City; Arnold Arboretum, Boston. Cincinnati and Pittsburgh have organized nature guide service free to community. Garden centers, cultural gardens (Shakespeare, Germanic, Hebrew), as in Cleveland.

Rochester, N. Y., has outstanding city parks. Their planning, as in Louisville, Ky., and other cities, was identified with Frederick Law

Olmsted. His counsel was always to develop treasures of rural and sylvan scenery and to have a regard for existing topographical peculiarities. He also said that recreation must not be discordant with the natural character of that site. The Fine Arts Garden of Cleveland is an excellent example of his work.

Radburn, N.J., is a community run on a cooperative basis including schools, stores, and operas as well as parks. The houses face the parks, and the streets are at the back. Children do not have to cross a street in going to school or to playgrounds. City planning commissions would do well to study the organization. See the booklet *Chicago's Parks* (1961), Chicago Park District, Administration Building, 425 East 14th Blvd., Chicago.

County and Metropolitan Parks. Well-developed natural areas are due to someone's planning. In Milwaukee, the excellent county-park system may be traced to the door of the father of Milwaukee county parks—Charles B. Whitnall—and to the practical carrying out of his vision by Alfred L. Boerner, county landscape engineer. Greenfield Park at West Allis has been chosen as an example of modern planning. A 450-ft. well on a hilltop with a turbine pump supplies 250 gal. water per min., which is used eight times as it winds its way through the park. It cascades for aeration. It receives copper sulphate to precipitate the lime. The stream empties into two lakes which simulate the kettle-hole lakes of the region. Technically, those lakes are warming basins for the swimming pool which holds 750,000 gal. for 500 swimmers. The water passes through a wading pool for the kiddies before reaching the pool where it goes to the lake for boating. Thence it passes over an artificial fall to a bog garden, after which it makes water hazards for the golf course. The bridges at Greenfield Park are made of limestone, whereas, in the glaciated park at Whitnall, the bridges are made of glacial boulders. Most of the county parks have lakes, bridle trails, swimming pools, and playfields where the participants do not fight the shrubbery. Each river is a unit that links the intercounty system and the new suburban development areas. Property owners donate land and pay one-half the cost of the boulevard construction.* They feel that it is a worth-while investment. See latest Biennial Report of the Milwaukee County Park Commission and the Milwaukee County Regional Planning Department, Court House, Milwaukee.

State and National Parks. Each national park has some outstanding natural feature, such as volcanic phenomena at Crater Lake National Park, ice action at Glacier National Park, geysers at Yellow-

*1940 statistics.

stone. New York is outstanding in its state-park development. Niagara, Letchworth, and the Palisades are worthy of study. Cook Forest in Pennsylvania has a primitive forest. Spring Mill Pioneer Village in Indiana exemplifies pioneer industries and the social life of 1816. Its stone gristmill and water-power sawmill operating in summer, its virgin timber, museum of tools, rock garden, blind aquatic life in underground streams are other features. The Indiana Dunes Park is again distinctive. All the nature guides in Indiana state parks are majors in natural science in Indiana universities. Bird hikes, evening lectures, all-day hikes, or auto tours are some of the nature opportunities that are offered.

References

FAIRBANKS. *Conservation Reader*, World Book Company, Yonkers, N.Y.
HALL. *Yosemite National Park*, Park Naturalist, Yosemite, Calif.
HODGE and DAWSON. *Civic Biology*, Ginn and Company, New York.
MILLS. *Your National Parks* and *Rocky Mountain National Park*, Houghton Mifflin Company, Boston.
MUIR. *Our National Parks*, Houghton Mifflin Company, Boston.
SKINNER. *The Yellowstone Nature Book*, A. C. McClurg & Company, Chicago.

Suggestions for a Nature Recreation Institute. "Learn by doing and not by talking." At the present time, the weakest link in the nature program is the lack of trained leadership. It is best organized by the Coordinating Council of Nature Activities with a local volunteer staff. One or two paid specialists may be brought in from the outside. A local camp is an ideal meeting place, and an organization camp can usually be obtained at a nominal fee. A two weeks' course held the last of June is the most suitable period, since camp counselors and playground leaders are seeking assistance at that time. Scouts and Camp Fire guardians welcome training periods over week ends.

The nearest college might be the logical organization for preparing skilled leaders. Most of these institutions have not yet recognized the opportunity as well as the necessity of training leaders in recreation and for outdoor programs. Until these institutions awaken to the situation, executives will have to meet the problem the best way possible.

There are several organizations that have short-term courses with the major emphasis on content, including the Nature Education Department, Oglebay Institute, Wheeling, W. Va., and the four National Audubon Society camps, located in Maine, Connecticut, Wisconsin, and California. The Yosemite School of Field Nature

History sent forth well-trained leaders until its closing in 1953.

The universities that supply the greatest number of informal outdoor nature leaders are Cornell and the College of Forestry at Syracuse. With the demand for leisure-time programs, there will undoubtedly be an increased opportunity for obtaining this service.

SUGGESTIONS FOR A NATURE PROGRAM

General Nature Activities*

Some nature service clubs

- Appalachian
- Auto tours
- Book study
- Campfire
- Canoeing naturalists
- Conservation
- First aid
- 4-H
- Future Farmers of America
- Junior Waltonians
- Hiking
- Leadership
- Microscope
- Museum
- Nature
- Nature guards
- Outing
- Pioneer
- Scouts
- Sea scouts
- Social hygiene
- Storytelling
- Wolf cubs
- Woodcraft

Some community nature projects

- Beautiful views (preserving)
- Billboard vs. scenery campaign
- Campfires for the public
- Clean-up campaign
- Guiding afield
- Mapping trails
- Nature column for daily paper
- Open-air services
- Outdoor good-manners campaign
- Park museums
- Roadside nature shrines
- Science fair
- Trails for hiking
- Trails, nature
- Trailside museum

Special days

- May Day
- June breakfast
- Flag Day
- Hallowe'en
- Old Home
- Columbus
- Husking Bee
- Thanksgiving
- Christmas
- Valentine's Day

Some worth-while nature trips

- Camera
- County fair
- Farm
- Good turn
- Map and compass
- Map trailing
- Museum
- State college
- State experiment station
- Trailing

Some naturalists' birthdays to celebrate

- Jan. 14. Thornton W. Burgess, 1874
- Feb. 3. Sidney Lanier, 1842
- Feb. 11. Thomas A. Edison, 1847
- Mar. 7. Luther Burbank, 1849
- Mar. 15. Liberty Hyde Bailey, 1858
- Apr. 3. John Burroughs, 1837
- Apr. 21. John Muir, 1838
- Apr. 22. Enos Mills, 1870
- Apr. 26. John James Audubon, 1785
- May 31. Walt Whitman, 1819
- June 21. Dan Beard, 1850
- July 12. Henry D. Thoreau, 1817

Some related handcraft units

- Aquarium
- Cabin
- Camp map
- Conservation posters
- Fireplaces outdoors
- Hike map
- Life-history charts
- Observation tower
- Photography
- Scenic locator

Nature classics worth telling about

- Alaskan seal
- Beaver life
- Bird migration
- Bubonic plague
- Cicada
- Dog heroes
- Golden plover
- Heroes of science
- Horse heroes
- Mormons and the Franklin gulls
- Pilgrims
- Reindeer
- Sequoia
- Yellow fever

* Date or number in order of expectancy.

Activities with Animals Other Than Birds*

Some animal service clubs	Some community animal projects	Some worth-while animal trips	Some related handcraft units
Fish:	Animal rescue league	Apiary	Aquariums
Anglers	Antisteel-trap campaign	Collecting	Bat belfry
Tropical	Clam farm	Dredging trip	Casts of footprints
General:	Deer salting	Fish hatchery	Cocoon exhibit
Animal conservation	Game farm	Fishing through ice	Exhibit case
Humane education	Insect zoo	Fox farm	Fishway
Pet club	Muskrat management	Fur shop	Habitat groups
Insects:	Observation hive	Livestock show	Insect nets
Bee	Pet loan shop	Milk plant	Life history charts
Entomologists	Releasing fur bearers	Museum	Models
Mammals:	Reptile census	Packing house	Pet cages
Baby beef	Skunk raising	Pet shop	Posters
Calf	Stocking waters	State game farm	Trail signs
Dairy	Stream improvement	Stockyards	Turtle pen
Horse	Wild-life refuge	Zoo	Wild-life shelters
Kennel			
Pig			
Reptile			
Shell			

* Date or number in order of expectancy.

ACTIVITIES WITH BIRDS*

Some bird clubs	Some community service projects	Some worth-while bird trips	Some related handcraft units
Birds	Banding	Canary show	Automatic feeder
Junior Audubon	Calendar	Chick hatching	Baths
Pigeon	Christmas tree	Hawk migration	City-block nest map
Poultry	Filling stations	Heron rookery	Collect foods
	Flicker hotels	Marsh	Feeding shelves
	Incubating chick eggs	Nest collecting (in fall)	Food chart
	Nest census	Pheasant farm	Houses
	Nest servicing material	Pigeon loft	Martin house
	Pheasant stocking	Poultry yard	Posters for bird day
	Quail food patch	Seashore	Shelters
	Sanctuary	Tern island	Suet basket
	Wild-fowl refuge	Wild-fowl sanctuary	Suet logs
	Winter feeding	Zoo	Tree-swallow houses around lake

* Date or number in order of expectancy.

EARTH, SKY, AND WATER ACTIVITIES*

Some service clubs	Some community projects	Some worth-while trips	Some related handcraft units
Airplane, model	Air and health	Astronomy observatory	Balanced aquarium
Electricity	Building-materials exhibit	Aviation field	Blueprints
Glider school	Building regulations	Battleship	Boat modeling
Lapidary	Canning demonstration	Beachcombing	Coal products exhibit
Mechanical toys	Christmas mechanical toys	Blast furnace	Color tops
Mineral	Combustible materials used in building a home	Coal mine	Kaleidoscope
Model boats	Firemaking	Cold-storage plant	Kites
Radio	Fire-prevention day	Dry-cleaning establishment	Magnet experiments
Rock	Fire, uses of	Dune area	Model airplanes
Sailing fleet	Fire extinguisher, homemade	Filtration plant	Paper gliders
Skyscrapers	Fuels, local	Lighthouse	Pin-hole camera
Star study	Geology shrines	Planetarium	Sand machines
Surveying	Record, daily (humidity, temperature, wind)	Quarry	Shadow stick data
Water craft	Soil conservation	Rock collecting	Soap making
Weather bureau	Storm signals	Sewage plant	Sun dial
	Star information	Shore line	Volcanic eruption model
	Water conservation	Star gazing	Water cycle chart
	Water recreation	Stones, to collect	Water wheels
	Water as a worker	Waterworks	Weather vanes
	Weather forecasting	Weather bureau	Windmills

* Date or number in order of expectancy.

Gardening Activities*

Some garden service clubs	Some community-garden projects	Some worth-while garden trips	Some related handcraft units
Mainly for beauty: City beautiful Flower garden Flowerpot Hospital flowers Japanese garden Memorial Native landscape Saucer gardens Wild flower Window box	Beautifying parks Beautifying road-sides Beautifying school grounds Bulb planting Garden tours Highway planting Landscaping campaign Park flower beds Table decorations Willow cuttings for improvement plantings	Bog garden Bulb garden Dish gardens Rock gardens Rose gardens Sunken gardens Terrace gardens Wall gardens Water gardens Wild-flower gardens	Autumn perennial exhibit Bulb show Dutch costumes Garden houses House plants from cuttings show Pergola Pool Porch baskets Spore prints Vines and trellises
Mainly for instruction: Arboretum Cactus Farm Fern Fruit Garden club Garden center Garden exchange Greenhouse Home gardens Prairie club School gardens Vegetable gardens	Garden calendar Garden fair Germanic garden Goldenrod garden Grandmother's garden Hebrew garden Indian garden Italian garden Plantings along fences School garden fair Shakespeare garden Wild aster garden Wild-flower garden	Blueberry farm Community market Cranberry bog Garden supply Gladiola farm Greenhouse Herb gardens Home gardens Industrial gardens Nursery Perennial gardens Truck gardens Vegetable gardens	Cold frame Garden stakes Homemade gadgets Hotbed Medicinal herbs Mushrooms Pottery Rocks for soil water experiments Sandbox for gardening Seed dispersal exhibit Seed mounts Weed exhibit Wild fruits

* Date or number in order of expectancy.

Trees and Forest Activities*

Some tree service clubs	Some community tree projects	Some worth-while tree trips	Some related handcraft units
Mainly trees as a group (Forests): Forest-fire patrol Forest rangers Forestry club School forest Town forest	Forest-fire prevention Forest-flower protection George Washington forest Memorial grove Shrubs for birds Tree nursery Tree planting on roadsides Trees for all, black walnut Walnut plantation Wild-flower reserve	Alpine zone Autumn foliage Dune trees Evergreen forest Landscape, native Swamp Timber line Town forest Tree nursery State forest	Autumn color chart Forest maps Forest museum Native dyes Ozalid-leaf prints Poisonous-plant exhibit Tree calendar Winter bouquets Winter-twigs exhibit Wood specimens
Mainly individual trees: Basket-willow growers Live Christmas trees Memorial trees Nut-tree club Tree club	Apple-blossom festival Basket-willow plantation Lilac week Tree pruning Tree-seed collecting Tree seedlings from historic trees Tree spraying Tree trails on streets Trees, community Christmas Trees, potted Christmas Walnut plantation Wild-flower protection	Arboretum Bayberrying Berrying Bog trotting Evergreens for window boxes Lumber yard Maple-sugar day Rhododendron time Sawmill Seed collecting State forest Wood-products museum	Basketry Bird-food exhibit Campfire circle Candleholders, rustic Historic tree labels Labels for trees Pine-needle basketry Terrariums Totem pole Tree protectors Willowware Wood carving

* Date or number in order of expectancy.

APPRAISAL SHEET FOR COMMUNITY NATURE RECREATION[1]

This is an attempt to assist in the self-analysis of community nature recreation. Each of these standards is being achieved in some community and a large per cent of them in many communities. No two individuals would agree on what the standards are or on the allocation of points to the separate items. However, the averaging of the estimate made by a group of community leaders should give a fair picture of the needs and accomplishments of the community. This appraisal sheet is presented to those desirous of obtaining a sincere view of the local situation. It is taken for granted that the schools, parks, playgrounds, a natural history museum, and a coordinating council may be equally effective in a community. Each is given a value of 20 points. Perhaps Pittsburgh, Pa., and Springfield, Mass., come nearest to fulfilling the requirements. The ideal community may score 100 points. The value of each item is given. Your estimate for the item should be written to the right of the maximum score allowed.

1. Elementary Schools (Grades I–VI).

a. No course.......................................0
Nature-study units often presented as part of social science.......1
"Paper course" (a printed course, but optional with teacher).....3
Course regularly given each schoolday in all elementary grades (if in 50 per cent of schools, allow 3 points; if fewer days, apportion points, and so on).......................................7

b. Supervisor of elementary science, gardening, or nature study, or a curriculum committee on same (full time: 10 mo.)................4

c. School gardens for at least half of the schools (every child has the opportunity).......................................3

d. Home gardening taught in at least one grade (if one grade in 50 per cent of schools, 1 point).......................................2

e. Community buildings. Auditorium suited for community use, housing free, Scouts, 4-H Clubs, adult garden clubs, and so on....4

f. Available materials, including visual aids (may be serviced by a department of visual education, School Nature League, a club, a natural environment, and so on).......................................3

g. Outdoor minded, six planned field trips for each grade during school year.......................................4

h. Home "chores" in form of assignments, pets, window boxes, and so on.......................................2

[1] This appraisal was first written by the author for the National Recreation Association and is included here through their courtesy.

i. Public school camp or equivalent opportunity....................4
j. School grounds satisfactorily landscaped..........................2
k. Teacher improvement in way of training classes, nature school, demonstration trips, institutes..3
l. Advantages of hobby show, science fair, birdhouse contest, 4-H exhibit, and so on..2
Possible score...20

Add points and divide by 2 for an estimate of what the schools are contributing.

FIG. 70.—Some of Boston's parks have become safe places for waterfowl. This is the happy result of a long process of education. It also takes a long period of education to bring young folks to the level that guarantees safety for wild ducks. Young folks from the Children's Museum are here seen assuming their responsibility of park citizenship. (*Photograph by Robert J. Keller and used through courtesy of the Children's Museum, Jamaica Plain, Boston.*)

2. Parks. (Rural communities may score available county or state parks.)

a. Community averages 1 acre per 100 population (if 1 acre per 300, give 1 point)..3
b. Superintendent with interest in and ability to appreciate an active nature program (estimate by activities he sponsors or inaugurates) 2

c. *Landscape engineer* who gives full time to this work or parks except natural areas satisfactorily landscaped (if gives one-third of time give 1 point, and so on) 4

d. *Wild-life areas* (have easy access or within hiking distance of woods and swamps left in natural condition without cleaning out of all underbrush) 3

e. *County parks* within 15 miles that are wild-life areas (2 points for 2 areas) 2

f. *Nature trails* (in at least one park area maintained for not less than 2 mo. in the year) 3

g. *Trailside museum* for all cities of 25,000 or more (at least one in a city park that is maintained not less than 2 mo. in the year and emphasizes local material) 4

h. *Park nature guide* for all cities of 25,000 or more (at least one trained leader who gives full time in one or more parks for at least 2 mo. in the year) 6

i. *Public camp* or youth hostels where nature groups may camp for one or more nights (if limited to summer months, 2 points) 3

All cities of 500,000 or more should have the following (check only one item under each heading):

j. *Botanical garden*. Plants formally labeled (scientific and common names) 1
Labels contain interesting information 2
Docent service (leaders available free) 3

k. *Public greenhouse*. Public merely gazes at plants 1
Printed information (booklets free), continuous exhibit 2
Leaders who will instruct classes 3
Includes practical work for children (if four activities or more, 4 points, if two activities, 2 points; cuttings, bulb growing, repotting, and so on) 4

l. *Arboretum*. Trees formally labeled, including common name 1
Labels contain more than scientific and common name and geographical origin 2
Leadership available for taking groups through the arboretum 3

m. *Zoo*. Public merely gazes at animals 1
An educational program 3

Total score for parks 20

Communities of less than 25,000 add first 6 units (may substitute 7 and 8).
Communities of 25,000 or more add first 8 units and divide by 1.5 for score.
Communities of 500,000 or more add units and divide by 2 for score.

3. Playgrounds (where complete area is not restricted to athletics).

a. What is the playground acreage per 1,000 school children? 3

b. Full-time *recreation director* with interest in and ability to appreciate an active nature program (estimate by what he does or sponsors) . . 3

c. *Supervisor of nature recreation* (not less than 3 mo. a year)
Equivalent of college education with major in nature education or training course annually in nature leadership....................3
d. *Minimum size* of 3 acres for at least 20 per cent of playgrounds...3
e. *Landscaped playgrounds.* Natural shading (at least one large shade tree)..1
(check only) Only inside and outside boundary fence.............2
(one item) Around buildings and play areas as well as boundary...3
f. *One leader on each playground* responsible for a nature program (if 40 per cent of playgrounds have a nature leader, allow 2 points, and so on)..5
g. *Nature-projects room*, workshop, or museum where children do nature work and exhibit under leadership (if only true of 20 per cent of playgrounds, give 1 point, and so on)..........................2
h. Definite *nature projects* involving daily care on the part of the children..2
i. *Recognition contests.* Birds, flowers, trees, and so on.............1
j. *Garden activities* (caring for shrubbery and window boxes every day) Caring for trees and flowers and having an individual garden plot.4
k. *Off-playground hikes* (not hikes without nature objectives. At least a hike a week)..4
l. *Other bona fide nature activities* program such as nature trails, nature stories, nature dramatizations, traveling exhibits, cow visiting playground, birdhouse competition (four activity periods per week) ...4
m. *Fall exhibition* of nature work.................................3
Total score for playground.......................................20

Add points and divide by 2 for an estimate of what the playgrounds are doing for community nature recreation.

4. **Natural-history Museum.** All cities of 500,000 should have a natural-history museum. (Rural communities may check individual schools)

a. *Specimens* merely in dead storage (no educational program). (If this is checked, do not check any other item.).......................3
b. A recognized *department of public instruction* with an individual definitely responsible for a program..........................8
c. A *free loan department* (films, slides, pictures, specimens)..........4
d. *Auditorium lectures* (at least weekly lectures free)................3
e. *Instruction* with aid of visual material (at least weekly)..........5
f. *Activity clubs* or classes—actually make things, take trips, or have at least weekly meetings..10
g. *Leadership training* (6 days, 10 points; 3 days, 5 points. Presumably a competent staff)...10
Possible score..20

Add points and divide by 2 for an estimate of what the museum is doing for the community.

5. **Coordinating Council of Nature Activities** ("home rule" whereby local activities are administered by representatives of local nature clubs, and so on. In rural communities, this may be the Grange, Izaak Walton League, or School Board).

An organized group encouraging nature activities, conservation of natural resources, landscaping of public property, observation of natural holidays, outdoor education, camping, and so on.

Representatives from schools, parks, playgrounds, museum, social agencies, and nature clubs of the community organized to make fullest use of facilities provided. At least four nature clubs such as bird, star, flower, garden, and so on..4

Exclusive function is responsibility for coordinating vital nature activities of the community for all ages and all kinds of people.

Made up of laymen serving without pay.

Meets at least once a year and whenever an urgent problem arises, such as play space plus landscaping for a new school, the conservation of a marsh, and so on. It is a policy-forming group that recommends to its constituent agencies..5

Newspapers—actual space devoted to nature, conservation, special celebrations such as Arbor Day and Bird Day, and so on, sponsored by Council..4

Training course for nature leaders—either in nearest teacher-training institution or university instigated by the Council (semester's course)..4

An intensive leaders' training institute in camp each spring—at least 2 weeks long so that activities in camp, on playground, in recreation-centers, in schools, parks, homes, and churches shall provide wholesome good times outdoors..3

Score for coordinating Council..20

Estimated total score__________

Appraisers may feel free to include items not mentioned in the list that they believe contribute to the nature recreation of the community. Community garden clubs, nature radio programs, bird clubs, and nature clubs have rating values that may be appended to the proper section. If the garden clubs sponsor a nature leader for the playground, for example, the club may be substituted for item *e* under Playgrounds.

CHAPTER XII

THE TECHNIQUE OF NATURE-CLUB LEADERSHIP

Study the Chapter on Leadership through Nature Clubs.

Additional Hints to Club Leaders. Put up a poster announcing the first meeting of the club. Make it artistic, to the point (such as garden club), limited in membership (fourth, fifth, and sixth grades), limited in number (16 members), and put in a mystery element. Make the first meeting an open meeting. If more than 16 appear, have them write down why they should belong. Then have a committee elected to select the members. It is good psychology to have a waiting list.

Post names of members and *know* the youngsters. Have your name so that they will know it. *Smile.*

Start on time, end on time, and keep things moving. Keep the business meeting at a minimum.

Drop members for nonattendance without valid excuses. Impress on new members that joining is an important step. Make clear the aim of the club, what it will do for the member, and what he can do for the club.

Start an *officers' council;* have it meet after club meeting and propose policies, dues. These policies are recommendations that are presented to the club at the next meeting, for action.

Anticipate what you need for the next meeting. If the officers' council decides that beans will be the price of admission, back them up.

Watch the finances closely. Do not allow them to be a temptation to the children. Club purchases should come from club dues or earnings. Never allow children to keep funds. A club member is treasurer and keeps good records. He turns his weekly account over to the leader at the close of each meeting.

Plan so that the members who come early have something to do. If you are at a library, have them get their books or arrange the museum table.

Every meeting must teach something new. Every meeting should have a new song, a new game, and handwork.

The nature experience of the day should make the club member go home enthusiastic.

Call on the sponsor and librarian. Let them know what happened tonight that was funny; what was worth while. Invite their suggestions. Plan weekly exhibits for the meeting place, the library, or the reading room.

FIG. 71.—The July Jaunters' Insect Club. Note materials needed and also compartments for individual belongings. (*Photograph by Robert J. Keller, and used through courtesy of the Children's Museum, Jamaica Plain, Boston.*)

Become acquainted with the parents. Welcome visitors. Have a guide in the club who will give time to the visitors. Keep your program going. Have your guide prepared to show what has been done and to answer questions about the club. Invite visitors to give their experiences and have them become acquainted with the club.

One of the tests of your efficiency is the active cooperation of the librarian, the parents, and the teachers. When the idea is sold to them, they will cooperate to make your work a success.

The spirit of the leader is the spirit of the club. If the leader is *sincere* and accepts *responsibility,* the club will be with him.

Outline Your Plan for Each Meeting.

4:30 P.M. Roll call by secretary. Collect dues by treasurer.

4:32 P.M. Present your materials—a new animal, such as a member's dog, for example. Hold conversation on adaptations, intelligence, how to train.

4:52 P.M. Club leaders' talk. Drive home the idea of humaneness, cleaness of the animal, his good teeth, and so on. Select one idea at a time and present it.

4:55 P.M. Activity such as a song about the animal you have.

5:00 P.M. Handwork. This is *not* a handwork club, but much handwork may be suggested that the children may do at home and bring for exhibition before the meeting. The making of animal tracks, plaster casts, block printing, soap carving, sketches, aquariums, cages, terrariums, silhouettes. In the case of the dog, it might be washing it or making it a dog collar.

5:20 P.M. Business meeting. Plan a dog show, the next hike, a trip to museum. To avoid discussion as to whether to go or not, say that you will go if 8, 10, or a certain number want to go. Plan a play.

5:25 P.M. Have a good, snappy game that you have planned for the meeting, perhaps identifying silhouettes of dogs.

5:35 P.M. Have a song period.

5:40 P.M. Tell a true story about the animal that you have brought. Story must be snappy, teach something, be interesting and true.

5:55 P.M. Remind the children of books to read about animals and of the things that each one has promised to do for next time. Adjourn.

The handwork and business meetings should be extended for longer periods if the club time allowance is 2 hr. For older children, this may be a wiser allotment.

Starting a Garden Club. *Selecting a Club.* If you decide to organize a garden club, for example, you must first of all select the institution that will sponsor the club. This may be a library, a settlement house, a community center, a neighborhood club, Scouts, Camp Fire Girls, Girl Reserves, or some other group. Meet the proper person, arrange materials, publicity for members, and other necessary details. Sponsors must agree to visit club meetings and report to the Department of Nature Education.

First Meeting. Requirements for joining. Willingness to have a garden even if limited to a box. Limit club to 16 members from fourth, fifth, and sixth grades. Requirements for first meeting, which will be a field trip, are a pair of rubbers and a shoe box or paper bag for collecting. Have field trip to gather sand, clay, gravel, loam, sandstone, shale, puddingstone. Show them your collection in vials and box for rocks. A quartz pebble, a granite pebble, a piece of flint, a black diamond (hard coal), a fossil in limestone, and pink feldspar may be added to the list. Show all these specimens before starting. Tell them that this is a game and that each specimen counts 1 point. You wish to see who has the best eyesight and is therefore the best collector. After the collecting game, have election of officers and naming of club. Tell them that, in a Scout troop, the members who join have to be able to tie knots and repeat the Scout oath and law. Ask them if they can think of any requirement for the next meeting besides being in the fourth grade or above and being willing to start a garden. Since the club will wish to be a live club, it may occur to them that no one be admitted at the next meeting unless he has at least four kinds of rocks in a mineral box. If they vote to do this, see that they carry it out. Encourage the exchange of specimens and the continuing of the collection for an exhibition at the next meeting. The secretary should write a report of the trip. Show what you wrote as a report of your trip with drawings. (Use Thoreau style with marginal sketches.)

Second Meeting. Appoint a door tender to see that each member has the price of admission. President calls the meeting to order and has secretary's report. May wish a ruling on new members. Have president, vice-president, and secretary choose teams. Sixteen members will make five to a team and a senior leader. Explain that there will be a contest between the three teams. Have instruction period on kinds and uses of rocks. Play a game. Put a chalk mark on the floor, line up teams at a line. Have the first one of each team throw a quartz pebble at the mark. The one coming nearest gets 3 points, next nearest 2 points, and others only 1 point. If pebble does not prove to be quartz, the player loses by default. Have the second member of each team throw a granite pebble. When each one has had a turn, add the scores and see which team is ahead, which second, and which third. Now tell them a story about a fossil. Tell them that four kinds of soil in clean bottles of same size will be the next price of admission. Tell them to save squash seed the next time they have that vegetable for dinner. Perhaps some of their mothers will be willing to have squash or pumpkin pie soon. Also have them bring a dozen beans. If you have dues, you may have one of the officers purchase beans at a chain store and other seeds as peas, corn, and squash at a seed store. The club leader and not club members should be the one to handle the money. Demonstrate how to plant the seeds and give them definite directions as to successive plantings. Each kind can be planted in a tin can so that at the fourth meeting they can bring the can with bean plants.

Conducting the Business Meetings. *The First Business Meeting of the Club.* A leader tells about the purpose of the club and plans with group. Have election of officers.

CHAIRMAN (usually the leader): The meeting will please come to order. (Explain the purpose of the club.) Nominations for president are in order.

MEMBER: I nominate ____________ for president.

SECOND MEMBER: I second the nomination. (After several nominations, someone arises and, when recognized by the chairman, says: "I move that the nominations be closed." The motion is seconded.)

CHAIRMAN: I appoint ______, ____________, ____________ as tellers. They may prepare the ballots. (Papers are then cut into small slips.)

CHAIRMAN: You may write the name of the one whom you wish for president upon the ballots. (After there has been time for this, the tellers collect and count.)

CHAIRMAN (after the election of the president): Will the new president take the chair? (The new president takes the chair.) Nominations for vice-president are now in order.

The same steps are gone through for electing vice-president, secretary-treasurer, and necessary committees.

Have discussion and voting on name of club.

The Second Club Meeting

PRESIDENT: The meeting will please come to order. The secretary will read the minutes of the last meeting.

SECRETARY: The ________ Club met on Thursday, Sept. 20, 1940, in room 115 . . .

PRESIDENT: Are there any additions or corrections of the minutes? If not, they stand approved as read.

PRESIDENT: We will now have the report of the program committee.

CHAIRMAN OF THE PROGRAM COMMITTEE: Mr. President and fellow members. Your committee . . .

PRESIDENT: You have heard the report of the program committee. Will someone move that this report be accepted?

MEMBER: I move that this report be accepted.

PRESIDENT: It has been moved and seconded that this report be accepted. Is there any discussion, or are there any errors? (Discussion may follow.)

PRESIDENT: Is there any further discussion? If not, are you ready for the question?

MEMBERS: Question.

PRESIDENT: All those in favor say "aye"; opposed, "no." The report is accepted. (The same procedure for reports of other committees.)

PRESIDENT: Is there any unfinished business? (If none has been left over, he says): We are now ready for the new business of the meeting, which is the question of the payment of dues. Will someone make a motion so that the question may be discussed?

MEMBER: I move that the club dues be 10 cents a month.

SECOND MEMBER: I second the motion.

PRESIDENT: It has been moved and seconded that the club dues be 10 cents a month. Is there any discussion? (Discussion follows.)

MEMBER: Question.

PRESIDENT: Are you ready for the question? All those in favor say "aye"; opposed "no." (If the ayes get it, the question is put before the house again and voted upon. All business must be put in the form of a motion and seconded before discussion and voting. Use same order of procedure as given above.)

PRESIDENT: The motion is in order to adjourn.

MEMBER: I move that we adjourn.

SECOND MEMBER: I second the motion. (This cannot be debated.)

PRESIDENT: You have heard the motion to adjourn. All those in favor say "aye." Opposed, "no."

The chair should always be addressed as "Madame President" or "Mister President." The president then says, "Miss A." Miss A cannot make her motion until she is recognized by the president.

A PROPOSED CONSTITUTION[1]

ARTICLE I. NAME

This Nature Club shall be called the________________________________

[1] This is a suggested form. The constitution should be made by the club and should be changed to suit the needs of the club. It should be posted in the clubroom where all can see it.

Article II. Purposes

The purposes of this club shall be 1.____________________
2.____________________ 3.____________________

Article III. Membership

Section 1. Any__________who is interested in____________________
(boy or girl)
and is__________years old shall be eligible, for membership.
(4, 5, 6th grade)

Section 2. The names of those proposed for membership shall be voted on by the members of the club. A majority vote of all members shall be sufficient to elect.

Section 3. Members are expected to participate in the activities of the club.

Section 4. There shall be no more than three unexcused absences.

Section 5. The membership shall be limited to 16 members in good standing.

Section 6. The dues shall be__________a meeting.

Section 7. Nonmembers may attend the club__________times.

Article IV. Officers

Section 1. The officers of this club shall be President____________________
Vice-president____________________Secretary____________________
Treasurer____________________Curator____________________
Membership chairman____________________

Section 2. These officers shall perform the duties usually falling to such officers.

Section 3. The officers make up the officers' council which shall make recommendations to the club for acceptance or rejection.

Article V. Meetings

Section 1. Regular weekly meetings shall be held on______ at______o'clock P.M.

Section 2. Meetings will be held at________, __________ Street,__________
(Number) (Name) (Library,
____
school, etc.)

Article VI. Amendments

This constitution may be amended by a two-thirds vote of the members, provided the amendment has been presented to the membership in writing at least one week before voting.

AN INVENTORY OF DESIRED OUTCOMES IN A NATURE CLUB

The club is an educational medium for its members. If it is a bird club, experiences with birds involve certain social habits. The following items are suggestive of some desirable outcomes. Recall some recent experiences in your club that indicate that the club members are gaining in these charac-

FIG. 72.—A museum is a workshop and not a biological morgue. Field exploration by the July Jaunters' Club is always followed by a "work period." The aquariums were maintained for a month. What is meant by orderly disorder? *(Photograph used through courtesy of the Children's Museum, Jamaica Plain, Boston.)*

teristics. Write the incident on a piece of paper, giving it the number that corresponds to the item which you feel is exemplified.

1. Responsibility.
2. Initiative.
3. Judgment.
4. Courtesy.
5. Helpfulness.
6. Patience.
7. Self-discipline.
8. Independence.
9. Loyalty.
10. Honesty.
11. Self-respect.
12. Unselfishness.
13. Thrift.
14. Freedom.
15. Creativeness.
16. Achievement.
17. Open-mindedness.
18. Cooperation.
19. Leadership.
20. Industry.

One reason for your selecting the "club route" was to gain practical experience in guiding children. It will be worth while to take an inventory now and then to find whether you are making progress. If you have evidence of this that relates to any of the following items, relate the incident on the back of the paper, numbering the experience so that it will correspond to the item illustrated.

1. You are accepted as a member of the group.
2. The members look to you for guidance.
3. Discipline is handled by the group.
4. The club recognizes that you have a sense of humor.
5. The club feels that the program is flexible.
6. The members realize that you prize originality.
7. The members do not feel that it is a school.
8. The club is a cooperative group life.
9. What do you plan to do while the members are arriving?
10. What do you enjoy most about your club?

A CHECK LIST FOR DISCUSSION OF CLUB LEADERSHIP

You have held several club meetings and, as a result, should be developing certain attitudes, habits, and skills. The following statements have to do with the technique of club leadership. Mark those statements that you believe to be true with a *T* and those that you believe to be false with an *F*. This should form the basis for leadership discussion.

_______1. The club program conforms to progressive educational thought.
_______2. The club program means the practice of good citizenship.
_______3. The main objective of a club is scholarship.
_______4. The club member chooses what to do.
_______5. The club is a secret society.
_______6. The leader decides the purposes of the club.
_______7. Parents interested in bird study should require their children to join the bird club.
_______8. It is desirable to admit new members on the basis of scholarship.
_______9. All members of a bird club should build a birdhouse.
_______10. All members of a bird club should participate.
_______11. The club leader dictates the program.
_______12. It is reasonable to restrict membership on the basis of interest.
_______13. It is desirable to have an initiation.
_______14. The best clubs will have a secret password.
_______15. The dues should be high enough to restrict the membership.
_______16. Valuable time may be wasted on a constitution.
_______17. The officers should determine the policies of the club.
_______18. Interest alone is a worthy objective.
_______19. Recreation can be pleasurable and profitable at the same time.

______20. Bird material should be collected for the club museum.

______21. The study of a hen with a thinking cap on baking a loaf of bread for the duck is more worth while than the hatching of a chick.

______22. The most progressive club will arrange for bird lecturers to come in to every meeting.

______23. A bird hike may be more worth while than a meeting in the club-room.

______24. A visit to a chick hatchery has no place on a bird club schedule.

Fig. 73.—Boston Children's Museum, Jamaica Plain. This geology room is ideally arranged. The colored wall panels illustrate the story of the Boston Basin. The rock specimens in front of the panels are local samples from each geologic age. In the show cases are local economic rocks and minerals orderly arranged. The young folks are solving problems. (*Photograph courtesy of Life Magazine.*)

______25. One corner of the active museum should have birds' eggs collected, identified, labeled with name, date, habitat, and collector.

______26. If there is a taxidermist in the neighborhood, he should be invited to teach the club how to stuff birds.

______27. It should be optional whether all members should keep a diary, make sketches, take snapshots, own field glasses, teach a song, or tell a story.

______28. Dues are necessary for a successful club.

______29. It is good pedagogy to offer prizes.

______30. One club meeting should be devoted to songs, another to stories, another to handwork, one to bird calls on the victrola, one to adaptations of birds, and another to nests.

______31. Program material for the bird club should be seasonal.

______32. Every meeting should have a game.

______33. It is legitimate and desirable to collect old nests for club museum.

______34. A progressive club could have all meetings in the open.

______35. A wise leader would make the following assignment: "Every member has two weeks in which to make a birdhouse."

______36. Every wide-awake club should own a canary, a parrot, and one other live bird, such as a goose, chicken, or duck.

______37. The following topics are particularly interesting and desirable for club meetings: Bird Pets of the Romans; Life of the Pterodactyl; Birds of the Tropics; Birds with Peculiar Anatomy; the Wooing of Birds; Methods of Preserving Birds; Skinning Birds; and the Cage Bird World.

______38. The following topics are really "time killers" and do not meet the most worthy objectives: Feeding Birds; Constructing Birdhouses; Visit to the Museum of Natural History; Listening to Bird Songs; Preparing a "Do" and "Don't" for Bird Lovers; Identifying Birds in an Orchard; Taking Snapshots of Birds; Bird Games; and Reading a Bird Poem.

______39. The purpose of a bird club is vocational—to make taxidermists, naturalists, artists, and other experts.

______40. Bird club members do not study.

______41. Ability in club leadership is a continuous growth.

______42. A club member participates in the things most interesting to him.

______43. The club program is arranged for amusement.

______44. The purpose of a nature club is to spread knowledge about insects, birds, trees, wild flowers, etc.

______45. The developing of mental characteristics guarantees the development of social characteristics.

______46. Good grades guarantee good citizenship.

______47. It is important to have club objectives.

______48. Training for club leadership is unnecessary.

______49. Failure in club leadership is impossible.

______50. A club is another class in x.

______51. The club method is good for the schoolroom.

______52. All schoolroom methods are good in a club.

______53. Schools and clubs use the same materials.

______54. The class is more informal than the club.

______55. A good club provides for individual interests and capacities.

______56. A club meeting should not be planned, but should be carried on according to circumstances.

______57. A club member may fail as such, although the club members do not realize it.

______58. A club is a lesson-hearing affair.

______59. A club is a "frill" or "fad."

______60. Clubs have existed long enough to justify their existence.

______61. Making, mounting, visiting, studying, walking, singing, playing, and conducting are all justifiable club activities.

______62. Homework is frequent among live club members.

______63. Conservation is a community project.

______64. Trips to museums, forests, farms, gardens, the zoo, neighbors, and reservations are legitimate club experiences.

______65. Drill can be made an attractive club activity.

INDEX

G

H

Q

R

S

T

CATALOGUE OF DOVER BOOKS

Books Explaining Science and Mathematics

WHAT IS SCIENCE?, N. Campbell. The role of experiment and measurement, the function of mathematics, the nature of scientific laws, the difference between laws and theories, the limitations of science, and many similarly provocative topics are treated clearly and without technicalities by an eminent scientist. "Still an excellent introduction to scientific philosophy," H. Margenau in PHYSICS TODAY. "A first-rate primer . . . deserves a wide audience," SCIENTIFIC AMERICAN. 192pp. 5⅜ x 8. S43 Paperbound **$1.25**

THE NATURE OF PHYSICAL THEORY, P. W. Bridgman. A Nobel Laureate's clear, non-technical lectures on difficulties and paradoxes connected with frontier research on the physical sciences. Concerned with such central concepts as thought, logic, mathematics, relativity, probability, wave mechanics, etc. he analyzes the contributions of such men as Newton, Einstein, Bohr, Heisenberg, and many others. "Lucid and entertaining . . . recommended to anyone who wants to get some insight into current philosophies of science," THE NEW PHILOSOPHY. Index. xi + 138pp. 5⅜ x 8. S33 Paperbound **$1.25**

EXPERIMENT AND THEORY IN PHYSICS, Max Born. A Nobel Laureate examines the nature of experiment and theory in theoretical physics and analyzes the advances made by the great physicists of our day: Heisenberg, Einstein, Bohr, Planck, Dirac, and others. The actual process of creation is detailed step-by-step by one who participated. A fine examination of the scientific method at work. 44pp. 5⅜ x 8. S308 Paperbound **75¢**

THE PSYCHOLOGY OF INVENTION IN THE MATHEMATICAL FIELD, J. Hadamard. The reports of such men as Descartes, Pascal, Einstein, Poincaré, and others are considered in this investigation of the method of idea-creation in mathematics and other sciences and the thinking process in general. How do ideas originate? What is the role of the unconscious? What is Poincaré's forgetting hypothesis? are some of the fascinating questions treated. A penetrating analysis of Einstein's thought processes concludes the book. xiii + 145pp. 5⅜ x 8. T107 Paperbound **$1.25**

THE NATURE OF LIGHT AND COLOUR IN THE OPEN AIR, M. Minnaert. Why are shadows sometimes blue, sometimes green, or other colors depending on the light and surroundings? What causes mirages? Why do multiple suns and moons appear in the sky? Professor Minnaert explains these unusual phenomena and hundreds of others in simple, easy-to-understand terms based on optical laws and the properties of light and color. No mathematics is required but artists, scientists, students, and everyone fascinated by these "tricks" of nature will find thousands of useful and amazing pieces of information. Hundreds of observational experiments are suggested which require no special equipment. 200 illustrations; 42 photos. xvi + 362pp. 5⅜ x 8. T196 Paperbound **$2.00**

THE UNIVERSE OF LIGHT, W. Bragg. Sir William Bragg, Nobel Laureate and great modern physicist, is also well known for his powers of clear exposition. Here he analyzes all aspects of light for the layman: lenses, reflection, refraction, the optics of vision, x-rays, the photoelectric effect, etc. He tells you what causes the color of spectra, rainbows, and soap bubbles, how magic mirrors work, and much more. Dozens of simple experiments are described. Preface. Index. 199 line drawings and photographs, including 2 full-page color plates. x + 283pp. 5⅜ x 8. T538 Paperbound **$1.85**

SOAP-BUBBLES: THEIR COLOURS AND THE FORCES THAT MOULD THEM, C. V. Boys. For continuing popularity and validity as scientific primer, few books can match this volume of easily-followed experiments, explanations. Lucid exposition of complexities of liquid films, surface tension and related phenomena, bubbles' reaction to heat, motion, music, magnetic fields. Experiments with capillary attraction, soap bubbles on frames, composite bubbles, liquid cylinders and jets, bubbles other than soap, etc. Wonderful introduction to scientific method, natural laws that have many ramifications in areas of modern physics. Only complete edition in print. New Introduction by S. Z. Lewin, New York University. 83 illustrations; 1 full-page color plate. xii + 190pp. 5⅜ x 8½. T542 Paperbound **95¢**

THE STORY OF X-RAYS FROM RONTGEN TO ISOTOPES, A. R. Bleich, M.D. This book, by a member of the American College of Radiology, gives the scientific explanation of x-rays, their applications in medicine, industry and art, and their danger (and that of atmospheric radiation) to the individual and the species. You learn how radiation therapy is applied against cancer, how x-rays diagnose heart disease and other ailments, how they are used to examine mummies for information on diseases of early societies, and industrial materials for hidden weaknesses. 54 illustrations show x-rays of flowers, bones, stomach, gears with flaws, etc. 1st publication. Index. xix + 186pp. 5⅜ x 8. T622 Paperbound **$1.35**

SPINNING TOPS AND GYROSCOPIC MOTION, John Perry. A classic elementary text of the dynamics of rotation — the behavior and use of rotating bodies such as gyroscopes and tops. In simple, everyday English you are shown how quasi-rigidity is induced in discs of paper, smoke rings, chains, etc., by rapid motions; why a gyrostat falls and why a top rises; precession; how the earth's motion affects climate; and many other phenomena. Appendix on practical use of gyroscopes. 62 figures. 128pp. 5⅜ x 8. T416 Paperbound **$1.00**

SNOW CRYSTALS, W. A. Bentley, M. J. Humphreys. For almost 50 years W. A. Bentley photographed snow flakes in his laboratory in Jericho, Vermont; in 1931 the American Meteorological Society gathered together the best of his work, some 2400 photographs of snow flakes, plus a few ice flowers, windowpane frosts, dew, frozen rain, and other ice formations. Pictures were selected for beauty and scientific value. A very valuable work to anyone in meteorology, cryology; most interesting to layman; extremely useful for artist who wants beautiful, crystalline designs. All copyright free. Unabridged reprint of 1931 edition. 2453 illustrations. 227pp. 8 x 10½. T287 Paperbound **$3.00**

A DOVER SCIENCE SAMPLER, edited by George Barkin. A collection of brief, non-technical passages from 44 Dover Books Explaining Science for the enjoyment of the science-minded browser. Includes work of Bertrand Russell, Poincaré, Laplace, Max Born, Galileo, Newton; material on physics, mathematics, metallurgy, anatomy, astronomy, chemistry, etc. You will be fascinated by Martin Gardner's analysis of the sincere pseudo-scientist, Moritz's account of Newton's absentmindedness, Bernard's examples of human vivisection, etc. Illustrations from the Diderot Pictorial Encyclopedia and De Re Metallica. 64 pages. **FREE**

THE STORY OF ATOMIC THEORY AND ATOMIC ENERGY, J. G. Feinberg. A broader approach to subject of nuclear energy and its cultural implications than any other similar source. Very readable, informal, completely non-technical text. Begins with first atomic theory, 600 B.C. and carries you through the work of Mendelejeff, Röntgen, Madame Curie, to Einstein's equation and the A-bomb. New chapter goes through thermonuclear fission, binding energy, other events up to 1959. Radioactive decay and radiation hazards, future benefits, work of Bohr, moderns, hundreds more topics. "Deserves special mention . . . not only authoritative but thoroughly popular in the best sense of the word," Saturday Review. Formerly, "The Atom Story." Expanded with new chapter. Three appendixes. Index. 34 illustrations. vii + 243pp. 5⅜ x 8. T625 Paperbound **$1.60**

THE STRANGE STORY OF THE QUANTUM, AN ACCOUNT FOR THE GENERAL READER OF THE GROWTH OF IDEAS UNDERLYING OUR PRESENT ATOMIC KNOWLEDGE, B. Hoffmann. Presents lucidly and expertly, with barest amount of mathematics, the problems and theories which led to modern quantum physics. Dr. Hoffmann begins with the closing years of the 19th century, when certain trifling discrepancies were noticed, and with illuminating analogies and examples takes you through the brilliant concepts of Planck, Einstein, Pauli, Broglie, Bohr, Schroedinger, Heisenberg, Dirac, Sommerfeld, Feynman, etc. This edition includes a new, long postscript carrying the story through 1958. "Of the books attempting an account of the history and contents of our modern atomic physics which have come to my attention, this is the best," H. Margenau, Yale University, in "American Journal of Physics." 32 tables and line illustrations. Index. 275pp. 5⅜ x 8. T518 Paperbound **$1.50**

SPACE AND TIME, E. Borel. Written by a versatile mathematician of world renown with his customary lucidity and precision, this introduction to relativity for the layman presents scores of examples, analogies, and illustrations that open up new ways of thinking about space and time. It covers abstract geometry and geographical maps, continuity and topology, the propagation of light, the special theory of relativity, the general theory of relativity, theoretical researches, and much more. Mathematical notes. 2 Indexes. 4 Appendices. 15 figures. xvi + 243pp. 5⅜ x 8. T592 Paperbound **$1.45**

FROM EUCLID TO EDDINGTON: A STUDY OF THE CONCEPTIONS OF THE EXTERNAL WORLD, Sir Edmund Whittaker. A foremost British scientist traces the development of theories of natural philosophy from the western rediscovery of Euclid to Eddington, Einstein, Dirac, etc. The inadequacy of classical physics is contrasted with present day attempts to understand the physical world through relativity, non-Euclidean geometry, space curvature, wave mechanics, etc. 5 major divisions of examination: Space; Time and Movement; the Concepts of Classical Physics; the Concepts of Quantum Mechanics; the Eddington Universe. 212pp. 5⅜ x 8. T491 Paperbound **$1.35**

Nature, Biology

NATURE RECREATION: Group Guidance for the Out-of-doors, William Gould Vinal. Intended for both the uninitiated nature instructor and the education student on the college level, this complete "how-to" program surveys the entire area of nature education for the young. Philosophy of nature recreation; requirements, responsibilities, important information for group leaders; nature games; suggested group projects; conducting meetings and getting discussions started; etc. Scores of immediately applicable teaching aids, plus completely updated sources of information, pamphlets, field guides, recordings, etc. Bibliography. 74 photographs. + 310pp. 5⅜ x 8½. T1015 Paperbound **$1.75**

HOW TO KNOW THE WILD FLOWERS, Mrs. William Starr Dana. Classic nature book that has introduced thousands to wonders of American wild flowers. Color-season principle of organization is easy to use, even by those with no botanical training, and the genial, refreshing discussions of history, folklore, uses of over 1,000 native and escape flowers, foliage plants are informative as well as fun to read. Over 170 full-page plates, collected from several editions, may be colored in to make permanent records of finds. Revised to conform with 1950 edition of Gray's Manual of Botany. xlii + 438pp. 5⅜ x 8½. T332 Paperbound **$2.00**

HOW TO KNOW THE FERNS, F. T. Parsons. Ferns, among our most lovely native plants, are all too little known. This classic of nature lore will enable the layman to identify almost any American fern he may come across. After an introduction on the structure and life of ferns, the 57 most important ferns are fully pictured and described (arranged upon a simple identification key). Index of Latin and English names. 61 illustrations and 42 full-page plates. xiv + 215pp. 5⅜ x 8. T740 Paperbound **$1.35**

MANUAL OF THE TREES OF NORTH AMERICA, Charles Sprague Sargent. Still unsurpassed as most comprehensive, reliable study of North American tree characteristics, precise locations and distribution. By dean of American dendrologists. Every tree native to U.S., Canada, Alaska, 185 genera, 717 species, described in detail—leaves, flowers, fruit, winterbuds, bark, wood, growth habits etc. plus discussion of varieties and local variants, immaturity variations. Over 100 keys, including unusual 11-page analytical key to genera, aid in identification. 783 clear illustrations of flowers, fruit, leaves. An unmatched permanent reference work for all nature lovers. Second enlarged (1926) edition. Synopsis of families. Analytical key to genera. Glossary of technical terms. Index. 783 illustrations, 1 map. Two volumes. Total of 982pp. 5⅜ x 8. T277 Vol. I Paperbound **$2.25**
T278 Vol. II Paperbound **$2.25**
The set **$4.50**

TREES OF THE EASTERN AND CENTRAL UNITED STATES AND CANADA, W. M. Harlow. A revised edition of a standard middle-level guide to native trees and important escapes. More than 140 trees are described in detail, and illustrated with more than 600 drawings and photographs. Supplementary keys will enable the careful reader to identify almost any tree he might encounter. xiii + 288pp. 5⅜ x 8. T395 Paperbound **$1.35**

GUIDE TO SOUTHERN TREES, Ellwood S. Harrar and J. George Harrar. All the essential information about trees indigenous to the South, in an extremely handy format. Introductory essay on methods of tree classification and study, nomenclature, chief divisions of Southern trees, etc. Approximately 100 keys and synopses allow for swift, accurate identification of trees. Numerous excellent illustrations, non-technical text make this a useful book for teachers of biology or natural science, nature lovers, amateur naturalists. Revised 1962 edition. Index. Bibliography. Glossary of technical terms. 920 illustrations; 201 full-page plates. ix + 709pp. 4⅝ x 6⅜. T945 Paperbound **$2.35**

FRUIT KEY AND TWIG KEY TO TREES AND SHRUBS, W. M. Harlow. Bound together in one volume for the first time, these handy and accurate keys to fruit and twig identification are the only guides of their sort with photographs (up to 3 times natural size). "Fruit Key": Key to over 120 different deciduous and evergreen fruits. 139 photographs and 11 line drawings. Synoptic summary of fruit types. Bibliography. 2 Indexes (common and scientific names). "Twig Key": Key to over 160 different twigs and buds. 173 photographs. Glossary of technical terms. Bibliography. 2 Indexes (common and scientific names). Two volumes bound as one. Total of xvii + 126pp. 5⅝ x 8⅜. T511 Paperbound **$1.25**

INSECT LIFE AND INSECT NATURAL HISTORY, S. W. Frost. A work emphasizing habits, social life, and ecological relations of insects, rather than more academic aspects of classification and morphology. Prof. Frost's enthusiasm and knowledge are everywhere evident as he discusses insect associations and specialized habits like leaf-rolling, leaf-mining, and case-making, the gall insects, the boring insects, aquatic insects, etc. He examines all sorts of matters not usually covered in general works, such as: insects as human food, insect music and musicians, insect response to electric and radio waves, use of insects in art and literature. The admirably executed purpose of this book, which covers the middle ground between elementary treatment and scholarly monographs, is to excite the reader to observe for himself. Over 700 illustrations. Extensive bibliography. x + 524pp. 5⅜ x 8. T517 Paperbound **$2.45**

COMMON SPIDERS OF THE UNITED STATES, J. H. Emerton. Here is a nature hobby you can pursue right in your own cellar! Only non-technical, but thorough, reliable guide to spiders for the layman. Over 200 spiders from all parts of the country, arranged by scientific classification, are identified by shape and color, number of eyes, habitat and range, habits, etc. Full text, 501 line drawings and photographs, and valuable introduction explain webs, poisons, threads, capturing and preserving spiders, etc. Index. New synoptic key by S. W. Frost. xxiv + 225pp. 5⅜ x 8. T223 Paperbound **$1.45**

THE LIFE STORY OF THE FISH: HIS MANNERS AND MORALS, Brian Curtis. A comprehensive, non-technical survey of just about everything worth knowing about fish. Written for the aquarist, the angler, and the layman with an inquisitive mind, the text covers such topics as evolution, external covering and protective coloration, physics and physiology of vision, maintenance of equilibrium, function of the lateral line canal for auditory and temperature senses, nervous system, function of the air bladder, reproductive system and methods—courtship, mating, spawning, care of young—and many more. Also sections on game fish, the problems of conservation and a fascinating chapter on fish curiosities. "Clear, simple language . . . excellent judgment in choice of subjects . . . delightful sense of humor," New York Times. Revised (1949) edition. Index. Bibliography of 72 items. 6 full-page photographic plates. xii + 284pp. 5⅜ x 8. T929 Paperbound **$1.65**

BATS, Glover Morrill Allen. The most comprehensive study of bats as a life-form by the world's foremost authority. A thorough summary of just about everything known about this fascinating and mysterious flying mammal, including its unique location sense, hibernation and cycles, its habitats and distribution, its wing structure and flying habits, and its relationship to man in the long history of folklore and superstition. Written on a middle-level, the book can be profitably studied by a trained zoologist and thoroughly enjoyed by the layman. "An absorbing text with excellent illustrations. Bats should have more friends and fewer thoughtless detractors as a result of the publication of this volume," William Beebe, Books. Extensive bibliography. 57 photographs and illustrations. x + 368pp. 5⅜ x 8½. T984 Paperbound **$2.00**

BIRDS AND THEIR ATTRIBUTES, Glover Morrill Allen. A fine general introduction to birds as living organisms, especially valuable because of emphasis on structure, physiology, habits, behavior. Discusses relationship of bird to man, early attempts at scientific ornithology, feathers and coloration, skeletal structure including bills, legs and feet, wings. Also food habits, evolution and present distribution, feeding and nest-building, still unsolved questions of migrations and location sense, many more similar topics. Final chapter on classification, nomenclature. A good popular-level summary for the biologist; a first-rate introduction for the layman. Reprint of 1925 edition. References and index. 51 illustrations. viii + 338pp. 5⅜ x 8½. T957 Paperbound **$1.85**

LIFE HISTORIES OF NORTH AMERICAN BIRDS, Arthur Cleveland Bent. Bent's monumental series of books on North American birds, prepared and published under auspices of Smithsonian Institute, is the definitive coverage of the subject, the most-used single source of information. Now the entire set is to be made available by Dover in inexpensive editions. This encyclopedic collection of detailed, specific observations utilizes reports of hundreds of contemporary observers, writings of such naturalists as Audubon, Burroughs, William Brewster, as well as author's own extensive investigations. Contains literally everything known about life history of each bird considered: nesting, eggs, plumage, distribution and migration, voice, enemies, courtship, etc. These not over-technical works are musts for ornithologists, conservationists, amateur naturalists, anyone seriously interested in American birds.

BIRDS OF PREY. More than 100 subspecies of hawks, falcons, eagles, buzzards, condors and owls, from the common barn owl to the extinct caracara of Guadaloupe Island. 400 photographs. Two volume set. Index for each volume. Bibliographies of 403, 520 items. 197 full-page plates. Total of 907pp. 5⅜ x 8½.
Vol. I T931 Paperbound **$2.50**
Vol. II T932 Paperbound **$2.50**

WILD FOWL. Ducks, geese, swans, and tree ducks—73 different subspecies. Two volume set. Index for each volume. Bibliographies of 124, 144 items. 106 full-page plates. Total of 685pp. 5⅜ x 8½.
Vol. I T285 Paperbound **$2.50**
Vol. II T286 Paperbound **$2.50**

SHORE BIRDS. 81 varieties (sandpipers, woodcocks, plovers, snipes, phalaropes, curlews, oyster catchers, etc.). More than 200 photographs of eggs, nesting sites, adult and young of important species. Two volume set. Index for each volume. Bibliographies of 261, 188 items. 121 full-page plates. Total of 860pp. 5⅜ x 8½.
Vol. I T933 Paperbound **$2.35**
Vol. II T934 Paperbound **$2.35**

THE LIFE OF PASTEUR, R. Vallery-Radot. 13th edition of this definitive biography, cited in Encyclopaedia Britannica. Authoritative, scholarly, well-documented with contemporary quotes, observations; gives complete picture of Pasteur's personal life; especially thorough presentation of scientific activities with silkworms, fermentation, hydrophobia, inoculation, etc. Introduction by Sir William Osler. Index. 505pp. 5⅜ x 8. T632 Paperbound **$2.00**

Puzzles, Mathematical Recreations

SYMBOLIC LOGIC and THE GAME OF LOGIC, Lewis Carroll. "Symbolic Logic" is not concerned with modern symbolic logic, but is instead a collection of over 380 problems posed with charm and imagination, using the syllogism, and a fascinating diagrammatic method of drawing conclusions. In "The Game of Logic" Carroll's whimsical imagination devises a logical game played with 2 diagrams and counters (included) to manipulate hundreds of tricky syllogisms. The final section, "Hit or Miss" is a lagniappe of 101 additional puzzles in the delightful Carroll manner. Until this reprint edition, both of these books were rarities costing up to $15 each. Symbolic Logic: Index. xxxi + 199pp. The Game of Logic: 96pp. 2 vols. bound as one. 5⅜ x 8. T492 Paperbound **$1.50**

PILLOW PROBLEMS and A TANGLED TALE, Lewis Carroll. One of the rarest of all Carroll's works, "Pillow Problems" contains 72 original math puzzles, all typically ingenious. Particularly fascinating are Carroll's answers which remain exactly as he thought them out, reflecting his actual mental process. The problems in "A Tangled Tale" are in story form, originally appearing as a monthly magazine serial. Carroll not only gives the solutions, but uses answers sent in by readers to discuss wrong approaches and misleading paths, and grades them for insight. Both of these books were rarities until this edition, "Pillow Problems" costing up to $25, and "A Tangled Tale" $15. Pillow Problems: Preface and Introduction by Lewis Carroll. xx + 109pp. A Tangled Tale: 6 illustrations. 152pp. Two vols. bound as one. 5⅜ x 8. T493 Paperbound **$1.50**

AMUSEMENTS IN MATHEMATICS, Henry Ernest Dudeney. The foremost British originator of mathematical puzzles is always intriguing, witty, and paradoxical in this classic, one of the largest collections of mathematical amusements. More than 430 puzzles, problems, and paradoxes. Mazes and games, problems on number manipulation, unicursal and other route problems, puzzles on measuring, weighing, packing, age, kinship, chessboards, joiners', crossing river, plane figure dissection, and many others. Solutions. More than 450 illustrations. vii + 258pp. 5⅜ x 8. T473 Paperbound **$1.25**

THE CANTERBURY PUZZLES, Henry Dudeney. Chaucer's pilgrims set one another problems in story form. Also Adventures of the Puzzle Club, the Strange Escape of the King's Jester, the Monks of Riddlewell, the Squire's Christmas Puzzle Party, and others. All puzzles are original, based on dissecting plane figures, arithmetic, algebra, elementary calculus and other branches of mathematics, and purely logical ingenuity. "The limit of ingenuity and intricacy," The Observer. Over 110 puzzles. Full Solutions. 150 illustrations. vii + 225pp. 5⅜ x 8. T474 Paperbound **$1.25**

MATHEMATICAL EXCURSIONS, H. A. Merrill. Even if you hardly remember your high school math, you'll enjoy the 90 stimulating problems contained in this book and you will come to understand a great many mathematical principles with surprisingly little effort. Many useful shortcuts and diversions not generally known are included: division by inspection, Russian peasant multiplication, memory systems for pi, building odd and even magic squares, square roots by geometry, dyadic systems, and many more. Solutions to difficult problems. 50 illustrations. 145pp. 5⅜ x 8. T350 Paperbound **$1.00**

MAGIC SQUARES AND CUBES, W. S. Andrews. Only book-length treatment in English, a thorough non-technical description and analysis. Here are nasik, overlapping, pandiagonal, serrated squares; magic circles, cubes, spheres, rhombuses. Try your hand at 4-dimensional magical figures! Much unusual folklore and tradition included. High school algebra is sufficient. 754 diagrams and illustrations. viii + 419pp. 5⅜ x 8. T658 Paperbound **$1.85**

CALIBAN'S PROBLEM BOOK: MATHEMATICAL, INFERENTIAL AND CRYPTOGRAPHIC PUZZLES, H. Phillips (Caliban), S. T. Shovelton, G. S. Marshall. 105 ingenious problems by the greatest living creator of puzzles based on logic and inference. Rigorous, modern, piquant; reflecting their author's unusual personality, these intermediate and advanced puzzles all involve the ability to reason clearly through complex situations; some call for mathematical knowledge, ranging from algebra to number theory. Solutions. xi + 180pp. 5⅜ x 8. T736 Paperbound **$1.25**

MATHEMATICAL PUZZLES FOR BEGINNERS AND ENTHUSIASTS, G. Mott-Smith. 188 mathematical puzzles based on algebra, dissection of plane figures, permutations, and probability, that will test and improve your powers of inference and interpretation. The Odic Force, The Spider's Cousin, Ellipse Drawing, theory and strategy of card and board games like tit-tat-toe, go moku, salvo, and many others. 100 pages of detailed mathematical explanations. Appendix of primes, square roots, etc. 135 illustrations. 2nd revised edition. 248pp. 5⅜ x 8. T198 Paperbound **$1.00**

MATHEMAGIC, MAGIC PUZZLES, AND GAMES WITH NUMBERS, R. V. Heath. More than 60 new puzzles and stunts based on the properties of numbers. Easy techniques for multiplying large numbers mentally, revealing hidden numbers magically, finding the date of any day in any year, and dozens more. Over 30 pages devoted to magic squares, triangles, cubes, circles, etc. Edited by J. S. Meyer. 76 illustrations. 128pp. 5⅜ x 8. T110 Paperbound **$1.00**

THE BOOK OF MODERN PUZZLES, G. L. Kaufman. A completely new series of puzzles as fascinating as crossword and deduction puzzles but based upon different principles and techniques. Simple 2-minute teasers, word labyrinths, design and pattern puzzles, logic and observation puzzles — over 150 braincrackers. Answers to all problems. 116 illustrations. 192pp. 5⅜ x 8.
T143 Paperbound **$1.00**

NEW WORD PUZZLES, G. L. Kaufman. 100 ENTIRELY NEW puzzles based on words and their combinations that will delight crossword puzzle, Scrabble and Jotto fans. Chess words, based on the moves of the chess king; design-onyms, symmetrical designs made of synonyms; rhymed double-crostics; syllable sentences; addle letter anagrams; alphagrams; linkograms; and many others all brand new. Full solutions. Space to work problems. 196 figures. vi + 122pp. 5⅜ x 8.
T344 Paperbound **$1.00**

MAZES AND LABYRINTHS: A BOOK OF PUZZLES, W. Shepherd. Mazes, formerly associated with mystery and ritual, are still among the most intriguing of intellectual puzzles. This is a novel and different collection of 50 amusements that embody the principle of the maze: mazes in the classical tradition; 3-dimensional, ribbon, and Möbius-strip mazes; hidden messages; spatial arrangements; etc.—almost all built on amusing story situations. 84 illustrations. Essay on maze psychology. Solutions. xv + 122pp. 5⅜ x 8.
T731 Paperbound **$1.00**

MAGIC TRICKS & CARD TRICKS, W. Jonson. Two books bound as one. 52 tricks with cards, 37 tricks with coins, bills, eggs, smoke, ribbons, slates, etc. Details on presentation, misdirection, and routining will help you master such famous tricks as the Changing Card, Card in the Pocket, Four Aces, Coin Through the Hand, Bill in the Egg, Afghan Bands, and over 75 others. If you follow the lucid exposition and key diagrams carefully, you will finish these two books with an astonishing mastery of magic. 106 figures. 224pp. 5⅜ x 8.
T909 Paperbound **$1.00**

PANORAMA OF MAGIC, Milbourne Christopher. A profusely illustrated history of stage magic, a unique selection of prints and engravings from the author's private collection of magic memorabilia, the largest of its kind. Apparatus, stage settings and costumes; ingenious ads distributed by the performers and satiric broadsides passed around in the streets ridiculing pompous showmen; programs; decorative souvenirs. The lively text, by one of America's foremost professional magicians, is full of anecdotes about almost legendary wizards: Dede, the Egyptian; Philadelphia, the wonder-worker; Robert-Houdin, "the father of modern magic;" Harry Houdini; scores more. Altogether a pleasure package for anyone interested in magic, stage setting and design, ethnology, psychology, or simply in unusual people. A Dover original. 295 illustrations; 8 in full color. Index. viii + 216pp. 8⅜ x 11¼.
T774 Paperbound **$2.25**

HOUDINI ON MAGIC, Harry Houdini. One of the greatest magicians of modern times explains his most prized secrets. How locks are picked, with illustrated picks and skeleton keys; how a girl is sawed into twins; how to walk through a brick wall — Houdini's explanations of 44 stage tricks with many diagrams. Also included is a fascinating discussion of great magicians of the past and the story of his fight against fraudulent mediums and spiritualists. Edited by W.B. Gibson and M.N. Young. Bibliography. 155 figures, photos. xv + 280pp. 5⅜ x 8.
T384 Paperbound **$1.35**

MATHEMATICS, MAGIC AND MYSTERY, Martin Gardner. Why do card tricks work? How do magicians perform astonishing mathematical feats? How is stage mind-reading possible? This is the first book length study explaining the application of probability, set theory, theory of numbers, topology, etc., to achieve many startling tricks. Non-technical, accurate, detailed! 115 sections discuss tricks with cards, dice, coins, knots, geometrical vanishing illusions, how a Curry square "demonstrates" that the sum of the parts may be greater than the whole, and dozens of others. No sleight of hand necessary! 135 illustrations. xii + 174pp. 5⅜ x 8.
T335 Paperbound **$1.00**

EASY-TO-DO ENTERTAINMENTS AND DIVERSIONS WITH COINS, CARDS, STRING, PAPER AND MATCHES, R. M. Abraham. Over 300 tricks, games and puzzles will provide young readers with absorbing fun. Sections on card games; paper-folding; tricks with coins, matches and pieces of string; games for the agile; toy-making from common household objects; mathematical recreations; and 50 miscellaneous pastimes. Anyone in charge of groups of youngsters, including hard-pressed parents, and in need of suggestions on how to keep children sensibly amused and quietly content will find this book indispensable. Clear, simple text, copious number of delightful line drawings and illustrative diagrams. Originally titled "Winter Nights Entertainments." Introduction by Lord Baden Powell. 329 illustrations. v + 186pp. 5⅜ x 8½.
T921 Paperbound **$1.00**

STRING FIGURES AND HOW TO MAKE THEM, Caroline Furness Jayne. 107 string figures plus variations selected from the best primitive and modern examples developed by Navajo, Apache, pygmies of Africa, Eskimo, in Europe, Australia, China, etc. The most readily understandable, easy-to-follow book in English on perennially popular recreation. Crystal-clear exposition; step-by-step diagrams. Everyone from kindergarten children to adults looking for unusual diversion will be endlessly amused. Index. Bibliography. Introduction by A. C. Haddon. 17 full-page plates. 960 illustrations. xxiii + 401pp. 5⅜ x 8½.
T152 Paperbound **$2.00**

Entertainments, Humor

ODDITIES AND CURIOSITIES OF WORDS AND LITERATURE, C. Bombaugh, edited by M. Gardner. The largest collection of idiosyncratic prose and poetry techniques in English, a legendary work in the curious and amusing bypaths of literary recreations and the play technique in literature—so important in modern works. Contains alphabetic poetry, acrostics, palindromes, scissors verse, centos, emblematic poetry, famous literary puns, hoaxes, notorious slips of the press, hilarious mistranslations, and much more. Revised and enlarged with modern material by Martin Gardner. 368pp. 5⅜ x 8. T759 Paperbound **$1.75**

A NONSENSE ANTHOLOGY, collected by **Carolyn Wells.** 245 of the best nonsense verses ever written, including nonsense puns, absurd arguments, mock epics and sagas, nonsense ballads, odes, "sick" verses, dog-Latin verses, French nonsense verses, songs. By Edward Lear, Lewis Carroll, Gelett Burgess, W. S. Gilbert, Hilaire Belloc, Peter Newell, Oliver Herford, etc., 83 writers in all plus over four score anonymous nonsense verses. A special section of limericks, plus famous nonsense such as Carroll's "Jabberwocky" and Lear's "The Jumblies" and much excellent verse virtually impossible to locate elsewhere. For 50 years considered the best anthology available. Index of first lines specially prepared for this edition. Introduction by Carolyn Wells. 3 indexes: Title, Author, First lines. xxxiii + 279pp. T499 Paperbound **$1.35**

THE BAD CHILD'S BOOK OF BEASTS, MORE BEASTS FOR WORSE CHILDREN, and A MORAL ALPHABET, H. Belloc. Hardly an anthology of humorous verse has appeared in the last 50 years without at least a couple of these famous nonsense verses. But one must see the entire volumes—with all the delightful original illustrations by Sir Basil Blackwood—to appreciate fully Belloc's charming and witty verses that play so subacidly on the platitudes of life and morals that beset his day—and ours. A great humor classic. Three books in one. Total of 157pp. 5⅜ x 8. T749 Paperbound **$1.00**

THE DEVIL'S DICTIONARY, Ambrose Bierce. Sardonic and irreverent barbs puncturing the pomposities and absurdities of American politics, business, religion, literature, and arts, by the country's greatest satirist in the classic tradition. Epigrammatic as Shaw, piercing as Swift, American as Mark Twain, Will Rogers, and Fred Allen, Bierce will always remain the favorite of a small coterie of enthusiasts, and of writers and speakers whom he supplies with "some of the most gorgeous witticisms of the English language" (H. L. Mencken). Over 1000 entries in alphabetical order. 144pp. 5⅜ x 8. T487 Paperbound **$1.00**

THE PURPLE COW AND OTHER NONSENSE, Gelett Burgess. The best of Burgess's early nonsense, selected from the first edition of the "Burgess Nonsense Book." Contains many of his most unusual and truly awe-inspiring pieces: 36 nonsense quatrains, the Poems of Patagonia, Alphabet of Famous Goops, and the other hilarious (and rare) adult nonsense that place him in the forefront of American humorists. All pieces are accompanied by the original Burgess illustrations. 123 illustrations. xiii + 113pp. 5⅜ x 8. T772 Paperbound **$1.00**

MY PIOUS FRIENDS AND DRUNKEN COMPANIONS and MORE PIOUS FRIENDS AND DRUNKEN COMPANIONS, Frank Shay. Folksingers, amateur and professional, and everyone who loves singing: here, available for the first time in 30 years, is this valued collection of 132 ballads, blues, vaudeville numbers, drinking songs, sea chanties, comedy songs. Songs of pre-Beatnik Bohemia; songs from all over America, England, France, Australia; the great songs of the Naughty Nineties and early twentieth-century America. Over a third with music. Woodcuts by John Held, Jr. convey perfectly the brash insouciance of an era of rollicking unabashed song. 12 illustrations by John Held, Jr. Two indexes (Titles and First lines and Choruses). Introductions by the author. Two volumes bound as one. Total of xvi + 235pp. 5⅜ x 8½. T946 Paperbound **$1.25**

HOW TO TELL THE BIRDS FROM THE FLOWERS, R. W. Wood. How not to confuse a carrot with a parrot, a grape with an ape, a puffin with nuffin. Delightful drawings, clever puns, absurd little poems point out far-fetched resemblances in nature. The author was a leading physicist. Introduction by Margaret Wood White. 106 illus. 60pp. 5⅜ x 8. T523 Paperbound **75¢**

PECK'S BAD BOY AND HIS PA, George W. Peck. The complete edition, containing both volumes, of one of the most widely read American humor books. The endless ingenious pranks played by bad boy "Hennery" on his pa and the grocery man, the outraged pomposity of Pa, the perpetual ridiculing of middle class institutions, are as entertaining today as they were in 1883. No pale sophistications or subtleties, but rather humor vigorous, raw, earthy, imaginative, and, as folk humor often is, sadistic. This peculiarly fascinating book is also valuable to historians and students of American culture as a portrait of an age. 100 original illustrations by True Williams. Introduction by E. F. Bleiler. 347pp. 5⅜ x 8. T497 Paperbound **$1.35**

THE HUMOROUS VERSE OF LEWIS CARROLL. Almost every poem Carroll ever wrote, the largest collection ever published, including much never published elsewhere: 150 parodies, burlesques, riddles, ballads, acrostics, etc., with 130 original illustrations by Tenniel, Carroll, and others. "Addicts will be grateful . . . there is nothing for the faithful to do but sit down and fall to the banquet," N. Y. Times. Index to first lines. xiv + 446pp. 5⅜ x 8.
T654 Paperbound **$2.00**

DIVERSIONS AND DIGRESSIONS OF LEWIS CARROLL. A major new treasure for Carroll fans! Rare privately published humor, fantasy, puzzles, and games by Carroll at his whimsical best, with a new vein of frank satire. Includes many new mathematical amusements and recreations, among them the fragmentary Part III of "Curiosa Mathematica." Contains "The Rectory Umbrella," "The New Belfry," "The Vision of the Three T's," and much more. New 32-page supplement of rare photographs taken by Carroll. x + 375pp. 5⅜ x 8.
T732 Paperbound **$2.00**

THE COMPLETE NONSENSE OF EDWARD LEAR. This is the only complete edition of this master of gentle madness available at a popular price. A BOOK OF NONSENSE, NONSENSE SONGS, MORE NONSENSE SONGS AND STORIES in their entirety with all the old favorites that have delighted children and adults for years. The Dong With A Luminous Nose, The Jumblies, The Owl and the Pussycat, and hundreds of other bits of wonderful nonsense. 214 limericks, 3 sets of Nonsense Botany, 5 Nonsense Alphabets, 546 drawings by Lear himself, and much more. 320pp. 5⅜ x 8. T167 Paperbound **$1.00**

THE MELANCHOLY LUTE, The Humorous Verse of Franklin P. Adams ("FPA"). The author's own selection of light verse, drawn from thirty years of FPA's column, "The Conning Tower," syndicated all over the English-speaking world. Witty, perceptive, literate, these ninety-six poems range from parodies of other poets, Millay, Longfellow, Edgar Guest, Kipling, Masefield, etc., and free and hilarious translations of Horace and other Latin poets, to satiric comments on fabled American institutions—the New York Subways, preposterous ads, suburbanites, sensational journalism, etc. They reveal with vigor and clarity the humor, integrity and restraint of a wise and gentle American satirist. Introduction by Robert Hutchinson. vi + 122pp. 5⅜ x 8½. T108 Paperbound **$1.00**

SINGULAR TRAVELS, CAMPAIGNS, AND ADVENTURES OF BARON MUNCHAUSEN, R. E. Raspe, with 90 illustrations by Gustave Doré. The first edition in over 150 years to reestablish the deeds of the Prince of Liars exactly as Raspe first recorded them in 1785—the genuine Baron Munchausen, one of the most popular personalities in English literature. Included also are the best of the many sequels, written by other hands. Introduction on Raspe by J. Carswell. Bibliography of early editions. xliv + 192pp. 5⅜ x 8. T698 Paperbound **$1.00**

THE WIT AND HUMOR OF OSCAR WILDE, ed. by Alvin Redman. Wilde at his most brilliant, in 1000 epigrams exposing weaknesses and hypocrisies of "civilized" society. Divided into 49 categories—sin, wealth, women, America, etc.—to aid writers, speakers. Includes excerpts from his trials, books, plays, criticism. Formerly "The Epigrams of Oscar Wilde." Introduction by Vyvyan Holland, Wilde's only living son. Introductory essay by editor. 260pp. 5⅜ x 8. T602 Paperbound **$1.00**

MAX AND MORITZ, Wilhelm Busch. Busch is one of the great humorists of all time, as well as the father of the modern comic strip. This volume, translated by H. A. Klein and other hands, contains the perennial favorite "Max and Moritz" (translated by C. T. Brooks), Plisch and Plum, Das Rabennest, Eispeter, and seven other whimsical, sardonic, jovial, diabolical cartoon and verse stories. Lively English translations parallel the original German. This work has delighted millions since it first appeared in the 19th century, and is guaranteed to please almost anyone. Edited by H. A. Klein, with an afterword. x + 205pp. 5⅝ x 8½.
T181 Paperbound **$1.15**

HYPOCRITICAL HELENA, Wilhelm Busch. A companion volume to "Max and Moritz," with the title piece (Die Fromme Helena) and 10 other highly amusing cartoon and verse stories, all newly translated by H. A. Klein and M. C. Klein: Adventure on New Year's Eve (Abenteuer in der Neujahrsnacht), Hangover on the Morning after New Year's Eve (Der Katzenjammer am Neujahrsmorgen), etc. English and German in parallel columns. Hours of pleasure, also a fine language aid. x + 205pp. 5⅝ x 8½. T184 Paperbound **$1.00**

THE BEAR THAT WASN'T, Frank Tashlin. What does it mean? Is it simply delightful wry humor, or a charming story of a bear who wakes up in the midst of a factory, or a satire on Big Business, or an existential cartoon-story of the human condition, or a symbolization of the struggle between conformity and the individual? New York Herald Tribune said of the first edition: ". . . a fable for grownups that will be fun for children. Sit down with the book and get your own bearings." Long an underground favorite with readers of all ages and opinions. v + 51pp. Illustrated. 5⅜ x 8½. T939 Paperbound **75¢**

RUTHLESS RHYMES FOR HEARTLESS HOMES and MORE RUTHLESS RHYMES FOR HEARTLESS HOMES, Harry Graham ("Col. D. Streamer"). Two volumes of Little Willy and 48 other poetic disasters. A bright, new reprint of oft-quoted, never forgotten, devastating humor by a precursor of today's "sick" joke school. For connoisseurs of wicked, wacky humor and all who delight in the comedy of manners. Original drawings are a perfect complement. 61 illustrations. Index. vi + 69pp. Two vols. bound as one. 5⅜ x 8½.
T930 Paperbound **75¢**

Say It language phrase books

These handy phrase books (128 to 196 pages each) make grammatical drills unnecessary for an elementary knowledge of a spoken foreign language. Covering most matters of travel and everyday life each volume contains:

Over 1000 phrases and sentences in immediately useful forms — foreign language plus English.

Modern usage designed for Americans. Specific phrases like, "Give me small change," and "Please call a taxi."

Simplified phonetic transcription you will be able to read at sight.

The only completely indexed phrase books on the market.

Covers scores of important situations: — Greetings, restaurants, sightseeing, useful expressions, etc.

These books are prepared by native linguists who are professors at Columbia, N.Y.U., Fordham and other great universities. Use them independently or with any other book or record course. They provide a supplementary living element that most other courses lack. Individual volumes in:

Russian 75¢ **Italian 75¢** **Spanish 75¢** **German 75¢**
Hebrew 75¢ **Danish 75¢** **Japanese 75¢** **Swedish 75¢**
Dutch 75¢ **Esperanto 75¢** **Modern Greek 75¢** **Portuguese 75¢**
Norwegian 75¢ **Polish 75¢** **French 75¢** **Yiddish 75¢**
Turkish 75¢ **English for German-speaking people 75¢**
English for Italian-speaking people 75¢ **English for Spanish-speaking people 75¢**

Large clear type. 128-196 pages each. 3½ x 5¼. Sturdy paper binding.

Listen and Learn language records

LISTEN & LEARN is the only language record course designed especially to meet your travel and everyday needs. It is available in separate sets for FRENCH, SPANISH, GERMAN, JAPANESE, RUSSIAN, MODERN GREEK, PORTUGUESE, ITALIAN and HEBREW, and each set contains three 33⅓ rpm long-playing records—1½ hours of recorded speech by eminent native speakers who are professors at Columbia, New York University, Queens College.

Check the following special features found only in LISTEN & LEARN:

- **Dual-language recording. 812 selected phrases and sentences,** over 3200 words, spoken first in English, then in their foreign language equivalents. A suitable pause follows each foreign phrase, allowing you time to repeat the expression. You learn by unconscious assimilation.
- **128 to 206-page manual** contains everything on the records, plus a simple phonetic pronunciation guide.
- **Indexed for convenience. The only set on the market** that is completely indexed. No more puzzling over where to find the phrase you need. Just look in the rear of the manual.
- **Practical.** No time wasted on material you can find in any grammar. LISTEN & LEARN covers central core material with phrase approach. Ideal for the person with limited learning time.
- **Living, modern expressions,** not found in other courses. Hygienic products, modern equipment, shopping—expressions used every day, like "nylon" and "air-conditioned."
- **Limited objective.** Everything you learn, no matter where you stop, is immediately useful. You have to finish other courses, wade through grammar and vocabulary drill, before they help you.
- **High-fidelity recording.** LISTEN & LEARN records equal in clarity and surface-silence any record on the market costing up to $6.

"Excellent . . . the spoken records . . . impress me as being among the very best on the market," **Prof. Mario Pei,** Dept. of Romance Languages, Columbia University. "Inexpensive and well-done . . . it would make an ideal present," CHICAGO SUNDAY TRIBUNE. "More genuinely helpful than anything of its kind which I have previously encountered," **Sidney Clark,** well-known author of "ALL THE BEST" travel books.

UNCONDITIONAL GUARANTEE. Try LISTEN & LEARN, then return it within 10 days for full refund if you are not satisfied.

Each set contains three twelve-inch 33⅓ records, manual, and album.

SPANISH	the set **$5.95**	GERMAN	the set **$5.95**
FRENCH	the set **$5.95**	ITALIAN	the set **$5.95**
RUSSIAN	the set **$5.95**	JAPANESE	the set **$5.95**
PORTUGUESE	the set **$5.95**	MODERN GREEK	the set **$5.95**
MODERN HEBREW	the set **$5.95**		

Americana

THE EYES OF DISCOVERY, J. Bakeless. A vivid reconstruction of how unspoiled America appeared to the first white men. Authentic and enlightening accounts of Hudson's landing in New York, Coronado's trek through the Southwest; scores of explorers, settlers, trappers, soldiers. America's pristine flora, fauna, and Indians in every region and state in fresh and unusual new aspects. "A fascinating view of what the land was like before the first highway went through," Time. 68 contemporary illustrations, 39 newly added in this edition. Index. Bibliography. x + 500pp. 5⅜ x 8. T761 Paperbound **$2.00**

AUDUBON AND HIS JOURNALS, J. J. Audubon. A collection of fascinating accounts of Europe and America in the early 1800's through Audubon's own eyes. Includes the Missouri River Journals —an eventful trip through America's untouched heartland, the Labrador Journals, the European Journals, the famous "Episodes", and other rare Audubon material, including the descriptive chapters from the original letterpress edition of the "Ornithological Studies", omitted in all later editions. Indispensable for ornithologists, naturalists, and all lovers of Americana and adventure. 70-page biography by Audubon's granddaughter. 38 illustrations. Index. Total of 1106pp. 5⅜ x 8. T675 Vol I Paperbound **$2.25**
T676 Vol II Paperbound **$2.25**
The set **$4.50**

TRAVELS OF WILLIAM BARTRAM, edited by Mark Van Doren. The first inexpensive illustrated edition of one of the 18th century's most delightful books is an excellent source of first-hand material on American geography, anthropology, and natural history. Many descriptions of early Indian tribes are our only source of information on them prior to the infiltration of the white man. "The mind of a scientist with the soul of a poet," John Livingston Lowes. 13 original illustrations and maps. Edited with an introduction by Mark Van Doren. 448pp. 5⅜ x 8.
T13 Paperbound **$2.00**

GARRETS AND PRETENDERS: A HISTORY OF BOHEMIANISM IN AMERICA, A. Parry. The colorful and fantastic history of American Bohemianism from Poe to Kerouac. This is the only complete record of hoboes, cranks, starving poets, and suicides. Here are Pfaff, Whitman, Crane, Bierce, Pound, and many others. New chapters by the author and by H. T. Moore bring this thorough and well-documented history down to the Beatniks. "An excellent account," N. Y. Times. Scores of cartoons, drawings, and caricatures. Bibliography. Index. xxviii + 421pp. 5⅝ x 8⅜. T708 Paperbound **$1.95**

THE EXPLORATION OF THE COLORADO RIVER AND ITS CANYONS, J. W. Powell. The thrilling first-hand account of the expedition that filled in the last white space on the map of the United States. Rapids, famine, hostile Indians, and mutiny are among the perils encountered as the unknown Colorado Valley reveals its secrets. This is the only uncut version of Major Powell's classic of exploration that has been printed in the last 60 years. Includes later reflections and subsequent expedition. 250 illustrations, new map. 400pp. 5⅝ x 8⅜.
T94 Paperbound **$2.25**

THE JOURNAL OF HENRY D. THOREAU, Edited by Bradford Torrey and Francis H. Allen. Henry Thoreau is not only one of the most important figures in American literature and social thought; his voluminous journals (from which his books emerged as selections and crystallizations) constitute both the longest, most sensitive record of personal internal development and a most penetrating description of a historical moment in American culture. This present set, which was first issued in fourteen volumes, contains Thoreau's entire journals from 1837 to 1862, with the exception of the lost years which were found only recently. We are reissuing it, complete and unabridged, with a new introduction by Walter Harding, Secretary of the Thoreau Society. Fourteen volumes reissued in two volumes. Foreword by Henry Seidel Canby. Total of 1888pp. 8⅜ x 12¼. T312-3 Two volume set, Clothbound **$20.00**

GAMES AND SONGS OF AMERICAN CHILDREN, collected by William Wells Newell. A remarkable collection of 190 games with songs that accompany many of them; cross references to show similarities, differences among them; variations; musical notation for 38 songs. Textual discussions show relations with folk-drama and other aspects of folk tradition. Grouped into categories for ready comparative study: Love-games, histories, playing at work, human life, bird and beast, mythology, guessing-games, etc. New introduction covers relations of songs and dances to timeless heritage of folklore, biographical sketch of Newell, other pertinent data. A good source of inspiration for those in charge of groups of children and a valuable reference for anthropologists, sociologists, psychiatrists. Introduction by Carl Withers. New indexes of first lines, games. 5⅜ x 8½. xii + 242pp. T354 Paperbound **$1.75**

Art, History of Art, Antiques, Graphic Arts, Handcrafts

ART STUDENTS' ANATOMY, E. J. Farris. Outstanding art anatomy that uses chiefly living objects for its illustrations. 71 photos of undraped men, women, children are accompanied by carefully labeled matching sketches to illustrate the skeletal system, articulations and movements, bony landmarks, the muscular system, skin, fasciae, fat, etc. 9 x-ray photos show movement of joints. Undraped models are shown in such actions as serving in tennis, drawing a bow in archery, playing football, dancing, preparing to spring and to dive. Also discussed and illustrated are proportions, age and sex differences, the anatomy of the smile, etc. 8 plates by the great early 18th century anatomic illustrator Siegfried Albinus are also included. Glossary. 158 figures, 7 in color. x + 159pp. 5⅝ x 8⅜. T744 Paperbound **$1.50**

AN ATLAS OF ANATOMY FOR ARTISTS, F Schider. A new 3rd edition of this standard text enlarged by 52 new illustrations of hands, anatomical studies by Cloquet, and expressive life studies of the body by Barcsay. 189 clear, detailed plates offer you precise information of impeccable accuracy. 29 plates show all aspects of the skeleton, with closeups of special areas, while 54 full-page plates, mostly in two colors, give human musculature as seen from four different points of view, with cutaways for important portions of the body. 14 full-page plates provide photographs of hand forms, eyelids, female breasts, and indicate the location of muscles upon models. 59 additional plates show how great artists of the past utilized human anatomy. They reproduce sketches and finished work by such artists as Michelangelo, Leonardo da Vinci, Goya, and 15 others. This is a lifetime reference work which will be one of the most important books in any artist's library. "The standard reference tool," AMERICAN LIBRARY ASSOCIATION. "Excellent," AMERICAN ARTIST. Third enlarged edition. 189 plates, 647 illustrations. xxvi + 192pp. 7⅞ x 10⅝. T241 Clothbound **$6.00**

AN ATLAS OF ANIMAL ANATOMY FOR ARTISTS, W. Ellenberger, H. Baum, H. Dittrich. The largest, richest animal anatomy for artists available in English. 99 detailed anatomical plates of such animals as the horse, dog, cat, lion, deer, seal, kangaroo, flying squirrel, cow, bull, goat, monkey, hare, and bat. Surface features are clearly indicated, while progressive beneath-the-skin pictures show musculature, tendons, and bone structure. Rest and action are exhibited in terms of musculature and skeletal structure and detailed cross-sections are given for heads and important features. The animals chosen are representative of specific families so that a study of these anatomies will provide knowledge of hundreds of related species. "Highly recommended as one of the very few books on the subject worthy of being used as an authoritative guide," DESIGN. "Gives a fundamental knowledge," AMERICAN ARTIST. Second revised, enlarged edition with new plates from Cuvier, Stubbs, etc. 288 illustrations. 153pp. 11⅜ x 9. T82 Clothbound **$6.00**

THE HUMAN FIGURE IN MOTION, Eadweard Muybridge. The largest selection in print of Muybridge's famous high-speed action photos of the human figure in motion. 4789 photographs illustrate 162 different actions: men, women, children—mostly undraped—are shown walking, running, carrying various objects, sitting, lying down, climbing, throwing, arising, and performing over 150 other actions. Some actions are shown in as many as 150 photographs each. All in all there are more than 500 action strips in this enormous volume, series shots taken at shutter speeds of as high as 1/6000th of a second! These are not posed shots, but true stopped motion. They show bone and muscle in situations that the human eye is not fast enough to capture. Earlier, smaller editions of these prints have brought $40 and more on the out-of-print market. "A must for artists," ART IN FOCUS. "An unparalleled dictionary of action for all artists," AMERICAN ARTIST. 390 full-page plates, with 4789 photographs. Printed on heavy glossy stock. Reinforced binding with headbands. xxi + 390pp. 7⅞ x 10⅝. T204 Clothbound **$10.00**

ANIMALS IN MOTION, Eadweard Muybridge. This is the largest collection of animal action photos in print. 34 different animals (horses, mules, oxen, goats, camels, pigs, cats, guanacos, lions, gnus, deer, monkeys, eagles—and 21 others) in 132 characteristic actions. The horse alone is shown in more than 40 different actions. All 3919 photographs are taken in series at speeds up to 1/6000th of a second. The secrets of leg motion, spinal patterns, head movements, strains and contortions shown nowhere else are captured. You will see exactly how a lion sets his foot down; how an elephant's knees are like a human's—and how they differ; the position of a kangaroo's legs in mid-leap; how an ostrich's head bobs; details of the flight of birds—and thousands of facets of motion only the fastest cameras can catch. Photographed from domestic animals and animals in the Philadelphia zoo, it contains neither semiposed artificial shots nor distorted telephoto shots taken under adverse conditions. Artists, biologists, decorators, cartoonists, will find this book indispensable for understanding animals in motion. "A really marvelous series of plates," NATURE (London). "The dry plate's most spectacular early use was by Eadweard Muybridge," LIFE. 3919 photographs; 380 full pages of plates. 440pp. Printed on heavy glossy paper. Deluxe binding with headbands. 7⅞ x 10⅝. T203 Clothbound **$10.00**

CATALOGUE OF DOVER BOOKS

THE AUTOBIOGRAPHY OF AN IDEA, Louis Sullivan. The pioneer architect whom Frank Lloyd Wright called "the master" reveals an acute sensitivity to social forces and values in this passionately honest account. He records the crystallization of his opinions and theories, the growth of his organic theory of architecture that still influences American designers and architects, contemporary ideas, etc. This volume contains the first appearance of 34 full-page plates of his finest architecture. Unabridged reissue of 1924 edition. New introduction by R. M. Line. Index. xiv + 335pp. 5⅜ x 8. T281 Paperbound **$2.00**

THE DRAWINGS OF HEINRICH KLEY. The first uncut republication of both of Kley's devastating sketchbooks, which first appeared in pre-World War I Germany. One of the greatest cartoonists and social satirists of modern times, his exuberant and iconoclastic fantasy and his extraordinary technique place him in the great tradition of Bosch, Breughel, and Goya, while his subject matter has all the immediacy and tension of our century. 200 drawings. viii + 128pp. 7¾ x 10¾. T24 Paperbound **$1.85**

MORE DRAWINGS BY HEINRICH KLEY. All the sketches from Leut' Und Viecher (1912) and Sammel-Album (1923) not included in the previous Dover edition of Drawings. More of the bizarre, mercilessly iconoclastic sketches that shocked and amused on their original publication. Nothing was too sacred, no one too eminent for satirization by this imaginative, individual and accomplished master cartoonist. A total of 158 illustrations. lv + 104pp. 7¾ x 10¾. T41 Paperbound **$1.85**

PINE FURNITURE OF EARLY NEW ENGLAND, R. H. Kettell. A rich understanding of one of America's most original folk arts that collectors of antiques, interior decorators, craftsmen, woodworkers, and everyone interested in American history and art will find fascinating and immensely useful. 413 illustrations of more than 300 chairs, benches, racks, beds, cupboards, mirrors, shelves, tables, and other furniture will show all the simple beauty and character of early New England furniture. 55 detailed drawings carefully analyze outstanding pieces. "With its rich store of illustrations, this book emphasizes the individuality and varied design of early American pine furniture. It should be welcomed," ANTIQUES. 413 illustrations and 55 working drawings. 475. 8 x 10¾. T145 Clothbound **$10.00**

THE HUMAN FIGURE, J. H. Vanderpoel. Every important artistic element of the human figure is pointed out in minutely detailed word descriptions in this classic text and illustrated as well in 430 pencil and charcoal drawings. Thus the text of this book directs your attention to all the characteristic features and subtle differences of the male and female (adults, children, and aged persons), as though a master artist were telling you what to look for at each stage. 2nd edition, revised and enlarged by George Bridgman. Foreword. 430 illustrations. 143pp. 6⅛ x 9¼. T432 Paperbound **$1.50**

LETTERING AND ALPHABETS, J. A. Cavanagh. This unabridged reissue of LETTERING offers a full discussion, analysis, illustration of 89 basic hand lettering styles — styles derived from Caslons, Bodonis, Garamonds, Gothic, Black Letter, Oriental, and many others. Upper and lower cases, numerals and common signs pictured. Hundreds of technical hints on make-up, construction, artistic validity, strokes, pens, brushes, white areas, etc. May be reproduced without permission! 89 complete alphabets; 72 lettered specimens. 121pp. 9¾ x 8. T53 Paperbound **$1.35**

STICKS AND STONES, Lewis Mumford. A survey of the forces that have conditioned American architecture and altered its forms. The author discusses the medieval tradition in early New England villages; the Renaissance influence which developed with the rise of the merchant class; the classical influence of Jefferson's time; the "Mechanicsvilles" of Poe's generation; the Brown Decades; the philosophy of the Imperial facade; and finally the modern machine age. "A truly remarkable book," SAT. REV. OF LITERATURE. 2nd revised edition. 21 illustrations. xvii + 228pp. 5⅜ x 8. T202 Paperbound **$1.75**

THE STANDARD BOOK OF QUILT MAKING AND COLLECTING, Marguerite Ickis. A complete easy-to-follow guide with all the information you need to make beautiful, useful quilts. How to plan, design, cut, sew, appliqué, avoid sewing problems, use rag bag, make borders, tuft, every other aspect. Over 100 traditional quilts shown, including over 40 full-size patterns. At-home hobby for fun, profit. Index. 483 illus. 1 color plate. 287pp. 6¾ x 9½. T582 Paperbound **$2.00**

THE BOOK OF SIGNS, Rudolf Koch. Formerly $20 to $25 on the out-of-print market, now only $1.00 in this unabridged new edition! 493 symbols from ancient manuscripts, medieval cathedrals, coins, catacombs, pottery, etc. Crosses, monograms of Roman emperors, astrological, chemical, botanical, runes, housemarks, and 7 other categories. Invaluable for handicraft workers, illustrators, scholars, etc., this material may be reproduced without permission. 493 illustrations by Fritz Kredel. 104pp. 6½ x 9¼. T162 Paperbound **$1.00**

PRIMITIVE ART, Franz Boas. This authoritative and exhaustive work by a great American anthropologist covers the entire gamut of primitive art. Pottery, leatherwork, metal work, stone work, wood, basketry, are treated in detail. Theories of primitive art, historical depth in art history, technical virtuosity, unconscious levels of patterning, symbolism, styles, literature, music, dance, etc. A must book for the interested layman, the anthropologist, artist, handicrafter (hundreds of unusual motifs), and the historian. Over 900 illustrations (50 ceramic vessels, 12 totem poles, etc.). 376pp. 5⅜ x 8. T25 Paperbound **$2.00**

Fiction

FLATLAND, E. A. Abbott. A science-fiction classic of life in a 2-dimensional world that is also a first-rate introduction to such aspects of modern science as relativity and hyperspace. Political, moral, satirical, and humorous overtones have made FLATLAND fascinating reading for thousands. 7th edition. New introduction by Banesh Hoffmann. 16 illustrations. 128pp. 5⅜ x 8.
T1 Paperbound **$1.00**

THE WONDERFUL WIZARD OF OZ, L. F. Baum. Only edition in print with all the original W. W. Denslow illustrations in full color—as much a part of "The Wizard" as Tenniel's drawings are of "Alice in Wonderland." "The Wizard" is still America's best-loved fairy tale, in which, as the author expresses it, "The wonderment and joy are retained and the heartaches and nightmares left out." Now today's young readers can enjoy every word and wonderful picture of the original book. New introduction by Martin Gardner. A Baum bibliography. 23 full-page color plates. viii + 268pp. 5⅜ x 8.
T691 Paperbound **$1.50**

THE MARVELOUS LAND OF OZ, L. F. Baum. This is the equally enchanting sequel to the "Wizard," continuing the adventures of the Scarecrow and the Tin Woodman. The hero this time is a little boy named Tip, and all the delightful Oz magic is still present. This is the Oz book with the Animated Saw-Horse, the Woggle-Bug, and Jack Pumpkinhead. All the original John R. Neill illustrations, 10 in full color. 287 pp. 5⅜ x 8.
T692 Paperbound **$1.50**

28 SCIENCE FICTION STORIES OF H. G. WELLS. Two full unabridged novels, MEN LIKE GODS and STAR BEGOTTEN, plus 26 short stories by the master science-fiction writer of all time! Stories of space, time, invention, exploration, future adventure—an indispensable part of the library of everyone interested in science and adventure. PARTIAL CONTENTS: Men Like Gods, The Country of the Blind, In the Abyss, The Crystal Egg, The Man Who Could Work Miracles, A Story of the Days to Come, The Valley of Spiders, and 21 more! 928pp. 5⅜ x 8.
T265 Clothbound **$4.50**

THREE MARTIAN NOVELS, Edgar Rice Burroughs. Contains: Thuvia, Maid of Mars; The Chessmen of Mars; and The Master Mind of Mars. High adventure set in an imaginative and intricate conception of the Red Planet. Mars is peopled with an intelligent, heroic human race which lives in densely populated cities and with fierce barbarians who inhabit dead sea bottoms. Other exciting creatures abound amidst an inventive framework of Martian history and geography. Complete unabridged reprintings of the first edition. 16 illustrations by J. Allen St. John. vi + 499pp. 5⅜ x 8½.
T39 Paperbound **$1.85**

SEVEN SCIENCE FICTION NOVELS, H. G. Wells. Full unabridged texts of 7 science-fiction novels of the master. Ranging from biology, physics, chemistry, astronomy to sociology and other studies, Mr. Wells extrapolates whole worlds of strange and intriguing character. "One will have to go far to match this for entertainment, excitement, and sheer pleasure . . . ," NEW YORK TIMES. Contents: The Time Machine, The Island of Dr. Moreau, First Men in the Moon, The Invisible Man, The War of the Worlds, The Food of the Gods, In the Days of the Comet. 1015pp. 5⅜ x 8.
T264 Clothbound **$4.50**

THE LAND THAT TIME FORGOT and THE MOON MAID, Edgar Rice Burroughs. In the opinion of many, Burroughs' best work. The first concerns a strange island where evolution is individual rather than phylogenetic. Speechless anthropoids develop into intelligent human beings within a single generation. The second projects the reader far into the future and describes the first voyage to the Moon (in the year 2025), the conquest of the Earth by the Moon, and years of violence and adventure as the enslaved Earthmen try to regain possession of their planet. "An imaginative tour de force that keeps the reader keyed up and expectant," NEW YORK TIMES. Complete, unabridged text of the original two novels (three parts in each). 5 illustrations by J. Allen St. John. vi + 552pp. 5⅜ x 8½.
T1020 Clothbound **$3.75**
T358 Paperbound **$2.00**

3 ADVENTURE NOVELS by H. Rider Haggard. Complete texts of "She," "King Solomon's Mines," "Allan Quatermain." Qualities of discovery; desire for immortality; search for primitive, for what is unadorned by civilization, have kept these novels of African adventure exciting, alive to readers from R. L. Stevenson to George Orwell. 636pp. 5⅜ x 8.
T584 Paperbound **$2.00**

A PRINCESS OF MARS and A FIGHTING MAN OF MARS: TWO MARTIAN NOVELS BY EDGAR RICE BURROUGHS. "Princess of Mars" is the very first of the great Martian novels written by Burroughs, and it is probably the best of them all; it set the pattern for all of his later fantasy novels and contains a thrilling cast of strange peoples and creatures and the formula of Olympian heroism amidst ever-fluctuating fortunes which Burroughs carries off so successfully. "Fighting Man" returns to the same scenes and cities—many years later. A mad scientist, a degenerate dictator, and an indomitable defender of the right clash—with the fate of the Red Planet at stake! Complete, unabridged reprinting of original editions. Illustrations by F. E. Schoonover and Hugh Hutton. v + 356pp. 5⅜ x 8½.
T1140 Paperbound **$1.75**